Contents

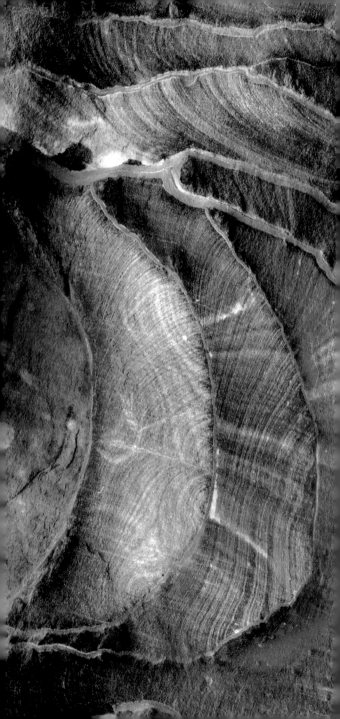

Geological History

J ordan's oldest rocks date to about 590 million years ago when Earth had a single supercontinent and no land animals. The ancient rocks are mostly *granite* formed from magma below ground. They are exposed in southern Jordan around Aqaba.

Between 550 and 20 million years ago, Earth's single landmass broke up, rejoined, and then broke up again to form the continents we know today. During these continental shifts, the ancient *Tethys Ocean* periodically flooded parts of what is now Jordan. This resulted in layers of sand deposits that formed *sandstone*, and layers of marine life sediment that formed *limestone*. The hard, red sandstone of Petra, Wadi Rum, and Wadi Dana formed between 550 and 500 million years ago. The white limestone around Amman formed in shallow reefs between 250 and 25 million years ago.

Around 35 million years ago, the Arabian plate began to separate from Africa forming the *Great Rift Valley*—a vast fault that runs under the Red Sea, along the entire length of the Jordan Valley, and continues north to Turkey. Around 3 million years ago, accelerated tectonic activities opened the rift to form the *Jordan Valley*, uplifting the sandstone and limestone deposits on the valley's eastern flank to form Jordan's highlands. Around the same time, the Mediterranean Sea regularly flooded the Jordan Valley, which formed large lakes that eventually evaporated to become the *Dead Sea* around 10,000 years ago.

Between 25 and 1 million years ago, a series of volcanic activities took place in northern Jordan and southern Syria. Jordan's northern desert is dotted with dark volcanic rocks called *basalt*.

Around 5,500 years ago, a change in the Earth's tilt shifted the tropical rain belt southwards and created the region's dry deserts.

Jordan's youngest rocks are *mudstones*. They can be found on dry lake beds south of the Dead Sea.

Pangaea - 225 Million Years Ago

Topography

Jordan enjoys three main topographic features with unique and diverse landscapes in a relatively small geographic area: the *Jordan Valley*, the *Highlands*, and the *Eastern Desert*.

The *Jordan Valley* extends the entire length of western Jordan. The northern part of the valley, watered by the Jordan River, is the fertile *Ghor*. The southern part is the arid and spectacular *Wadi Araba*. In the middle is the *Dead Sea* region, the lowest point on Earth.

Jordan's highlands extend the entire length of the country, forming the eastern ridge of the Jordan Valley. The northern part enjoys a Mediterranean climate, receives the country's highest rainfall, and includes woodland habitats. The southern part is intersected by spectacular valleys such as Wadi Mujib, Wadi Hasa, and Wadi Musa.

The *Eastern Desert* covers 75% of Jordan. It includes the Basalt Desert in the north, the Ruwayshid Desert in the north-east, the Central Desert in central Jordan, and the Mudawwara and Rum deserts in the south.

□ SEDIMENT

Sediment is particles of matter that settle to the bottom of liquids. Over long periods, deposits of mineral and organic sediment accumulate at the bottom of lakes, seas, or flood plains. They often cement into rocks, and then occasionally get exposed or uplifted by geological activities to form new mountains. Once exposed, erosion reverses the process by gradually wearing them away. Each color band visible in sedimentary deposits represents a distinct geological event. **Location** Limestone sedimentary rocks form the *Northern Highlands*, including *Ajloun*, *Amman*, and *Karak*. Sandstone sedimentary rocks form the *Southern Highlands*, including *Wadi Dana*, *Petra*, and *Wadi Rum*.

□ UPLIFT

Uplift is the geological process through which land is pushed upwards, increasing its elevation. Jordan's highlands were once flat sedimentary deposits buried below ground, as they still are in the flat Eastern Desert. The highlands were uplifted around three million years ago by accelerated tectonic activities that formed the Jordan Valley. The pictured mountains show sedimentary rock layers uplifted and tilted from their original horizontal position. **Location** The highlands east of the Jordan Valley. Clear examples are south of the *Dead Sea*, around the GPS coordinates: 31.2436°, 35.5772°.

☐ CROSS-BEDDING

Cross-bedding is the way new sedimentary deposits are affected by water or wind currents. When sediment slowly settles down, it accumulates in parallel, horizontal layers. When moved by currents, it accumulates at an angle, sloping down in the direction of the current. The cross-bedding patterns in exposed sandstone rocks in southern Jordan tell a story of periodic floods depositing sand sediment. The presence of rounded pebbles or marine fossils in the rocks indicates that the cross-bedding was caused by water, not wind currents. **Location** Common in sedimentary rocks in southern Jordan, including *Wadi Dana*, *Wadi Rum*, and *Mudawwara*.

 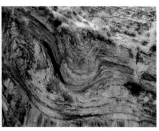

☐ FOLD

Fold is the bend in ground layers caused by geological pressures. Folds are mostly visible in sedimentary rock layers that usually run in parallel horizontal lines, but bend in areas of increased pressure. Folds are a visual reminder of the slow, but constant shifts in the Earth's crust and the enormous forces that shape it. **Location** Found in some exposed hillsides of western Jordan. An example is in *Wadi Hidan* at the GPS coordinates: 31.5655°, 35.7408°.

☐ CONCRETIONS

Concretions are hard structures that form among sedimentary deposits early in the process of rock formation. They form when minerals concentrate and harden in one area before the surrounding areas. Chert and limestone concretions form in concentric layers as minerals build up around a small nucleus such as a pebble, leaf, or bone. They grow over a long period to form disks and other shapes of up to several meters in diameter. Irregular sandstone concretions form within sand sediment when minerals are deposited unevenly, when they concentrate in air pockets, or when they aggregate in crystal-like bodies. Despite some resemblance to fossils, concretions are not fossils. **Location** Disk-shaped chert and limestone concretions are common on Highway 5 between *Azraq* and *Jafr*. They are naturally exposed by erosion or excavated for commercial use. Also found on exposed hillsides of western Jordan, including south of *Petra* at the GPS coordinates: 30.1380°, 35.3640°. Irregular sandstone concretions are found in *Wadi Dana*, *Wadi Rum*, and *Petra*.

☐ FOSSILS

Fossils are the remains or prints of old organisms preserved in sedimentary rocks. The fossils of extinct or primitive marine creatures are found in the Northern Highlands. Dinosaur and plant fossils were recently discovered in the Eastern Desert. The oldest mammal fossil found in Jordan belongs to a prehistoric whale with legs (before whales evolved into sea mammals). It was found in Wadi Dahek, where shark teeth can also be found embedded in rocks. **Location** Fossils are common in the limestone mountains of western Jordan. An example of a fossil crop is down in the valley of *Wadi al-Seer*, at the GPS coordinates: 31.8831°, 35.7549°. Another small fossil patch is on the Desert Highway, south of *Qatranah*, at the GPS coordinates: 30.9991°, 36.0105°. *Wadi Dahek* is southeast of *Azraq*, around the GPS coordinates: 31.5717°, 37.1217°.

□ LIESEGANG BANDING

Liesegang banding refers to the rings and fan-shaped color patterns that appear in some sedimentary rocks such as Petra's sandstone. The colorful patterns are formed by mineral-rich groundwater that flows and deposits minerals through the sedimentary layers. Different minerals produce different colors, and some act as natural cements that help turn loose sediment into rocks. Minerals commonly seen in liesegang banding are red iron oxide (rusted iron), black manganese, yellow sulfur, and green copper carbonate. **Location** Common in and around *Petra*, and in the *Mujib Gorge* (see *Mujib Nature Reserve*).

☐ ANCIENT LAKES

Evidence of periodic sea transgression over Jordan has been well preserved in the Mudawwara Desert. Large lakes covered the region over 450 million years ago, leaving layers of silty sediment, fossils of marine life, small islands sculpted by waves, and even wave-formed ripple marks (see *Fossilized Ripples*). **Location** Around *Mudawwara* in southern Jordan. An example is at the GPS coordinates: 29.4197°, 35.9735°.

☐ FOSSILIZED RIPPLES

Fossilized ripples are sedimentary deposits shaped by currents, which later hardened into rocks, preserving the ripple marks. Found mostly around Mudawwara in southern Jordan, they were formed over 450 million years ago when silty deposits hardened into laminate rocks. The ripple marks are high relative to their wavelength, which indicates they were formed by water, not wind. They are symmetrical, which indicates they were formed by shallow waves, not strong currents. **Location** Around *Mudawwara* in southern Jordan. A small example on Highway 5 is at the GPS coordinates: 29.3504°, 36.0227°.

☐ ANCIENT SEABED

Wadi Dahek is a valley cut by two faults and widened by erosion. It offers a spectacular look into the substrata of the Eastern Desert that formed in a marine environment between 65 and 25 million years ago (known as Wadi Shallala formation). Visible in the exposed layers is marl (clay & lime), chalk, limestone, gypsum, chert, flint, concretions, hoodoos, buttes, pinnacles, and marine fossils (especially durable shark teeth). **Location** Wadi Dahek, with its deep end in Jordan and its shallow end in Saudi Arabia, is south of Azraq, about 8 km northeast of Umari, around the GPS coordinates: 31.5717°, 37.1217°.

☐ ANCIENT PEBBLES

Erosion in Wadi Rum and Wadi Dana has exposed ancient pebbles embedded in sandstone rocks. The pebbles were smoothed and rounded by water currents, evidence of the periodic floods that deposited them over 400 million years ago. **Location** Common in *Wadi Rum* and *Wadi Dana*.

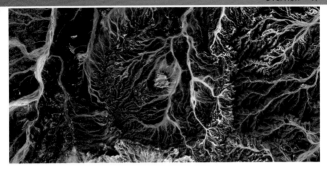

☐ IMPACT CRATER

A crater 6 km in diameter has recently been discovered in Jordan's Eastern Desert. It is believed to have been created by a meteor over 100 meter in diameter, impacting Earth at a velocity of 40-50 kilometer/second. The impact force is estimated to be the equivalent of 5,000 Hiroshima atomic bombs, ejecting enough dust, smoke, and vapor into the atmosphere to circle and darken the whole planet, and causing continuous rain and floods for months or years. This is a significant crater in that it is the largest and youngest in the Middle East; it is the only known crater in chert sedimentary layers, and it is well preserved in the dry desert climate. The exact age of the crater has yet to be determined, but it is less than 34 million years old. **Location** *Waqf al-Suwwan* in the *Eastern Desert*, northeast of *Bayer*; at the GPS coordinates: 31.0463°, 36.8062°.

☐ BASINS

Basins are large depressions in the land that water drains into from higher terrain. Jordan is composed of several large basins, including the Dead Sea, Aqaba, Azraq, and Jar basins. With the exception of the Aqaba basin, Jordan's drainage basins have no outlets to other bodies of water (endorheic basins). The water they collect in rainy years either seeps into underground aquifers or evaporates, leaving a high concentration of salts and minerals as in the Dead Sea and Azraq. In most desert depressions, the high evaporation rate turns shallow rainwater pools into mudflats known as *Qa'* in Arabic. **Location** Jordan is composed of the *Zarqa*, *Azraq*, and *Hamad* basins in the north; the *Dead Sea*, *Wadi Araba*, and *Aqaba* basins in the west; the *Hasa* and *Jafr* basins in central Jordan; and the *Disi* basin in the south. Desert pools occur in rainy winters and can last through spring.

Dead Sea

The Dead Sea is part of the *Great Rift Valley*, a vast fault in the Earth's crust formed by the drift in opposite directions of the Arabian and African tectonic plates. This ongoing geological process lowers the Dead Sea by about half a millimeter per year, and slides its flanks past each other by about 5 millimeters per year.

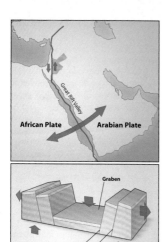

☐ GRABEN

The Earth's crust floats on liquid magma. As the Arabian and African plates drift apart, the rift line tends to stretch and swell under internal pressure. It eventually cracks in parallel step faults, dropping the middle section called a *graben* (meaning *ditch* in German). The Jordan Valley is a series of grabens, the lowest of which is the Dead Sea area. While the Dead Sea is the lowest point on Earth at 418 meters below sea level, the Dead Sea graben lies much lower, buried under 14 kilometers of sediment washed down the rift margins. **Location** The *Jordan Valley*, which extends the entire length of western Jordan and includes the *Jordan River Valley* (*Ghor*), the *Dead Sea*, and *Wadi Araba*.

☐ LISAN FORMATION

Lake Lisan preceded the present-day Dead Sea. Around 65,000 years ago, the larger Lake Lisan extended from Lake Tiberias in the north, to 35 kilometers south of the Dead Sea. Throughout its life, the size and level of Lake Lisan fluctuated, reflecting the regional and global climate changes. During warming events, lake evaporation caused the precipitation of white calcium carbonates (chalk) on the bottom of the lake. In wet years, gray silt and clay washed down the surrounding mountains to the bottom of the lake. The alternating white and gray sedimentary layers are called *Lisan Formation*. It is an important,

natural climate record. **Location** The sedimentary layers of Lake Lisan form the white, soft hillsides of some areas in the *Jordan River Valley* and along the *Dead Sea*. An example is south of the *Dead Sea* at the GPS coordinates: 31.2363°, 35.5202°.

☐ SALTS AND MINERALS

The Dead Sea is nine times saltier than the oceans and has minerals that constitute up to 35% of its weight. The high salinity and mineral content make it 30% denser than freshwater, giving it an oily feel and a remarkable buoyancy (swimmers float effortlessly in the Dead Sea). Salts and minerals continue to concentrate in the Dead Sea as rivers and hot springs bring them in and evaporation leaves them behind. The Dead Sea is rich in calcium, magnesium, bromine, and other minerals. **Location** The *Dead Sea* is south of the *Jordan River*.

☐ EVAPORATION PONDS

Evaporation ponds are shallow, man-made ponds for evaporating sea water and harvesting the minerals left behind. The minerals and algae concentrations in the ponds produce crystalline structures and vivid brines. **Location** The southern *Dead Sea* basin.

☐ SALT FORMATIONS

As the mineral-rich water evaporates on the Dead Sea shores, it leaves behind crystallized salt called *halite*. Over time, the gradual buildup of salt coats entire beaches, while the waves smooth and sculpt it into spectacular random formations. Other minerals and organic matter trapped within the crystalline structures commonly give them soft hues or bright colors. **Location** Common on the *Dead Sea* beaches untouched by recent development. An example is south of the *Mujib Bridge* at the GPS coordinates: 31.4317°, 35.5628°.

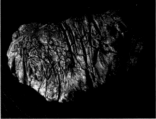

□ HEALTH EFFECTS

The Dead Sea's low elevation and high mineral content make it a unique environment for a variety of recuperative and cosmetic treatments. The lower elevation results in increased oxygen levels, increased atmospheric pressure, and reduced ultraviolet radiation, which are beneficial for lung, skin, and joint ailments. The mineral-rich water and the unique black muds rich in minerals and organic matter are beneficial for skin and joint ailments. **Location** Health spas are common in hotels and resorts around the *Dead Sea*, and in *Ma'in* hot springs west of *Madaba*.

□ BITUMEN

Bitumen is a heavy, black byproduct of crude oil distillation, used today mostly for paving roads (asphalt). Bitumen occurs naturally only in the Dead Sea where it is released from the bottom of the lake by earthquakes. The Dead Sea bitumen was used in prehistoric times to attach arrow heads to wooden shafts; the Ain Ghazal inhabitants used it to decorate their statues; the Babylonians used it to waterproof boats; the Sumerians used it as a cement; the Egyptians used it in cosmetics, medicine, and mummy embalmment; the Romans used it as a waterproof sealer; and the Nabateans extracted and traded it. **Location** South of the *Dead Sea*. Found floating on the surface or washed onto the shore in large or small blocks, mainly after earthquake activities.

□ PINK WATER

Although the high salinity of the Dead Sea makes it inhospitable to aquatic life, the floods during rainy seasons temporarily drop the lake's salinity to levels where it can support salt-loving microbes. Among them is the red *Halobacterium*, which contains the same red carotenoid pigment found in tomatoes and red peppers. Under the right conditions, Halobacterium thrives, turning the blue Dead Sea pink. Halobacterium has the ability to survive in extreme conditions by repairing its damaged DNA. It has been studied in the search for a cure to cancer and to counter the damaging effects of radiation. **Location** Small pools with lower

salinity around the *Dead Sea*. The actual Dead Sea turns pink only under the right conditions after heavy rains, mostly where the Jordan River terminates. This is becoming a rare occurrence as fresh water is increasingly diverted away from the Dead Sea. Pink water is not to be confused with the red-brown *bromine* common in Dead Sea brines.

Volcanos

A series of volcanic activities took place in Jordan between 25 and 1 million years ago. As the Arabian and African plates drifted apart, the Earth's crust stretched thin along the fault line, and lava erupted out of the Jabal al-Durz volcano in southern Syria and out of smaller volcanic vents in northern and western Jordan.

☐ VOLCANIC CONES

A *volcanic cone* is a pile of volcanic matter that accumulates around an erupting volcanic vent. Small volcanic cones erode rapidly, generally losing the central crater characteristic of larger volcanos. **Location** Common in the *Basalt Desert* of northern Jordan. One of largest is on Highway 10, southwest from *Safawi*, at the GPS coordinates: 32.1167°, 36.8717°.

☐ VOLCANIC PLUGS

A *volcanic plug* forms when lava hardens inside the vent of an active volcano, trapping the magma beneath it. Volcanic plugs become exposed when softer volcanic cones erode around them. **Location** South of *Karak*, near the *Tannoor Dam*, at the GPS coordinates: 30.9733°, 35.7300°. Other volcanic plugs exposed by quarries or mines are near the village of *Mukawir*, overlooking the *Dead Sea*, at the GPS coordinates: 31.5804°, 35.6298°; and on Highway 5, just north of *Azraq*, at the GPS coordinates: 31.9566°, 36.9069°.

☐ LAVA FLOW

A *lava flow* is a stream of molten rock that flows out of a volcanic vent. When thick lava cools evenly and slowly, it contracts and develops vertical cracks (columnar joints). This process produces a tiled surface and a pillared cross-section. Extreme climate temperatures break the hardened lava into smaller rocks, then into iron-rich sand (see *Metal Deposits*). Because molten lava can spread thinly over large areas, it is not always near the volcanic vent it originated from. **Location** Common in the *Basalt Desert* of northern Jordan. Also found in *Wadi Hidan* at the GPS coordinates: 31.5065°, 35.6863°.

☐ LAVA CAVES

As lava flows above ground, the exposed lava surface cools down and forms a hard crust. The hot lava beneath the crust continues to flow downslope until it drains out, leaving empty caves behind. The caves become accessible when their fragile ceilings collapse, normally within 10,000 years after they form. Jordan's lava caves were formed at least 400,000 years ago; they are among the oldest in the world. Stone tools found around some caves suggest that they were used by humans in prehistoric times. **Location** At least seven lava caves are found in the *Basalt Desert*. The longest is *Beer al-Hammam*, 445 meters long; it is located at the GPS coordinates: 32.1326°, 36.8233°. The most accessible is the *Azzam Cave* at the GPS coordinates: 32.2850°, 36.6099°.

☐ CRYSTALS

Crystals are mineral formations that have a regular, geometric structure. They commonly form when minerals are melted by a heat source such as a volcano and then slowly cool down, allowing the atoms to rearrange into orderly patterns. They also form when mineral-rich water evaporates, leaving the crystallized minerals behind. One of the commonly found crystals is *quartz*, which gives off sparks when struck together (visible in the dark). With the exception of rare and unique specimens, most crystals have little or no value. **Location** Quartz is common around volcanic vents. Examples are in the *Mujib Dam* area, and south of *Karak* around the GPS coordinates: 30.9658°, 35.7250°. Crystals on the surface of boulders are also found in the valley of *Wadi al-Seer*, at the GPS coordinates: 31.8831°, 35.7550°. Gypsum crystals are common in *Wadi Dahek*, southeast of *Azraq*, around the GPS coordinates: 31.5700°, 37.1217°.

☐ METAL DEPOSITS

Earth's interior consists mostly of iron, nickel, and smaller amounts of other metals. Lava flows generally bring out traces of metals that are mixed with molten rock. If the lava encounters concentrated chemical solutions, some metals may become separated and pooled into ores that can be mined. **Location** Copper is found in *Wadi Finan* around the GPS coordinates: 30.6233°, 35.5000°. It is reached from *Wadi Araba* about 100 km south of the *Dead Sea* (see *Dana Nature Reserve* and *Finan Copper Mines*). The sand in the *Basalt Desert* is rich in iron.

☐ HOT SPRINGS

A *hot spring* is a naturally occurring flow of hot water out of the ground. The water is heated by Earth's internal heat, which increases with depth. In regions with geological activities such as the Great Rift Valley, the Earth's crust is thinner, bringing hot molten magma closer to the surface and increasing the occurrence of hot springs. Because minerals readily dissolve in hot water, hot springs are rich in minerals and even contain traces of naturally occurring radioactive elements. **Location** Along the *Jordan Valley* margins, including *Ma'in* west of *Madaba*, *Burbayta* in *Wadi Hasa*, and *Hemma* north of *Irbid*.

☐ SILLS & DIKES

As molten lava pushes out of the ground, it flows horizontally between existing rock layers, and vertically through cracks. When lava cools near the surface inside horizontal lava conduits, it forms *sills*. When it cools inside vertical conduits, it forms *dikes*. Sills and dikes make the dark streaks in the exposed granite hillsides of southern Jordan. **Location** Granite mountains north and south of *Aqaba*.

Deserts

Jordan is located at the northern edge of the vast *Arabian Desert*, which covers most of the Arabian peninsula, most of Jordan, and extends into southern Iraq and eastern Egypt.

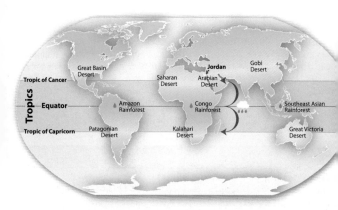

☐ ARIDIFICATION

Contrary to initial impressions, the world's deserts are not on the equator where the sun is the hottest. Deserts occur on two separate latitudes known as the *tropic of Cancer* and the *tropic of Capricorn*, 23° north and south of the equator. As the sun heats the equator, the rising hot currents pull large amounts of water vapor from the oceans. As these currents move over the tropics, they lose most of their moisture in heavy monsoon rains that create the world's rainforests, while the remaining dry currents that reach the margins of the tropics create the world's driest regions in a natural process called *aridification*. Once lush grasslands, Jordan's dry deserts were formed by aridification around 5,500 years ago when a change in the Earth's tilt moved the tropical rain belt southwards. Regular wobble in Earth's rotational axis shifts the tropics and swings the Middle East between wet and dry once every 20,000 years. **Location** Jordan is located at the margins of the *Arabian Desert*, just north of the *tropic of Cancer*.

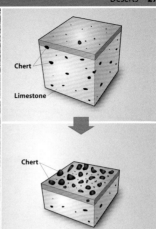

Chert

Limestone

Chert

☐ DESERT PAVEMENT

Desert pavement is a desert surface composed of tightly packed stones and rocks. The Central Desert is tightly packed with chert and flint stones, left behind after erosion removes the softer limestone and chalk around them (lag deposits). Finer sand is either blown away by the wind or gradually carried to lower elevations by water. The Basalt Desert is tightly packed with basalt stones produced by lava flows and broken up by extreme temperatures. Despite their barren appearance, the stones and rocks provide shady habitats for desert wildlife and function as mulch for desert plants. Sandy deserts such as Wadi Rum and Wadi Araba are exceptions; their sandstone mountains are constantly being eroded, replenishing the surrounding desert with fine sand. **Location** The *Central Desert* and the *Basalt Desert*.

☐ DESERT VARNISH

Desert rocks can acquire a thin, dark coating known as *desert varnish*. It is usually dismissed as a stain or discoloration caused by water or sun. In fact, it is caused by colonies of microscopic bacteria that live on the surface of the rocks and can survive in arid climates. Their biochemistry requires manganese and iron, which they absorb in tiny amounts from the air and deposit on rocks as black manganese oxide and red iron oxide. These deposits are combined with clay to shield the bacteria from heat and radiation. A full coating of desert varnish takes over 10,000 years to build up. See *Rock Art*. **Location** Common in *Wadi Rum* and *Petra*. The dark coating looks like spilled paint on rocky cliffs.

Erosion

Erosion is the continuous, natural process in which rocks are broken apart and moved by the mechanical forces of water, wind, and even living organisms. *Weathering* is a parallel process in which rocks are broken apart by chemical reactions.

☐ MESAS

A *mesa* (meaning *table* in Spanish) is a flat-topped mountain with vertical cliffs. Wadi Rum's mesas were once just a single sandstone mass that had been uplifted by tectonic activities around three million years ago. The hard, upper crust of this mass developed fractures, which erosion first deepened into vertical gorges, and then gradually widened to form sand-filled valleys and the isolated mesas. When a small mesa has almost completely worn away, it is called a *butte*. **Location** *Wadi Rum* and *Petra*.

☐ HOODOOS

Hoodoos are mushroom-shaped rocks that form in a process called *differential erosion*. They form when lower rock layers wear away faster than higher layers, either because they are softer or because they are more exposed to floods or blowing sand. **Location** The pictured hoodoo is in *Wadi Araba*, southwest of *Petra*, at the GPS coordinates: 30.2733°, 35.3454°. Other hoodoos are found in rocky regions such as *Wadi Rum*, *Wadi Dana*, and *Petra*.

☐ NATURAL BRIDGES

Natural bridges and *arches* generally start forming when water seeps between layers of sedimentary rock and expands the gaps between them. When the lower layers continue to erode or collapse, they leave the upper layers suspended over an open space.

Natural bridges form and collapse in less than 20,000 years. They are young and short-lived, considering that the surrounding rocks might be hundreds of millions of years old. **Location** The most noted natural bridges are in *Wadi Rum* at the GPS coordinates:

29.4688°, 35.4491°;
29.4733°, 35.5000°;
29.8086°, 35.4542°;
29.5747°, 35.5033°;
29.5202°, 35.4427°.

Other natural bridges and arches are found in *Pella* and rocky regions such as *Wadi Dana* and *Petra*.

☐ TAFONI

Tafoni (meaning *small caverns* in Italian) are spectacular random pits in rocky cliffs produced by thousands of years of weathering. When water is absorbed by porous rocks, it mixes with the calcium inside the rock. As the water evaporates, it draws out some of the calcium to the surface, forming a hard layer called *duricrust*. This causes the remaining calcium inside the rock to be distributed unevenly. When the duricrust breaks off, erosion wears away the rock at different rates, starting with the soft parts that have the least calcium. **Location** Common in the sandstone cliffs of *Wadi Rum*, *Petra*, and *Wadi Dana*.

☐ ONION-SKIN WEATHERING

Onion-skin weathering (or *spheroidal weathering*) occurs mainly in deserts where extreme temperatures repeatedly expand and contract rocks, causing the outer layers to peel off like onion skin. **Location** Common in basalt rocks in the *Eastern Desert* and in concretions south of the *Toba Palace*, around the GPS coordinates: 31.3257°, 36.5700°.

☐ SOLUTION WEATHERING

Rainwater mixed with carbon dioxide forms a mild acid similar to that present in soda. When the acidic water comes into contact with carbonate rocks such as limestone, it dissolves away the parts it flows over, affecting less the other parts (*differential weathering*). Over long periods, this produces random channels, dimples, and holes in exposed rocks. **Location** Common in *Wadi Araba* and the *Northern Highlands*.

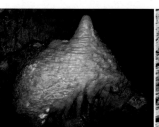

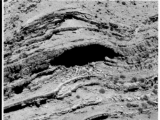

☐ SOLUTION CAVES

Rainwater mixed with carbon dioxide forms a mild acid similar to that present in soda. As the acidic water seeps below ground, it dissolves carbonate rocks such as limestone. When this process occurs for thousands of years, large spaces can open up, forming caves. As water continues to drip down through the cave, it redeposits some minerals, producing formations such as *stalactites* and *stalagmites*. **Location** The *Burqush Cave*, also known as *Zubia Cave*, is located north of *Ajloun* at the GPS coordinates: 32.4368°, 35.7440°.

☐ FRACTURE CAVES

Fracture caves commonly start with the slow erosion of lower rock layers, triggering the sudden collapse of unsupported rocks above. This process forms underground voids, some of which develop into caves with accessible entrances. **Location** Common in limestone hillsides in the *Northern Highlands*.

☐ ALLUVIUM

Alluvium is sediment washed down by water to lower elevations. Over long periods, alluvium deposits accumulate in flood planes or at the bottom of bodies of water and form thick sedimentary layers. They often cement into rocks and occasionally get uplifted by geological activities to form new mountains. **Location** Common in western Jordan where the mountains meet *Wadi Araba*. The above photo shows the red alluvium in the background, washed down the red granite mountains of *Wadi Araba* in the foreground.

☐ ALLUVIAL FANS

Alluvial fans form when rapidly flowing waters deposit sediment onto plains at the end of their run. Sediment builds up over thousands of years, forming fan-shaped deposits. In dry seasons, slow-flowing streams carry less sediment, eroding paths in existing fans instead. **Location** Common in western Jordan where canyons terminate at the *Dead Sea* and *Wadi Araba* (north of *Aqaba*). The pictured alluvial fan is where *Wadi Mujib* terminates at the *Dead Sea*, at the GPS coordinates: 31.4666°, 35.5726°.

☐ SCREE

Scree (or *talus*) is a heap of loose stones that form into a slope at the bottom of a rocky cliff. The scree slope builds up as erosion breaks off pieces of the cliff through a process called *frost heaving*. The repeated freezing and thawing of water inside cracks and crevices in the rocky cliff causes rocks to break off. This process takes place even in deserts, and even on the moon and planets with minimal soil moisture. **Location** Common in rocky regions such as *Wadi Rum*.

☐ SINKHOLES

Sinkholes are ground depressions that form when the ceiling of underground cavities collapse under their own weight, or by an external force. They vary in size from a few centimeters to hundreds of meters in both depth and diameter. Sinkholes around the Dead Sea are increasingly common due to the falling sea level. They form when rainwater dissolves away underground salt deposits, leaving cavities behind. **Location** Around the *Dead Sea*. Examples are at the GPS coordinates: 31.3405°, 35.5477°.

Rock Identification

A *rock* is a hard, naturally formed aggregate of minerals. Rocks reveal important geological clues, making rock identification a key to reconstructing Earth's history.

Rock Type:

- **Igneous Rock:** Igneous is from the Latin word *ignis*, meaning *fire*. This rock starts as magma below the Earth's surface and then solidifies either below the surface forming plutonic igneous rock (intrusive), or above ground forming volcanic igneous rock (extrusive).

- **Sedimentary Rock:** Forms from layers of compacted sediment.

- **Metamorphic Rock:** Started as igneous or sedimentary rock, but then underwent changes caused by heat, pressure, or both.

Hardness Value:

- **Hard:** The rock can scratch glass, which indicates that it contains quartz or feldspar.

- **Soft:** The rock cannot scratch glass, but can scratch a fingernail.

- **Very Soft:** A fingernail can scratch the rock.

Grain Size:

- **Fine:** The grains are visible only under a microscope.

- **Medium:** The grains are small, but visible with the naked eye or a hand lens.

- **Coarse:** The grains are clearly visible with the naked eye, and the individual minerals are identifiable.

☐ GRANITE

Hard, plutonic igneous rock that consists of coarse-grained minerals such as quartz (gray to white), feldspar (white or pink), and mica (black). Forms when underground magma cools slowly, allowing the different minerals to crystallize. Commonly used in buildings and monuments. **Location** Jordan's oldest rocks are mostly granite. They lie under mountains like *Wadi Rum*'s, but they are exposed in southern Jordan, south and north of *Aqaba*.

☐ BASALT

Dark, hard, fine-grained, volcanic igneous rock that consists mostly of iron and some other minerals such as feldspar; poor in silica. Starts as liquid magma below ground, then flows and cools above ground. Gas pockets trapped in the lava often expand and produce surface pores. When shot in the air, lava bombs cool more quickly, producing glassier, rounder rocks. **Location** The *Basalt Desert* of northern Jordan is dotted with basaltic rocks. See *Volcanos*.

☐ SANDSTONE

Soft, medium-grained, sedimentary rock that consists of compacted sand (mostly quartz and feldspar), usually held together by natural cements such as clay, silica, and iron oxide. The contents of both the sand and cement determine the sandstone's color. Iron oxide (rusted iron) is red; manganese is black; sulfur is yellow; silica and calcite are lighter colors. When there is a lack of cement, the

sandstone is usually brittle and white. **Location** *Petra*, *Wadi Dana*, and *Wadi Rum*. See *Liesegang Banding*.

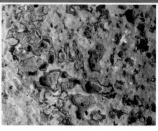

☐ LIMESTONE

Soft, fine-grained, sedimentary rock that consists of calcite minerals (calcium carbonate). It forms mainly from marine life sediment such as sea shells, corals, and algae secretions; and often contains fossils of marine creatures. The limestone around Amman formed in shallow reefs between 250 and 25 million years ago. Limestone is usually white, but can be gray, yellow, or red depending on the other organic and mineral sediment mixed with it. *Chalk* is a very soft type of limestone that forms from the sediment of microscopic organisms. The Dead Sea region produces color-banded limestone resembling marble called *Travertine*, which might have formed in hot springs from evaporating mineral-rich water. Limestone fizzes in vinegar and dissolves in stronger acids, making it vulnerable to pollution and acid rain. **Location** Common in western Jordan, including *Amman, Ajloun, Karak, Ma'an,* and *Hallabat* (east of *Zarqa*). Widely used as a building stone in Jordan, and to manufacture lime and cement.

☐ MUDSTONE & SHALE

Mudstone is a soft, fine-grained, sedimentary rock that consists of thick clay and silt. When mudstone forms in thin layers, it is called *shale* instead. **Location** Jordan's youngest rocks are mudstones found on dry lake beds south of the *Dead Sea*. Mudstone and shale are also common on ancient lake beds in the *Mudawwara* region.

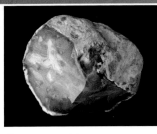 

☐ CHERT & FLINT

Chert is a hard, fine-grained, sedimentary rock with a dark, glassy appearance. It is a form of quartz that occurs within limestone sediment, found in nature after the softer limestone around it wears away. *Flint* is a variety of chert that occurs as nodules in chalk and marly limestone, commonly considered to be a higher quality chert. Flint produces very sharp edges when broken; used by early humans to make hunting tools. It gives sparks when struck with steel; used in modern lighters to ignite fuel. **Location** Around limestone rocks in western Jordan. The *Central Desert* pavement is tightly packed with chert and flint.

☐ MARBLE

Soft, fine- to medium-grained, metamorphic rock. Forms when limestone is exposed to intense heat that causes the minerals in the stone to melt and then crystallize. The veins and blotchy patterns found in marble come from impurities in the limestone. The intense temperatures destroy any fossils present in the original rock. Marble dissolves in acid just like limestone, making it vulnerable to pollution and acid rain. **Location** *Hallabat* (east of *Zarqa*), *Ajloun*, *Tafilah*, *Dab'a* (south of *Amman*), and *Karak*. Used in buildings and monuments.

☐ CONGLOMERATE ROCK

Coarse-grained, sedimentary rock that forms when different stones cement together. The individual stones are mostly rounded; they are held together by finer sand and natural cements, such as clay, calcite, or iron oxide. **Location** Around old alluvial deposits in the *Dead Sea* and *Wadi Araba* regions. Common around *Lut's Cave*, just south of the *Dead Sea*.

☐ BRECCIA

Coarse-grained, sedimentary rock that forms when stone fragments cement together. Differs from conglomerate rock in that the individual stones are mostly angular, having been broken apart by geological forces. As with conglomerate rock, the individual stones are held together by finer sand and natural cements, such as clay or calcite. **Location** *Wadi Araba*, where old scree deposits cemented into breccia.

Early Inhabitants

The earliest evidence of humans in Jordan dates to over half a million years ago. Stone tools made by pre-modern humans from this period have been found mostly in the once lush hunting plains of central Jordan.

Around 50,000 years ago, modern humans (*Homo sapiens*) began to spread out from Africa, driving pre-modern humans to extinction during the next 20,000 years. Around 10,000 years ago, modern humans began to settle in small farming communities; archaeological remains of early houses from this period have been discovered in over 150 sites in Jordan.

Around 5,500 years ago, climate changes created the region's dry deserts and drove the human population to concentrate in the *Fertile Crescent*, a geographical area watered by the Nile, Jordan, Euphrates, and Tigris rivers. The establishment of larger communities led to the dawn of civilization in Mesopotamia and Egypt, and to the transition from the Stone to the Copper and Bronze Age around 5,000 years ago, and then to the Iron Age around 3,000 years ago.

Jordan's strategic location on trade routes gave rise to the Nabateans over 2,000 years ago and linked what is now Jordan to several classical civilizations, including the Sumerian, Babylonian, Egyptian, Persian, Greek, Roman, Byzantine, and Arab civilizations.

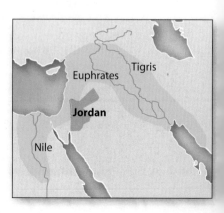

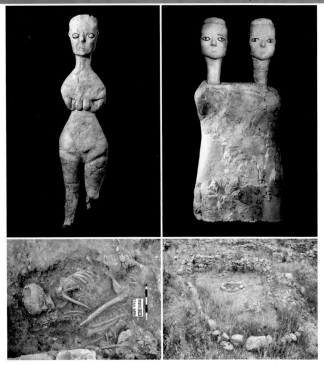

☐ AIN GHAZAL

Ain Ghazal is one of the largest prehistoric human settlements in the Middle East. The archaeological remains of the early houses date as far back as 7,250 BC when humans began to settle in small farming communities during the pre-pottery Stone Age.

The statues that have been found in Ain Ghazal are among the oldest in the world. They were made of reed bundles covered with plaster and decorated with pigments and bitumen. Other artifacts that have been found in Ain Ghazal include human skulls covered with plaster, human and animal clay figurines, tokens, painted walls and floors, and stone tools.

Ain Ghazal remained continuously inhabited for over 2,000 years, providing significant archaeological evidence of environmental degradation due to human activities. Among the evidence are the decline in charcoal fragments from the oak trees that once grew there and the decline in animal remains of over 50 species that once depended on the woodland. Overgrazing and tree depletion is also evident in the decline of plaster quantity and quality in later Ain Ghazal artifacts, which suggests a shortage of wood needed to heat gypsum rocks. Today's barren Ain Ghazal stands in stark contrast to the woodland it used to be. **Location** The prehistoric settlement was discovered during a road construction, which resumed after an emergency, archaeological excavation. The remains of the site are located northeast of *Amman* in *Ain Ghazal*. Some of Ain Ghazal's artifacts are exhibited in the *Jordan Archaeological Museum* in Amman.

☐ BEIDA

Beida was inhabited by early nomads as far back as the 11th millennium BC. It developed into one of the earliest prehistoric human settlements in the Middle East over 9,000 years ago. Important evidence of early goat domestication has been found in Beida. The bone remains of consumed goats that have been excavated in this area are mostly from immature goats, which indicates that they were domesticated, not hunted in the wild. Remains of wheat and barley in the early stages of domestication from wild grasses have also been found in Beida. **Location**

Beida is near Little Petra, 10 km north of Petra, at the GPS coordinates: 30.3709°, 35.4475°. Other pre-pottery human settlements near Petra are *Basta,* 25 km south of Petra, and *Shkarat Msaied,* 15 km north of Petra.

☐ DOLMENS

Dolmens (meaning *stone tables* in the Celtic language *Breton)* are cubic structures with upright stone slabs that support horizontal capstones. They date roughly to the Bronze Age (3500-1200 BC) or earlier. The discovery of skeletal remains in some of the dolmens indicates that they had been used as burial chambers. The dolmens were designed either with movable slabs or with square portholes that could be reopened and used for multiple burials.

They were originally sealed with earth mounds, which have subsequently eroded away. **Location** A large dolmen concentration is found in Jordan, although some have been damaged or are now endangered by encroaching development. The biggest dolmen field spreads over several kilometers north of the *Dead Sea,* around the GPS coordinates: 32.1033°, 35.6038°. Other dolmens can be found around *Irbid, Jerash, Amman,* and *Mount Nebo.*

☐ KITES

Kites are traps of piled-rock walls that guide animals into smaller enclosures with camouflaged structures (hides) where the hunters lie in wait. Hundreds of kites were built in the Basalt Desert as early as the 7th millennium BC through the beginning of the 5th millennium BC to hunt predominantly gazelles. Kites are so named for resembling flying kites when seen from the air. Most kites are connected to form a system of long chains and most are oriented eastward, which suggests seasonal hunting of animals moving from east to west. The large concentration of kites in the Basalt Desert is not indicative of a dense human population, but represents several millennia of kite building and sustainable hunting by small communities. Kites evolved over time from simple structures with circular enclosures near Azraq to more complex star-shaped enclosures throughout the Basalt Desert. Some kites were modified several times to pave the way for animal domestication and pastoralism. **Location** Common in the entire *Basalt Desert*. Examples are north of *Azraq* at and around the GPS coordinates 31.9243°, 36.8665°; south of *Safawi* at and around 32.1233°, 37.1633°; and in a chain over 100 km long that stretches south from *Burqu'* all the way to the Saudi border.

☐ MENHIRS

Menhirs (meaning *long stones* in the Celtic language *Breton*) are upright-standing stones that appear either alone or in groups. They date roughly to the Bronze Age (3500-1200 BC) or earlier. It is speculated that menhirs had been erected for religious purposes or rituals related to seasonal cycles. **Location** Over 27 menhirs can be found in Jordan, although some have been damaged by encroaching development. An example is near the village of *Lejjun*, east of Karak, at the GPS coordinates: 31.23900°, 35.8573°. The tallest is five meters high in the town of *Adir* near *Karak*. Other menhirs can be found around *Irbid*, *Ajloun*, *Jerash*, *Ma'in*, *Mount Nebo*, and *Wadi Waleh* south of *Madaba*.

Old Testament Kingdoms

The Iron Age (1200-332 BC) saw the rise of three kingdoms in Jordan: *Ammon* in the north with its capital Rabbath Ammon (present-day Amman), *Moab* in central Jordan with its capitals Karak and Dibon (present-day Diban), and *Edom* in the south with its capital Bozrah (present-day Busayra). All three kingdoms appear in the Old Testament's account of Moses leading the Israelites to the Promised Land. As these kingdoms accumulated wealth, they became targets for the Israelites, Assyrians, Babylonians, and Persians, culminating with the Greek invasion by Alexander the Great in 332 BC.

☐ KING'S HIGHWAY

The King's Highway is an ancient trade route that linked Ammon, Moab, and Edom to present-day Syria and Egypt. Many of the early wars were waged to exert control over this vital route. The King's Highway was later used by the Nabateans, paved by the Romans (see *Via Nova Traiana*), disrupted by the Crusaders, and then evolved over the centuries into the present-day King's Highway (Highway 35). **Location** The King's Highway began in *Heliopolis*, one of the most ancient cities of Egypt. It passed through the *Sinai Desert* to *Aqaba, Wadi Araba, Shobak, Karak, Madaba, Amman, Jerash,* and then to the Syrian cities of *Bosra, Damascus,* and *Resafa*.

□ RABBATH AMMON

Located in the Citadel of present-day Amman, Rabbath Ammon (meaning the *Great City of the Ammonites*) was the capital of the kingdom of Ammon around the 1st millennium BC. Over 150 Ammonite sites have been discovered around Amman, most have yet to be fully excavated. Rujm al-Malfouf is one of several Ammonite towers built around the capital in the 1st millennium BC to defend against King David of Israel. The Citadel is also the site of structures from earlier and later periods, including early Bronze Age tombs,

the world's earliest fortifications from the 2nd millennium BC, and the remains of the Roman temple of Hercules, a Byzantine basilica, and an Islamic Palace. The Jordan Archaeological Museum within the Citadel houses antiquities that date as far back as prehistoric times. The collection includes artifacts from Ain Ghazal and the Dead Sea Copper Scroll. **Location** The Citadel is on *Jabal al-Qal'a* overlooking downtown Amman. Rujm al-Malfouf is located on *Jabal Amman*, beside the Department of Antiquities.

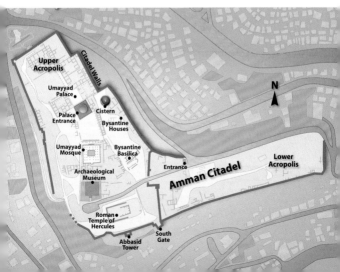

☐ DEIR ALLA

Deir Alla is believed to be the biblical settlement of Succoth, named by Jacob. It is the site of an ancient Ammonite temple built around 1,500 BC. A text inscribed with black and red ink on 119 pieces of plaster was found here. The text dates to around the 8th century BC and contains the account of a prophet named Balaam and his previously unknown prophecy. Numerous pottery fragments from

trade caravans can be found in this area. **Location** The hill of *Deir Alla* in the *Jordan River Valley*, 30 km west of *Jerash*

☐ DIBON

Ancient Dibon dates as far back as the third millennium BC. Along with Karak, it became the capital of the kingdom of Moab around the first millennium BC. Discovered in Dibon in 1868, the Mesha stele is a black basalt stone that records King Mesha's victories and building projects that included fortifications and water reservoirs. Dibon was later occupied by the Romans, Byzantines, and Muslims. **Location** The kingdom of Moab occupied the Dead Sea's eastern shore and plateau. Partial excavations of Dibon are adjacent to the present-day town of *Diban*, 25 km south of *Madaba*. The Mesha stele is part of the Louvre Museum collection in Paris.

☐ LEHUN

Located on the northern rim of Wadi Mujib for its natural defenses and water sources, Lehun is the site of prehistoric finds that go back 150,000 years, a fortified town from the 4th millennium BC, a walled village from the 12th-11th century BC, a Moabite fortress from the 10th-5th century BC, and traces of Nabatean, Roman, Islamic, and Ottoman occupation. **Location** Lehun (present-day *Lahun*) is 30 km south of *Madaba* and 7 km east from *Diban*, around the GPS coordinates: 31.4667°, 35.8500°.

☐ BOZRAH

Ancient Bozrah was a pastoral city and probably the capital of the kingdom of Edom in the 7th-6th century BC. Archaeological excavations of Edomite sites have yielded mostly small villages and semi-nomadic structures. However, the copper industry, pottery manufacturing, and trade activities suggest a complex, urbanized society. Edom was conquered by the Babylonians, Persians, and Greeks, and then became the Nabatean kingdom by 200 BC. **Location** Edom extended south from the *Dead Sea* and included *Wadi Araba* and *Petra*. Bozrah is present-day *Busayra*, between *Tafilah* and *Shobak*.

☐ SELA

Sela is an Edomite city dating as far back as the 8th century BC. It is near Bozrah (Busayra), the capital of the Biblical kingdom of Edom. The vertical cliffs and the flat top of Sela Mountain made it an ideal natural fortress against raids. It is believed to be one of the first places the Nabateans settled before establishing their new kingdom. The site includes the ruins of the ancient city of Sela, and Nabatean structures such as dams and high places. **Location** Opposite the present-day town of *Sela*, south of *Tafilah*, at the GPS coordinates: 30.7808°, 35.5750°.

☐ SHRINE OF PROPHET AARON

This shrine is believed to be the resting place of the prophet Aaron, the elder brother of the prophet Moses. Aaron died in the Petra region and was buried by Moses on Mount Hor, later renamed Mount Aaron. The small structure that marks the site was originally a Byzantine church built around the 7th century AD, later converted to a domed mosque in 1459 AD. **Location** The 2-3 hours hike starts at the heart of the ancient city of *Petra* and ends five km southwest at the summit of *Mount Aaron*, the highest peak in the city (1,350 meters).

☐ MOUNT NEBO

Mount Nebo is believed to be the place where Moses finally saw the Promised Land and where he spent his final days. The modern-day shrine on Mount Nebo incorporates both the foundation of a 4th century AD chapel built to commemorate the place of Moses' death and the remains of a Byzantine monastery that had been built on the same site in the 6th century AD. The structure contains six tombs beneath the mosaic floor. **Location** Seven km west of *Madaba*.

☐ LOT'S CAVE

Lot's cave is believed to be where prophet Lot and his two daughters took refuge after God's destruction of the village of Sodom. A Byzantine monastery and a basilica mark the cave's entrance at the southern end of the Dead Sea. A few kilometers to the north is a pillar of salt believed to be Lot's wife, turned into salt for disobeying God's order not to look back at Sodom. **Location** Lot's cave is at the southern end of the *Dead Sea* near *Safi*, at the GPS coordinates: 31.0468°, 35.5028°. The pillar of salt is 4 km south of the Mujib bridge, at the GPS coordinates: 31.4319°, 35.5632°.

☐ FINAN COPPER MINES

The Finan Valley is the site of the largest ancient copper mines. Early farming communities made beads from copper stones found in the valley around 8,000 years ago. Copper mining began in the Copper Age around 6,000 years ago. The copper industry reached its first peak under the Edomites in the Iron Age around 3,000 years ago. It reached its second peak under the Romans when convicts and Christian slaves were worked to death in the mines. Thousands of graves have been found in the area, together with the ruins of several Byzantine churches built later to honor early Christians. The remains of furnaces and heaps of black slag from the smelting process are also common in the area. The surrounding hills remain completely barren today, having been deforested to fuel the industry. **Location** At the border of *Dana Nature Reserve* around the GPS coordinates: 30.6233°, 35.5000°. It is reached from *Wadi Araba* about 100 km south of the *Dead Sea*. See *Dana Nature Reserve*.

Greek Period

The Greek period in Jordan began with the conquest of the Middle East by Alexander the Great in 332 BC and ended with the Roman conquest in the 1st century BC. The Greeks built new structures and cities in Jordan, influenced Nabatean architecture, and renamed the city of Rabbath Ammon (Amman), Philadelphia. Most of the Greek structures in Jordan were subsequently damaged or altered.

☐ QASR AL-ABD

Qasr al-Abd (palace of the slave) is a two-story, Greek-style palace built by the governor of Ammon *Hyrcanus* in the 2nd century BC. The palace is adorned with lions and other animals, and had originally been surrounded by a lush park with a lake. It is constructed with some of the largest stone blocks of any building in the Middle East, which makes it particularly vulnerable to earthquakes. It was flattened by an earthquake in 362 AD and remained in ruins until recently when it was partially reconstructed. Parts of the palace grounds are still buried under the adjacent village of Iraq al-Amir where there are 11 man-made caves that might have been used as stables. **Location** West of *Amman* at the village of *Iraq al-Amir*, 10 km down from *Wadi al-Seer,* at the GPS coordinates: 31.9130°, 35.7520°.

Petra

Petra (meaning *stone* in Greek) served as the capital of the Nabatean kingdom and a crossroads on trade routes to Egypt, Arabia, Syria, and beyond.

The Nabateans began migrating from western Arabia and settling in Petra around the 6th century BC. In their early history, they led a nomadic life, traveling and trading goods. They originally established Petra as a religious burial site and lived in tents around the public structures. As they developed trade routes and accumulated wealth, they settled in houses in a crowded city center and in small villages around the city.

Petra came under the control of the Romans in 106 AD, acquiring a few Roman-style structures such as the Colonnade Street, and later acquiring churches during the Byzantine era. Petra's decline started around the 7th century AD with the shift in trade routes and occurrence of violent earthquakes. It slowly slipped into obscurity until its rediscovery in 1812.

☐ SIQ

The *Siq* is a kilometer-long natural gorge and the main entrance to the ancient city of Petra. The Moses Spring originally flowed through the Siq until the Nabateans diverted it to prevent floods, opting instead to bring water into the city through controlled water channels on both sides of the Siq. The Siq is adorned with a number of niches depicting Nabatean deities, an eroded relief of a camel caravan, and some inscriptions. A triumphal arch originally spanned the Siq's entrance. To the right of the entrance, there is another narrow and rugged *Small Siq*, which a dam diverts water into. **Location** The main Siq begins a short distance from the Petra Visitors Center (entrance and parking area) and ends at the Treasury monument. The Small Siq begins to the right of the main Siq's entrance and leads north of the city.

☐ TREASURY

The *Treasury* is an elegant, 2-story structure over 40 meters tall, carved out of solid rock. Despite its name, the Treasury is believed to have been built in the 1st century BC to serve as a royal tomb, possibly for King Aretas III. The facade is ornate with Greek-style columns, triangular pediments, a rotunda topped by a symbolic funerary urn, and figures of Greek gods, all symbolizing the death of a hero. The interior consists of a porch flanked by two small rooms and a larger central hall. The structure was originally painted, and the plaza in front was originally four meters lower than its present level. **Location** The first monument that comes into view at the end of the Siq.

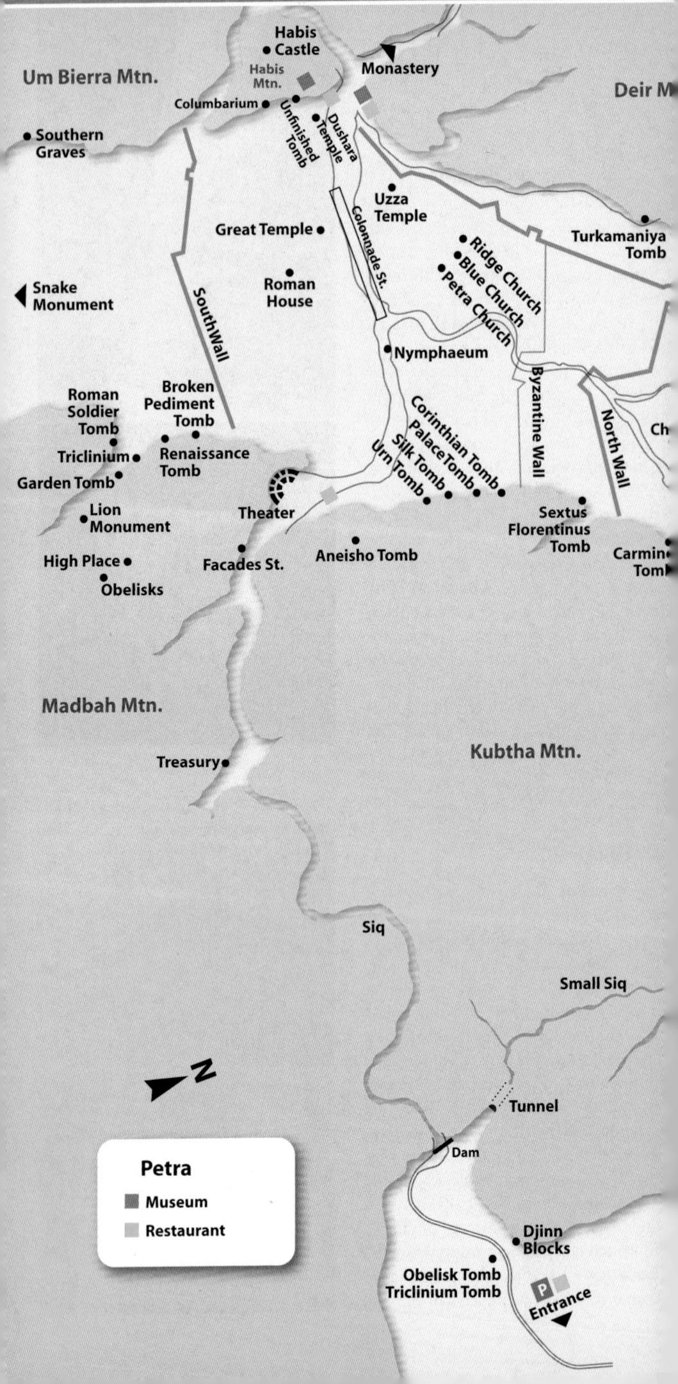

Um Bierra Mtn.

Habis
Castle

Monastery

Habis
Mtn.

Deir M

Columbarium

Unfinished
Tomb

Dushara
Temple

Southern
Graves

Uzza
Temple

Turkamaniya
Tomb

Great Temple

Colonnade St.

Ridge Church
Blue Church
Petra Church

Snake
Monument

South Wall

Roman
House

Nymphaeum

Byzantine Wall

North Wall

Ch

Roman
Soldier
Tomb

Broken
Pediment
Tomb

Corinthian Tomb
Palace Tomb

Triclinium

Renaissance
Tomb

Silk Tomb
Urn Tomb

Garden Tomb

Lion
Monument

Theater

Sextus
Florentinus
Tomb

Carmin
Tom

High Place

Facades St.

Aneisho Tomb

Obelisks

Madbah Mtn.

Kubtha Mtn.

Treasury

Siq

Small Siq

N

Tunnel

Petra

■ Museum
■ Restaurant

Dam

Djinn
Blocks

Obelisk Tomb
Triclinium Tomb

P
Entrance

☐ TOMBS

There are over 100 tombs within Petra, each was likely the burial site for a whole family or tribe. Evidence suggests that the Nabateans might have buried only the bones after exposing bodies to the elements, which would have made it practical to transport remains from distant trade routes as well as to bury entire families in common ceremonial tombs.
Location In addition to the Treasury and Monastery, there are royal tombs east of Colonnade Street: Urn, Silk, Corinthian, and Palace Tombs. Over 100 smaller tombs are also scattered around the city.

☐ UNFINISHED TOMB

The *Unfinished Tomb* was abandoned before it was completed for unknown reasons. It is nevertheless an important structure that reveals the Nabateans' building process. It shows that they removed the face of the mountain until they reached solid rock and then carved the structure from the top down, using the unfinished bottom part as a scaffold. In this case, only a small portion at the top of the tomb had been finished.

Location The base of the Habis Mountain, west of Colonnade Street.

☐ THE THEATER

This is a large, Roman-style amphitheater, seating about 6,000 spectators. It was built in the 1st century AD by the Nabateans, before the Roman conquest of the city. The theater has a stage, an orchestra area, a seating area, vaulted passageways through which the audience entered, and side-doors through which the actors entered. The caves along the back of the theater are remnants of older tombs that the theater displaced. The lower section of the theater, including the stage, was badly damaged by floods before the dam at the Siq's entrance was repaired. **Location** Past the Treasury and the Street of Facades, just before reaching the heart of *Petra*.

☐ THE GREAT TEMPLE

Despite its name, it is unlikely that this building served as a temple. This large structure consists of two levels. The upper terrace was built in the 1st century BC, and then remodeled with the addition of the lower courtyard in the 1st century AD. The upper level has a colonnaded hall and a small theater, likely to have served as an assembly hall. It contains walls with the remains of brightly decorated plasters and column capitals decorated with elephant heads. The lower courtyard had originally been flanked by a roofed triple colonnade. To the east of the temple is another recently excavated structure with the remains of a pool and surrounding gardens. **Location** In the center of *Petra*.

☐ TEMPLE OF DUSHARA

Also known as *Qasr al-Bint*, this large temple was built in the 1st century BC by Obodas III. The temple stood at the end of a long, sacred precinct (temenos), starting from a gate at the end of the Colonnade Street. The altar in front of the temple was the place for public worship, while the temple housed images of the gods. The temple originally had a staircase leading to a portico supported by four columns and to the arched entrance still standing today. The three inner chambers might have been dedicated to

three gods: Al Uzza, Ba'al-Shamin, and Dushara. The impressive roof spans exceed those of later Roman temples in Jerash. **Location** At the end of the Colonnade Street in the center of *Petra*.

☐ WATER

The Nabateans collected and managed water by building elaborate systems of channels, pipes, dams, and underground cisterns. They made great advances in manufacturing ceramic pipes and developed durable, waterproof cement to line and seal porous sandstone cisterns. Secret water collection systems were built far beyond Petra, allowing the Nabateans to travel the deserts unchallenged. Many water collection systems are still in use today by locals, while others have yet to be discovered. **Location** Common in and around *Petra*. Examples of channels are on both sides of the Siq; pipes are exhibited at the *Petra Archaeological Museum* north of the Dushara Temple; a cistern is near Petra's entrance at the GPS coordinates: 30.3268°, 35.4686°.

☐ WRITING

The Nabatean alphabet was derived from Aramaic and written right to left. It evolved into the Arabic alphabet around the 4th century AD. The spoken Nabatean language is related to old Arabic. Despite their ability to write and speak multiple languages, the Nabateans neither recorded their history nor produced literature. Writing was limited to simple inscriptions on tombs, graffiti, and some legal documents in their late history. **Location** Common throughout *Petra* and the

entire region. Examples are found off the Monastery path at the GPS coordinates: 30.335083°, 35.439450° and near the Monastery at the GPS coordinates: 30.340050°, 35.429133°.

☐ MONASTERY

The *Monastery* is a massive, 2-story structure nearly 50 meters tall, carved out of solid rock. The ornate facade is topped by a symbolic funerary urn and the interior consists of a single small hall. Despite its name, this structure is not a monastery. It is believed to have been carved in the 1st century AD to serve as a meeting hall for the cult of Obodas, which elevated the Nabatean King Obodas I to a divinity. It may also have been used as a tomb by the Obodas family. **Location** It is a one-hour hike to the monastery, starting at the foot of Habis Mountain, up a series of paths to the top of the *Deir Mountain*.

☐ BOARD GAMES

The Nabateans carved and played board games on flat surfaces and benches all over Petra. It is not known how these games were played. At first glance, the carved game boards look like variations on the ancient game of *Mancala*. Mancala, however, requires bigger holes and side-stores to hold a large numbers of seeds. **Location** Common in *Petra*. Examples are found behind the shops before entering Petra at the GPS coordinates: 30.324483°, 35.467217° and 30.324033°, 35.467300°; near the Jinn Blocks; to the left of the Siq's entrance; to the side of the Urn Tomb; and in front of the Monastery.

☐ HIGH PLACES

High Places are sites of religious significance on high mountains or hills. There are hundreds of high places in Petra and around other Nabatean burial sites. They generally have altars, wash basins, and other ceremonial structures. Some have large cisterns for collecting rainwater. High places might have served as places of sacrifice or as sites to expose the dead to the elements so that only their bones would need to be buried (see *Tombs*). The hike up to high places is difficult, but the views are worthwhile.

Location The trail up to the high place on *Madbah Mountain* is just before the amphitheater. The trail up to the high place on *Kubtha Mountain* is between the Palace and Sextius Florentinus tombs.

☐ BYZANTINE CHURCHES

In the Byzantine period, many of Petra's tombs were modified into churches. Three new churches were also constructed in the city center: the *Petra Church*, the *Blue Church*, and the *Ridge Church*. The Petra Church was built in the late 5th century. It contains exquisite mosaics depicting personifications of nature and animals, which represent God's domain. The Blue Church is so called for its blue Egyptian granite columns adorned with Nabataean horned capitals.

Location The three main churches are north of the Colonnade Street in the center of Petra. Among the tombs modified into churches are the Urn Tomb east of Colonnade Street and the Christian Tombs north of the city.

□ LITTLE PETRA

Also known as *Siq al-Barid*, *Little Petra* is a natural gorge and the site of a number of remarkable Nabatean tombs, divinity blocks, cisterns, and dining halls with benches and hand-washing sinks used for commemorative meals. Among the dining halls is the *Painted Biclinium* which contains the remains of a Nabatean wall-painting. The large number of broken dishes found during excavations in Little

Petra suggests that breaking dishes was a ritual at the end of commemorative meals. **Location** 10 km north of *Petra*.

□ ROCK ART

Early inhabitants, Nabateans, and desert travelers etched thousands of images and inscriptions on desert rocks throughout the years. Among them are petroglyphs depicting camel caravans, hunting scenes, and wild animals. They were made by pecking into the dark *desert varnish*, exposing the rock's lighter color underneath (see *Desert Varnish*). Many of the petroglyphs in Wadi Rum can be attributed to the Thamud Arab tribe that inhabited the valley alongside the Nabateans around 2,000 years ago. Some petroglyphs in the Basalt Desert are prehistoric, dating over 8,000 years. **Location** Petroglyphs are common in *Wadi Rum*, *Petra*, the *Azraq* region, and rocky areas in all of Jordan's deserts. An example in *Wadi Rum* is at the GPS coordinates: 29.5560°, 35.4528°.

☐ ARAB WALL

The *Arab Wall* is a defensive Edomite or Nabatean wall that extends 100 km from Wadi Hasa to Ras al-Naqb. The wall consists of boulders piled less than one meter high. It was rendered more effective by Nabatean watchtowers that communicated by flash-signals and larger forts behind the wall to send reinforcements. Interestingly, the original design of the Roman Hadrian's Wall, built later in Great Britain, matches this wall. **Location** Much of the wall has been destroyed by neglect or development. The wall intersects the road between *Petra* and *Ma'an*, east of the village of *Ail*, at the GPS coordinates: 30.1848°, 35.5684°. Rubble from a watchtower is located on the wall half a kilometer north from this point at the GPS coordinates: 30.1866°, 35.5724°. The Grayn Fort is 10 km south of the village of *Ail* at the GPS coordinates: 30.1241°, 35.4794°.

☐ HUMEIMA

Humeima (ancient *Hawara*) is a town founded by the Nabatean king Aretas around the 2nd century BC. According to legend, the site was revealed to the king by an apparition. The lack of nearby water sources prompted the building of an aqueduct from the Qana springs 25 km to the north, bringing water to a number of originally covered cisterns and to a large uncovered pool. Some cisterns are still in use today, while other structures have yet to be excavated. Humeima remained inhabited through the early Islamic period. Its ruins include the foundation of the earliest, large Roman fort in Jordan, at least five Byzantine churches, and an Abbasid mosque and palace. The Abbasid family launched a takeover of the Muslim Empire in the 8th century AD from Humeima. **Location** Between *Ma'an* and *Aqaba*, off Highway 15, at the GPS coordinates: 29.9503°, 35.3468°.

Roman Period

The Roman conquest of the Syrian province in 63 BC expanded the Roman Empire to include northwestern Jordan. In southern and eastern Jordan, the Nabateans maintained their independence from Rome until 106 AD. In the following four centuries, the Romans built a network of cities, forts, and roads in Jordan, many of which are still prominent today.

Decapolis

Decapolis (meaning *10 cities* in Greek) was a league of 10 Roman cities in the Syrian province that formed strong cultural, commercial, and political ties. Four cities in this league are located in Jordan: Philadelphia (Amman), Gerasa (Jerash), Gadara (Umm Qais), and Pella (Tabaqat Fahl). Hippos, Dion, Canatha, Raphana, and Damascus are in Syria. Scythopolis is west of the Jordan River.

☐ AMMAN

During the Roman rule, the city of *Philadelphia* (*Amman*) was at the crossroads of lucrative trade routes connecting the Empire with the south and Far East. The city flourished and was rebuilt in the Roman style with colonnaded streets, fountains, a bathhouse, a temple, and other public buildings. Only a few Roman structures in Amman remain well perservered. Among them is the amphitheater, built around 150 AD. It is the largest in Jordan, it seats over 6,000 spectators, and is still used today for cultural events. Just north of the amphitheater stands another smaller theatre (Odeon) that seats 500 spectators. It was originally roofed over and was used for smaller events. Other Roman structures in Amman are the Nymphaeum and the ruins of Hercules Temple. **Location** The theaters are in downtown *Amman*. The Nymphaeum is southwest from the theaters. The Hercules Temple is on the Citadel overlooking the downtown area.

□ UMM QAIS

The town of *Umm Qais* is the site of the ancient city of *Gadara*, dating as far back as the 7th century BC. It was inhabited by the Greeks around the 4th century BC, and was then taken over by the Romans in the 1st century BC. According to the Bible, it is the location where Jesus healed two men by casting their demons into a herd of pigs. Gadara prospered from its strategic location on trade routes, its fertile fields, and the nearby Hemma hot springs that attracted vacationing Romans. In addition to its commercial success, Gadara developed into a cultural center that attracted philosophers, writers, artists, and poets. Among Gadara's public structures are two theatres, a vaulted terrace, a bath complex, colonnaded streets, and a church and a basilica added during the Byzantine period. Most of Gadara's structures were built with black basalt stones, common in the surrounding volcanic area. In 747 AD, a devastating earthquake severely damaged the city and reduced it to a small village. **Location** Overlooking the *Yarmouk River* and *Lake Tiberias* 20 km northwest of *Irbid*. The Hemma hot springs are 10 km north of *Umm Qais*, near the *Yarmouk River*.

□ PELLA

Nestled between hills around a water spring, *Pella* is the site of the most ancient and diverse archaeological ruins in Jordan. They include prehistoric finds that date to around 100,000 years ago; the remains of human settlements and walled cities which were continuously inhabited between 6,000 and 4,000 years ago; and structures from the Greco-Roman, Byzantine, and early Islamic periods. Muslims won the decisive Battle of Fahl against the Byzantines here in 636 AD. Among Pella's structures are a Canaanite temple, a small Roman theater, Byzantine

churches, and a medieval mosque. Pella was destroyed by a devastating earthquake in 747 AD. Most of its ancient structures have yet to be excavated and restored. **Location** Overlooking the *Jordan River Valley* 25 km southwest of *Irbid*. Pella is the present-day town of *Tabaqat Fahl*.

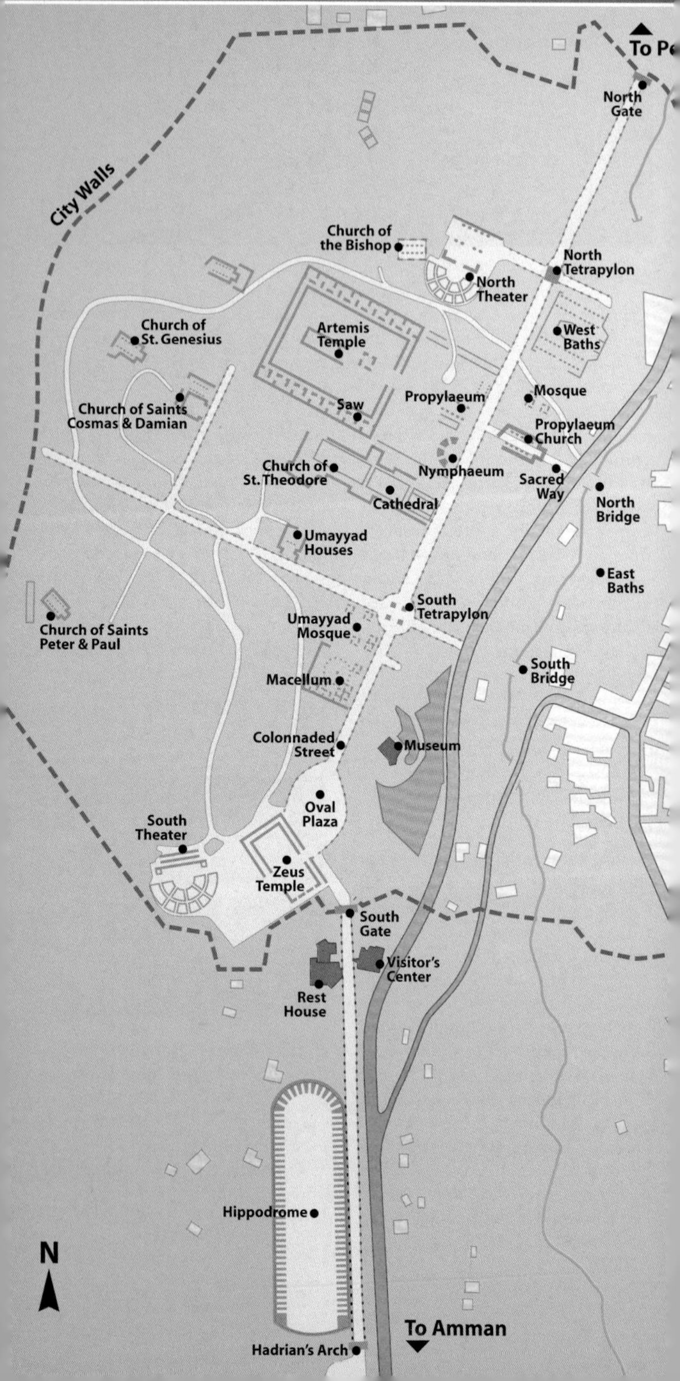

To Pe

North Gate

City Walls

Church of the Bishop

North Theater

North Tetrapylon

West Baths

Artemis Temple

Church of St. Genesius

Saw

Propylaeum

Mosque

Propylaeum Church

Church of Saints Cosmas & Damian

Nymphaeum

Sacred Way

North Bridge

Church of St. Theodore

Cathedral

East Baths

Umayyad Houses

Church of Saints Peter & Paul

South Tetrapylon

Umayyad Mosque

Macellum

South Bridge

Colonnaded Street

Museum

Oval Plaza

South Theater

Zeus Temple

South Gate

Visitor's Center

Rest House

Hippodrome

N

To Amman

Hadrian's Arch

Jerash

Jerash dates back to over 6,500 years ago. It is the site of prehistoric human settlements and was inhabited by early Arabs in the 1st millennium BC, by Greeks around the 2nd century BC, and then taken over by the Romans in the 1st century BC. Known by the Romans as *Gerasa*, it became one of the great cities of the Decapolis. Today, it is one of the largest and best-preserved Roman cities outside Italy. Within its walls are structures from later periods, including at least 15 Byzantine churches, two Islamic mosques, and Umayyad houses.

A devastating earthquake reduced the city to a small village in 747 AD. Ancient structures remained buried until they were rediscovered in 1806. Half of the Roman city is still buried under modern Jerash.

☐ HADRIAN'S ARCH

Ornate, triumphal arch commemorating Emperor Hadrian's visit to Jerash in 129 AD. Hadrian was the Governor of Syria before becoming emperor. As emperor, he is known for securing the Empire by building frontier defenses, including Hadrian's Wall in Great Britain. Interestingly, the original design of Hadrian's Wall matches a Nabatean wall in Jordan (see *Arab Wall*). **Location** Hadrian's Arch was to become a southern city gate, but it remained south of the walled city.

☐ HIPPODROME

Hippodrome is from the Greek word *hippos* meaning *horse*, and *dromos* meaning *race*. The hippodrome is an arena for horse races, chariot races, and other sporting events. The Jerash hippodrome was built during the reign of Hadrian in the 2nd century AD. Despite its large size, it is the smallest of its kind with only 10 starting gates instead of the typical 12. Performances are held in the arena almost daily, displaying chariot races, army drills, and gladiator fights. **Location** Outside the city walls between Hadrian's Arch and the South Gate.

☐ SOUTH GATE & CITY WALLS

The *South Gate* is the southern entrance to the walled city, dating to 130 AD. It is decorated with columns, leaves of acanthus, and statue niches. The gate was part of the original thin city wall, which was later strengthened in the 4th century AD. A small section of this 3-meter thick wall is still standing near the gate. The present city walls date to the Byzantine period. Inside the gate is an open area that served as a marketplace. **Location** The southern end of the walled city.

☐ ZEUS TEMPLE

Built in 162 AD in dedication to Zeus, the king of the gods in Greek mythology. It was built on the site of earlier religious sites. It faces toward the rising sun as most Roman temples did. The temple is currently under reconstruction. A model of the temple is on display in the vaults accessible from the side of the temple's first staircase. **Location** Past of the South Gate, on the hill adjacent to the Oval Plaza.

☐ OVAL PLAZA

Uniquely shaped oval plaza, paved and lined by 1st century Ionic columns. A statue might have originally stood in the middle of the plaza where a Byzantine fountain was later added in the 7th century AD. Currently, only the remains of the fountain stand at the intersection of water-pipe grooves that enter the plaza from the north and exit to the west. A column was recently erected nearby to hold the Jerash Festival flame. **Location** Between the South Gate and the Colonnaded Street.

☐ SOUTH THEATER

Built around 90 AD, the South Theater is the largest of three theaters in Jerash. The other two are the North Theater within the walled city and the Festival Theater two km north of the walled city. The south theater has a seating capacity of over 3,000 spectators. It has a standard design with a stage, orchestra area, seating area, and vaulted passageways through which the audience enters. The ornate stage was originally two stories high. Some seats are marked with Greek letters, denoting assigned seating. **Location** On top of the hill, west of the Oval Plaza.

☐ COLUMN STYLES

The three basic column styles that originated in Greece and were later adopted by the Romans are *Doric*, *Ionic*, and *Corinthian*. The Doric is the oldest and simplest style, characterized by a smoothly rounded column capital. The Ionic style is characterized by a column capital with a pair of spirals. The Corinthian style is characterized by a column capital elaborately decorated with leaves and scrolls. **Location** Doric columns can be found in Qasr al-Abd near *Amman*. Ionic columns are common in the oldest structures in *Jerash*, including the Oval Plaza. Corinthian columns are common in the newest structures in *Jerash*, including the section of the colonnaded street between the Oval Plaza and the Artemis Temple, which was upgraded in the 2nd century AD.

☐ COLONNADED STREETS

Like most Roman cities, Jerash has a north-south primary street called *cardo*, and east-west intersecting streets called *decumani*. The streets are still paved with the original stones that were grooved by chariot wheels. They are all lined by Ionic columns from the 1st century AD with the exception of the lower cardo, which was widened and upgraded to Corinthian columns around the 2nd century AD. The columns get gradually shorter on upslopes to maintain the level of the connecting beams (architraves). These beams eventually connect to the side of a tall column to start a new higher section. Tall columns also mark important points such as the entrance to the food market (macellum). A complex drainage system runs under the full length of the cardo. **Location** The cardo runs between the south and north gates. It is intersected by two east-west streets: the south decumanus and north decumanus.

☐ MACELLUM

Macellum is a food market. The Jerash macellum is an octagonal, colonnaded courtyard with a central fountain, originally surrounded by shops. The inscription on the pedestal that originally stood in the middle of the fountain dates the macellum to 130 AD. Adjacent to the macellum is a lion's head fountain that dates to 211 AD. **Location** On the main colonnaded street (cardo) between the Oval Plaza and the first intersecting street (south decumanus). The entrance is marked by taller street columns. Opposite the macellum is a small museum displaying Roman and prehistoric artifacts.

□ SOUTH TETRAPYLON

Tetrapylon is from the Greek word *tetra* meaning *four*, and *pylon* meaning *gate*. Tetrapylon is a monument at a major street intersection with arches on four sides, allowing traffic in all directions. Only the pedestals of the South Tetrapylon remain standing today. Heading east, the street leads first to the South Bridge, then to the East Baths, then the residential neighborhoods buried under modern *Jerash*, and finally, the East Gate. The ruins at the southwest corner of the tetrapylon belong to an Umayyad mosque from the 8th century AD. Farther west are the ruins of Umayyad houses. **Location** At the intersection of the main street (cardo) and the first cross-street (south decumanus).

□ CATHEDRAL

The Byzantine *Cathedral* was built in the 4th century on a 2nd century Roman Temple dedicated to Dionysus, the god of wine. The ornate gate leading to a staircase is from the original Roman temple. At the top of the stairs is the Cathedral's exterior wall embellished with the Shrine of St. Mary. Inside are the remains of the Cathedral and the Roman fountain court. The Romans reported that the water in the square fountain turned to wine during the Roman Dionysian festivals. Above the Cathedral is the Church of Saint Theodore built in 496 AD; the remains include twin colonnades and an apse. **Location** The Cathedral is on the main street (cardo), just south of the nymphaeum.

□ NYMPHAEUM

A *nymphaeum* is a monument for the mythological spirit of nature (nymph), commonly depicting a beautiful female in a river or in the woods. Built in 191 AD, the Jerash nymphaeum is an ornamental fountain originally decorated with marble, painted plaster, and lion heads spouting water into sidewalk basins that overflowed into the street's drainage system. **Location** On the main street (cardo) between the Cathedral and the staircase leading up to the Artemis Temple.

☐ PROPYLAEUM

Propylaeum is an ornate, monumental gateway leading from the main street (cardo) up to the Artemis Temple. Built in 150 AD, the Propylaeum was originally approached from the east via a street called the *Sacred Way*. This street started from the residential neighborhoods buried under modern Jerash and ended at the main street (cardo) in front of the Propylaeum. The Sacred Way was sealed off in the Byzantine period to build the Propylaeum Church, opposite the Propylaeum, incorporating the street's columns into the church. North of the church are the ruins of the Ayyubid or Mamluk Naghawi's Mosque, built between the 12th and 15th centuries. **Location** On the main street (cardo) just north of the nymphaeum.

☐ ARTEMIS TEMPLE

Built in 150 AD in dedication to Artemis, the goddess of the hunt and the wild, and patron of Jerash. The temple is in a vast courtyard (sacred precinct) originally surrounded by a colonnade. An altar in front of the temple, which now stands in ruin, was the place for public worship. The temple itself likely housed a statue of Artemis. The temple's staircase leads to a high portico with tall Corinthian columns and an inner chamber, now exposed. Despite their massive size, the columns sway in the wind, as demonstrated by the movement of a long object, like a knife, inserted between a column and its base. Some missing temple elements suggest that it was never finished in Roman times. A new discovery at the temple might prove to be the world's oldest church, dating from the 2nd century AD. **Location** On a hill in the heart of the walled city. Reached from the main street (cardo) through the propylaeum.

☐ WATER-POWERED SAW

The oldest known water-powered stone saw was discovered in *Jerash*. The saw, from the 6th century Byzantine period, was powered by a water wheel that simultaneously drove two saws. Prior to this discovery, it was believed that transferring circular to linear motion had been pioneered 500 years later. Similar electricity-powered saws are still used today to cut stones.

Location The southeastern corner of the Artemis courtyard (sacred precinct).

☐ NORTH THEATER

The *North Theater* was originally built around 165 AD with only 14 rows of seats. It was used for hosting the city council and for small performances. Greek inscriptions found on some of the seats reserved them for different voting tribes. The theater was later enlarged in 235 AD to accommodate up to 1,600 spectators. **Location** North of the Artemis Temple.

☐ NORTH TETRAPYLON

Tetrapylon is from the Greek word *tetra* meaning *four*, and *pylon* meaning *gate*. Tetrapylon is a monument at a major street intersection with arches on four sides, allowing traffic in all directions. Jerash's North Tetrapylon was built in the late 2nd century AD and later dedicated to Julia Domna, the Syrian wife of Emperor Lucius Severus. At the southeast corner of the tetrapylon are the ruins of the West Baths. **Location** At the intersection of the main street (cardo) and the second cross-street (north decumanus).

☐ NORTH GATE & BEYOND

The *North Gate* dates to 115 AD. It leads out of the city to the Roman road to Pella. Beyond the gate is a large Roman reservoir that supplied the city with water. Adjacent to the reservoir is a small theater and a bath for the spring and water festivals which involved nude bathing. Just north of the reservoir is the Tomb of Germanus. **Location** The North Gate is at the northern end of the walled city. The reservoir is two kilometers north of the gate.

Roman Forts

The Romans marked their borders and defended them tirelessly. The Roman forts in Jordan are part of a defense system that guarded the Empire's southeastern desert frontier (Limes Arabicus). The forts were linked by watchtowers only 15 km apart in some places.

☐ BSHIR FORT

A Roman fort built between 293 and 305 AD. It is one in a chain of forts and watchtowers from Umm al-Rasas to Lejjun that defended the Empire's southeastern borders. The fort is a square structure with 3-story corner towers, a central courtyard, soldier barracks, stables, and a nearby water reservoir. It was abandoned by the Romans in the 5th century AD, and then used by the Umayyads until it was damaged by an earthquake in the 8th century AD. Despite the damage, the fort's remote location kept it better preserved than other Roman forts in the region. **Location** 15 km northwest of *Qatranah* at the GPS coordinates: 31.3372°, 35.9810° (requires 4x4).

☐ LEJJUN FORTRESS

A Roman legionary fortress built around 300 AD. It was one in a chain of forts and watchtowers stretching from Umm al-Rasas to Lejjun that defended the Empire's southeastern borders. Only the outlines of this large, square fortress survived. Two rows of Ottoman barracks, commonly mistaken as Roman, stand 250 meters southwest of the fortress. The ruins of a prehistoric settlement are also nearby (see *Menhirs*).

Location Near the village of *Lejjun*, between *Karak* and *Qatranah*, at the GPS coordinates: 31.2370°, 35.8683°.

☐ UMM AL-JIMAL

Also known as the Black Oasis, the town of *Umm al-Jimal* (mother of camels) is believed to have been established by the Nabateans on a trade route around 2,000 years ago. Umm al-Jimal developed into Roman barracks around 200 AD and later expanded into forts and a town of several thousand people. Umm al-Jimal now consists of two forts at the northern and southern ends of the town, two Byzantine towers, about 15 Byzantine churches built around 600 AD, and town houses. All the structures were constructed with black basalt stones abundant in this area. Umm al-Jimal fell into ruins after an earthquake in 747 AD. **Location** 80 km northeast of Amman; 20 km east of *Mafraq*, near the border with Syria.

☐ AZRAQ FORT

One of several forts that defended the springs of the Azraq Oasis. Although the Azraq Oasis was distant from major cities, controlling it was important both to protect trade routes and to deny enemies access to water. The Azraq Fort was originally built by the Romans in the 3rd century AD, later used by the Byzantines and Umayyads, rebuilt by the Mamluks in 1237, and used by the Ottomans in the 16th century. Lawrence of Arabia spent the winter of 1917 in this fort during the Great Arab Revolt against the Ottoman Empire. The fort is square-shaped with corner-towers, a central courtyard, a small mosque, and a water well. It was built with black basalt stones and massive granite doors that seal the entrance. **Location** The Azraq Oasis 90 km east of Amman.

☐ BURQU' FORT

Built by the Romans in the 3rd century AD to defend the Ghadir Burqu' water spring. Although the spring was distant from major cities, controlling it was important both to protect trade routes and to deny enemies access to water. The fort is a square structure with a 4-story tower surrounded by rooms, walls, a gatehouse, and a nearby spring-fed, dammed water reservoir. The Burqu' fort became a Byzantine monastery in the 3rd and 4th century AD, and then an Umayyad

palace around 700 AD. **Location** Northeastern Jordan, 20 km northwest of *Ruwayshid*, at the GPS coordinates: 32.6133°, 37.9672° (requires 4x4).

☐ VIA NOVA TRAIANA

One of the most significant achievements of the Romans in Jordan was the building of the *Via Nova Traiana*, a paved road along the ancient King's Highway trading route. It was built by Emperor Trajan around 112-114 AD. It linked Aqaba, Amman, Jerash, Pella, Umm Qais, and Umm al-Jimal with the Syrian cities of Bosra and Damascus, and with trade routes from the Mediterranean and Egypt. **Location** A few sections of the road have survived in remote locations, while most of it evolved into the present-day King's Highway (Highway 35). Some milestones are exhibited on Mount Nebo, in Aqaba Fort, and in other museums. Some Roman forts along the road are still standing today (see *Roman Forts*).

☐ MACHAERUS FORTRESS

Built around 100 BC by the Hasmonean king Alexander Jannaeus to defend against the Nabateans. It was destroyed by the Romans in 57 BC, then rebuilt by the Roman client-king Herod the Great in 37-34 BC. It was here that Herod's son, Herod Antipas, honored Salome's wishes by presenting her with the head of the prophet John the Baptist on a plate. The fortress was again destroyed by the Romans in 72 AD after the Judaean war. The fortress is comprised of towers, rooms, a courtyard, a bath, and an aqueduct. **Location** A hill summit by the village of *Mukawir*, overlooking the *Dead Sea*; 30 km southwest of *Madaba*.

Byzantine Period

The Byzantine period began when the first Christian Roman Emperor, Constantine I, founded the Eastern Roman Empire in 324 AD, with its capital Constantinople in present-day Turkey. Christianity in Jordan began to develop earlier in the first century, but flourished in the Byzantine period. A large number of Byzantine churches lavished with exquisite mosaics were built in Madaba, Jerash, Petra, and other cities.

☐ **THE BAPTISM SITE**

Known as *Bethany beyond the Jordan* or *Bethabara*, it is believed to be the location on the Jordan River where Jesus Christ was baptized by John the Baptist. It is also identified as the location where the prophet Elijah ascended to heaven. The site includes the ruins of three Byzantine churches built over each other in the 5th-6th centuries AD. **Location** A short distance east of the *Jordan River*, just north of the *Dead Sea*. Follow the signs before reaching the Dead Sea from Amman.

☐ **CHURCH OF ST. GEORGE**

Also known as the *Church of the Map*, this Greek Orthodox church was built in 1884 on the ruins of an older Byzantine church. It incorporates sections of a mosaic floor that date to around 560 AD. The mosaic is a map of the Holy Land with the oldest existing representation of Jerusalem. Among other locations, it depicts the Jordan River, the Dead Sea, Egypt, Lebanon, and Turkey. **Location** The Church of St. George is at the center of the city of *Madaba*, 30 km southwest of Amman.

☐ ARCHAEOLOGICAL PARK

Madaba's *Archaeological Park* is a partially-roofed museum that displays structures and mosaics from the Roman, Byzantine, and Umayyad periods. The park was established after the excavation of the Byzantine Church of the Virgin, which led to the excavation of an adjacent Roman road, a Byzantine mansion (the Hippolytus Hall), and other structures. **Location** The park is at the center of the city of *Madaba*, walking distance from the Church of St. George. Adjacent to the park is the Madaba School of Mosaics, which conserves and restores ancient mosaics.

☐ CHURCH OF THE APOSTLES

A Byzantine church built in 568 AD. The remaining spectacular mosaic floor, known as the *Personification of the Sea*, is by an artist named Salamanios. It depicts a female figure emerging from the sea, surrounded by mythical sea creatures, exotic animals, and vegetation. **Location** The southern entrance to *Madaba* at the GPS coordinates: 31.7118°, 35.7950°.

☐ UMM AL-RASAS

Umm al-Rasas is an ancient city with origins that date as far back as the 6th or 7th century BC. It was later fortified by the Romans to serve as a military station, and was most active in the Byzantine and Umayyad periods when the Christian inhabitants constructed several churches adorned with mosaic floors. The Church of St. Stephen boasts the largest mosaic floor in Jordan, containing inscriptions, geometrical patterns, portraits, and depictions of 27 cities, including Jerusalem and Madaba. Umm al-Rasas consists of a fortified camp in the southern part of the city and open quarters to the north. About one km north of the city, there is a stone quarry, a cistern, and a 15 meter tower. The tower has a small room at the top without stairs to reach it; it is believed to have been a retreat for hermit monks. **Location** 30 km southeast *Madaba*.

☐ JERASH CHURCHES

The Church of Saints Cosmas and Damian is among a group of Byzantine churches in the western end of the Roman city of Gerasa (Jerash). It was built in 533 AD in dedication to the martyred twin doctors known for providing free medical care. The church has splendid floor mosaics depicting animals, geometric designs, and donor portraits. There are two neighboring churches: the Church of John the Baptist, whose mosaics are displayed in the Roman Theatre in Amman, and the Church of St. George. A total of 15 churches have been unearthed in Jerash. **Location** Within the walls of Roman *Jerash*, west of the Cathedral.

☐ PETRA CHURCHES

In the Byzantine period, many of Petra's tombs were modified into churches. Three new churches were also constructed in the city center: the Petra Church, the Blue Church, and the Ridge Church. The Petra Church was built in the late 5th century. It contains exquisite mosaics depicting personifications of nature and animals, which represent God's domain. The Blue Church is so called for its blue Egyptian granite columns adorned with Nabataean horned capitals. **Location** The three main churches are north of the Colonnade Street in the center of *Petra*. Among the tombs modified into churches are the Urn Tomb east of Colonnade Street and the Christian Tombs north of the city.

☐ ICONOCLASM

Iconoclasm is the destruction of images and statues for religious or political purposes. Iconoclasm took place during both the Byzantine and Islamic periods in Jordan. The careful erasing of icons in churches such as the Church of St. Stephen in Umm al-Rasas suggests changes introduced by the Christian community in the Byzantine period. In the Islamic period that followed, iconography was tolerated, except under the brief rule of the Umayyad caliph Yazid II (720-724 AD). The destruction of iconography in open areas, such as the figures on Petra's Treasury, might be by individuals, not systematic campaigns. **Location** Common in Byzantine churches such as the Church of St. Stephen in *Umm al-Rasas*.

Early Islamic Period

The Islamic campaign against the Byzantines began in the town of Mu'ta near Karak in 629 AD. Muslims won the decisive Battle of Fahl in Pella in 636 AD. Tombs and shrines of many of the Prophet's companions and military leaders can be found in Karak, Irbid, and other cities in Jordan.

Scattered around Jordan's Eastern Desert are palaces from the early Islamic Umayyad period, 661-750 AD. Their lack of defensive features and the scarcity of pottery shards around these palaces suggest they were used only sporadically for desert retreats, rest-houses, or for maintaining contact with Bedouin tribes.

☐ QASTAL PALACE

One of the oldest Umayyad palaces, believed to have been built by the Caliph Abd al-Malik, the builder of the Dome of the Rock Mosque in Jerusalem. Despite the modern construction on the site, the Qastal Palace has been well preserved and plans are underway to restore it. The palace is a square structure with corner and side towers, 30 rooms grouped into six independent living areas, and a central courtyard. The complex includes over 100 cisterns, a dammed reservoir, baths, the oldest Muslim cemetery in Jordan, and a mosque with the remains of a minaret that might be the oldest in the Islamic world. **Location** On Highway 15, 25 km south of *Amman,* at the GPS: 31.7460°, 35.9405°.

☐ HALLABAT PALACE

The *Hallabat Palace* was originally a Roman fort built in 198-217 AD. It was converted into a monastery in the Byzantine period and then rebuilt by the Umayyads in the 7th century AD. The palace has ornate frescos, mosaics, and carvings. It includes an adjacent mosque, a reservoir, eight cisterns, an irrigated agricultural area, small independent houses, and the Sarah bath complex two km to the east. **Location** Off Highway 30, 25 km east of *Zarqa*. The Sarah bath complex is closer to the main highway; the palace is two km past the baths at the GPS coordinates: 32.0929°, 36.3280°.

☐ KHARANA CASTLE

Well-preserved Islamic castle built in 711 AD. The square, two-story building consists of 61 rooms grouped into independent living areas, arranged around a central courtyard. Although it looks like a fort, the towers are not massive enough for defense, and the windows are not wide enough from the inside to have been used as arrow slits. The building was more likely used as a rest-house for desert caravans or as a retreat for the Umayyad leaders. Greek inscriptions found on some stones indicate that this castle was built on the site of an older building. **Location** Highway 40; 60 km east of Amman at the GPS: 31.7293°, 36.4646°.

☐ AMRA PALACE

Small, well-preserved, Islamic palace built in the early 8th century AD. It consists of a triple-vaulted hall, two private rooms, a bath complex, a ground-water well, and a water tank. The bath complex provided cold, warm, and hot rooms. An external furnace provided hot water to the bath and circulated hot air under the floors. The interiors are ornate with murals and mosaics in the Byzantine style. They depict historical figures, activities, and leisure scenes such as hunting and dancing. The palace might have been used as a desert retreat by the Umayyad leaders. **Location** Highway 40, 80 km east of Amman, at the GPS coordinates: 31.8029°, 36.5884°.

☐ THE PALACE

Simply known as *the Palace*, this complex was built by the Umayyads in the 8th century AD. It consists of a reception hall, a mosque, a courtyard, a colonnaded street, a bathhouse, and a large cistern. It is located within Amman's Citadel, which is also the site of the world's earliest fortifications, early Bronze Age tombs, the Ammonites' capital, and the remains of the Roman temple of Hercules and a Byzantine basilica. Nearby is the Jordan Archaeological Museum which houses antiquities that date as far back as prehistoric times. The collection includes artifacts from Ain Ghazal and the Dead Sea Copper Scroll. **Location** Jabal al-Qal'a overlooking downtown *Amman*.

☐ TOBA PALACE

Built with baked bricks along the Syria-Hejaz caravan route in the mid 8th century AD, but never fully completed. The unpreserved palace is a vast, walled, rectangular enclosure with corner and side towers; two symmetrical structures with vaulted reception halls and living quarters; and three nearby wells. **Location** 70 km east of *Qatranah*, at the GPS coordinates 31.3257°, 36.5700°. Requires 4x4.

☐ MUSHATTA PALACE

The largest and most lavish Umayyad palace. Built in 743-744 AD, but never fully completed. It consists of a monumental gateway, a reception-hall, living quarters, a mosque, vast brick walls, and at least 23 towers. The original, ornate gate facade is on display in the Pergamum Museum in Berlin, sent as a gift by the Ottomans. **Location** South of *Amman*, adjacent to the *Queen Alia International Airport*, at the GPS coordinates: 31.7383°, 36.0100°.

☐ AYLA

The town of Ayla (present day Aqaba) dates back to the 4th millennium BC. It was inhabited by early Arabs, the Nabateans, Romans, Byzantines, and then came under Islamic rule in 630 AD. Islamic Ayla is a rare example of an Islamic urban plan known as *misr*. The rectangular walled town has two intersecting axial streets that lead to four side gates. Within the walls is an early Islamic mosque from the 8th or 9th century AD, a governor's residence, and tribal quarters. **Location** *Aqaba's* main waterfront road, near the hotel district.

☐ SUGAR MILLS

At least 30 sugar mills from the Islamic Ayyubid and Mamluk periods (11th-13th century AD) are located in the Jordan Valley. The sugar industry was introduced into the valley from southern Iraq and later spread to North Africa, Spain, and the rest of Europe. The mills consist of water channels, water-powered grinding stones for crushing sugar cane, furnaces for boiling water, and storage rooms. The word *sugar* derives from the Arabic *sukkar*. **Location** An example is at Tawahin al-Sukkar near *Safi*, at the southern end of the *Dead Sea*.

Crusades

The Pope's call to seize Jerusalem in 1096 AD started the military campaigns known as the *Crusades*, which established the Christian Kingdom of Jerusalem five years later. This led to building a chain of Crusader castles in present-day Jordan to disrupt the route between Muslim bases in Damascus and Cairo.

☐ SHOBAK CASTLE

The earliest Crusader fortress in Jordan, built in 1115 AD. The castle was surrendered to Saladin in 1189 AD, one year after he conquered the Karak Castle. The Shobak Castle was refortified in the following centuries by the Mamluks. The castle includes massive walls, towers, two churches, an olive-press, cisterns, baths, and a spring at the bottom of a deep well. **Location** A hill summit northeast of *Shobak* and 20 km north of Petra, at the GPS coordinates: 30.5207°, 35.6161°.

☐ WADI MUSA CASTLE

Built in 1115-1116 AD, this Crusader castle is surrounded by two outer walls and square watchtowers, and takes advantage of difficult, mountainous terrain for protection. It includes a church, a gatehouse, cisterns, and communication bridges. The Wadi Musa Castle was the last of Jordan's Crusader castles to fall to Saladin in 1189 AD. **Location** Overlooking *Wadi Wu'ayra*, one km north of *Petra* before reaching *Little Petra*, at the GPS coordinates: 30.3324°, 35.4679°.

☐ HABIS & HIGH PLACE CASTLES

In addition to the Wadi Musa Castle just outside Petra, two more Crusader castles were built inside Petra to serve as watchtowers and signaling posts on the sight line with Jerusalem. The two castles currently lie in ruins from past earthquakes. **Location** Within the ancient city of Petra. The Habis Castle is atop the *Habis Mountain* (where the Unfinished Tomb is located). The High Place Castle is atop the *Madbah Mountain* (where the Treasury building is located).

☐ KARAK CASTLE

Crusader fortress built in 1142 AD, incorporating stones from older Nabatean, Roman, and Byzantine ruins. It served as the main link in a chain of Crusader fortifications in present-day Jordan. Among its inhabitants was Reynald de Chatillon, renowned for his brutality. He was defeated by Saladin in the Battle of Hattin, and the castle was conquered soon after in 1188 AD.

The castle was then refortified in the following two centuries by the Mamluks. It remained in continuous use by various groups, including the Ottomans, into the 19th century. The castle has arrow-slit walls, towers, a dungeon, vaulted halls, courtyards, a school, a mosque, and a large kitchen. **Location** A hill summit in the city of *Karak*, 120 km south of *Amman*.

☐ AQABA FORT

With the conquest of Aqaba in the early 12th century AD, the Crusaders built the Helim fortress and fortified the Pharaoh's Island to deny Muslims access to the port. Aqaba was recaptured by Saladin in 1182. The Crusader fortress was rebuilt by the Mamluks in 1587 and has been modified several times since. The present-day Aqaba Fort is a square structure with semicircular towers and walls adorned with Arabic inscriptions. The Hashemite Coat of Arms was added above the main gate at the end of the Ottoman rule. **Location** The Aqaba Fort is on the city's waterfront. The Pharaoh's Island is in Egyptian waters, 7 km offshore.

☐ RABADH CASTLE

Islamic military castle built by Saladin's nephew in 1183-1185 AD, during the rule of Saladin. It served as a strategic military post overlooking the Jordan River Valley and defending against the Crusaders. It also protected the iron mines around Ajloun, needed for military use. The castle has five towers, vaulted rooms, a surrounding moat, arrow slits, and other defensive features. **Location** A hill summit above *Ajloun* at the GPS coordinates: 32.3250°, 35.7275°. Iron debris from the smelting process can be found on the same hill right before reaching the castle. The iron mines are at the al-Warda caves near Ajloun.

Ottoman Period

Jordan came under the control of the Ottoman Turks after they defeated the Mamluks in 1516 AD. The Ottoman rule lasted four centuries, during which time they generally neglected the region, limiting their attention to pilgrimage routes. The Ottoman rule ended with the end of World War I and the Great Arab Revolt in 1918 AD.

Pilgrimage Road

Darb al-Shami (the Northern Way) is a pilgrimage route connecting Damascus with Mecca. It was established by the Ottomans around the 17th century AD and was strategically built on flat desert terrain, unlike the older routes to the west that stretch through mountainous Karak, Shobak, and Petra. To insure safe passage and water supply, the Ottomans built or reused existing structures to form a chain of 15 forts between Damascus and Aqaba.

☐ **MA'AN FORT**

Built in 1532 AD by the Ottomans, the Ma'an Fort is the oldest fort along the pilgrimage road in Jordan. It was also one of the most popular since the lush Ma'an oasis served as a welcome respite for pilgrims on their way to Mecca. While the Ma'an Fort currently serves as a cultural center, it was used as a prison for much of the last century. **Location** In *Ma'an*'s old quarter.

☐ DAB'A FORT

Built in the 16th century by the Ottomans, the Dab'a Fort is one of the oldest forts along the pilgrimage road in Jordan. The fort is a square, two-story building with rooms arranged around a central courtyard. It is surrounded by walls with arrow slits and square corner towers. The adjacent water reservoir (recently covered) is supplied by flood water through a smaller tank that collects sediments. **Location** 45 km south of *Amman*, off the Desert Highway (Highway 15), at the GPS coordinates: 31.5962°, 36.0505°.

☐ QATRANAH FORT

Two-story Ottoman fort, built in 1559 AD to guard a water reservoir on the pilgrimage road. The reservoir is a large open tank supplied by flood water in rainy seasons. Dams and channels diverted the water, first through a small settling tank to collect the sediments, then to the reservoir. **Location** In the town of *Qatranah*, on the Desert Highway (Highway 15).

☐ HASA FORT

Ottoman fort built in the 18th century to protect a water reservoir on the pilgrimage road. It is the last fort to have been built on this road. It is a square building with a central courtyard and a well. It is flanked by an open water tank on one side and a paved portion of the pilgrimage road on the other. The paved road extends over one km to avoid muddy conditions after rainfall and leads to a well-preserved bridge over the shallow start of the Wadi Hasa. **Location** Near the town of *Hasa*, 130 km south of Amman. The fort is on a dirt road off the Desert Highway (Highway 15), at the GPS coordinates: 30.8396°, 35.9333°.

☐ QASR SHABIB

Located in Zarqa, *Qasr Shabib* is the most northern surviving fort on the Ottoman's pilgrimage road before Damascus. The only fort farther north, in Mafraq, did not survive. Qasr Shabib was originally built by the Mamluks, and later used by the Ottomans to guard several water cisterns around it. The building consists of a single room and a tower with massive walls. **Location** In the heart of the city of *Zarqa*.

□ JIZA FORT

The *Jiza* complex consists of a massive 18 million gallon water tank and a fort that currently serves as a police station. The reservoir is believed to be Nabatean or Roman in origin. It later became a vital stop along the Ottoman's pilgrimage road. **Location** 30 km south of *Amman* on Route 25, past the *Queen Alia International Airport*. GPS coordinates: 31.7017°, 35.9524°.

□ HEJAZ RAILWAY

Towards the end of their rule, the Ottomans constructed the Hejaz Railway along the old pilgrimage road. Some train stations were built a close distance from the forts that protected the road. During the Great Arab Revolt (1916-1918), successful raids on the railway by Lawrence of Arabia and the Arab army disrupted the line only a few years after it opened. **Location** The Hejaz Railway ran through *Mafraq, Zarqa, Amman, Jiza, Qatranah, Ma'an, Mudawwara,* and several stations in between, many of which are still standing or in use today. Most Arab raids took place south of *Ma'an,* damaging and later dismantling the railroad section north of *Mudawwara.* Several sections farther north are still operational such as the route between *Amman* and *Damascus,* and between *Hasa* and *Aqaba.*

Environment

Habitats

Jordan is at the intersection of the Mediterranean region, central Asia, and the Arabian desert. It enjoys diverse ecosystems, ranging from woodlands to shrublands to deserts. Created by the Great Rift Valley, Wadi Araba also enjoys an Afrotropical ecozone with a unique mix of Arabian wildlife and African vegetation.

☐ NORTHERN HIGHLANDS

The Northern Highlands enjoy a Mediterranean climate, receive the country's highest rainfall, and have the richest vegetation. They are habitats for natural oak and pine forests, wild flowers, and numerous animal species such as insects, birds, rodents, bats, and foxes. **Location** The *Northern Highlands* extend southwards from *Irbid* to *Amman*. They include the *Ajloun Woodland Reserve* and the *Dibbin Nature Reserve*.

☐ SOUTHERN HIGHLANDS

The Southern Highlands feature rugged mountains and dramatic elevation changes that form a variety of habitats. They are home to numerous plant species, including juniper and wild almond trees, and numerous animal species. The mammalian species include the caracal, rock hyrax, and Nubian ibex. The rugged rock cliffs are ideal nesting sites for a number of birds of prey. **Location** The *Southern Highlands* extend southwards from *Shobak* to *Ras al-Naqb*. They include the *Dana Nature Reserve*.

☐ WADIS

Wadi is Arabic for *valley,* generally referring to a valley with flowing water in rainy years. Wadis with flowing water are ideal habitats for oleander, cattail, reed, and other plants that require constant water. They are breeding grounds for amphibians, fish, and insects such as dragonflies and horseflies.

Wadis also attract larger animals, including carnivores and migrant birds. **Location** Most wadis with flowing water intersect Jordan's highlands and terminate in the Jordan Valley. Examples are Wadi Mujib, Wadi Hasa, and Wadi Zarqa. Examples around *Amman* are Wadi al-Seer and Wadi Shita.

☐ RESERVOIRS

Although man-made, dam and sewage reservoirs are habitats for numerous indigenous animals and vital roosting sites for migrant birds. They are breeding grounds for invertebrates, fish, and amphibians; hunting grounds for insectivores and carnivores; and waterholes for herbivores. **Location** Wadi Arab and Wadi Ziqlab dams are west of *Irbid*; Buwayda, Ghadeer al-Abyad, and Sama al-Sarhan dams are around *Mafraq*; King Talal dam is south of *Jerash*; Khaldiyeh Dam is east of *Zarqa*; Karama, Shu'ayb and Kafrein dams are north of the *Dead Sea*; Wala and Mujib Dams are south of *Madaba*; Swaqa, Qatranah, and Sultani dams are around *Qatranah*; Tannoor dam is south of *Karak*; Wadi Rajil dam is east of *Azraq*; Ruwayshid, Sha'lan, and Burqu' dams are around *Burqu'*.

☐ DEAD SEA

The safety of the rugged mountains and river valleys around the Dead Sea make this region an ideal habitat for animals such as the Nubian ibex, golden jackal, and eagles. Mammals such as the crested porcupine often venture to the shores of the Dead Sea at night to lick salt. The Mujib Nature Reserve is home to over 400 plant species, and over 200 mammal, fish, amphibian, and reptile species. **Location** The Mujib bridge is a good location to observe soaring birds of prey and the passage of migrant birds. The Mujib gorge is a nesting site for numerous birds. The *Mujib Nature Reserve* offers campsites and hiking trails for wildlife observation.

□ DESERTS

Despite their barren appearance, deserts support a variety of vegetation, including some trees. Insects, reptiles, and small mammals are abundant in shady places, under rocks, or in sandy burrows. They minimize water loss by moving in cooler hours, and some get all of their water from the food they eat. Rainy winters create desert pools that can last through spring, supporting even migrant birds. Some animals indigenous to the Basalt Desert have evolved dark variations in response to their dark habitat, including the black morph of the mourning wheatear and the black agama. **Location** The *Basalt Desert* is in northern Jordan, the *Ruwayshid Desert* is in the northeast, the *Central Desert* is in central Jordan, the *Rum* and *Mudawwarah* deserts are in the south, and *Wadi Araba* is in southwestern Jordan.

☐ JORDAN RIVER VALLEY

The combination of water from the *Jordan River*, fertile soils, and low-elevation make the *Jordan River Valley* a natural greenhouse, ideal for both wild and cultivated vegetation. It is also an ideal habitat for pollinators and leaf-eating invertebrates, which in turn attract larger insectivores and carnivores, including the European otter. **Location** Known as *Ghor*, the *Jordan River Valley* extends southwards from the *Yarmouk River* to the *Dead Sea*.

☐ RED SEA

The shallow depth and lack of sea currents in the Gulf of Aqaba produce clear water and enable light-loving algae and corals to thrive. This in turn attracts other marine life, including crabs, urchins, sea turtles, and dolphins. Over 1,100 fish species and over 1,000 invertebrates have been recorded in the *Red Sea*, around 10% are unique to these waters. **Location** *Aqaba* is on the *Red Sea* in southern Jordan.

☐ HUMAN ENVIRONMENT

Urban gardens, parks, and undeveloped lots are habitats for numerous wild and cultivated plants, which attract pollinators and herbivores. Urban trash sites are breeding and feeding grounds for many insects and rodents. They all in turn attract predatory insectivores and carnivores, including reptiles, hedgehogs, and even foxes. Animals that have adapted to urban environments tend to be secretive, nocturnal, or elusive to humans. Many make their homes in building crevices. **Location** Cities, towns, and villages.

Human Impact

☐ DESERTIFICATION

Desertification is the loss of fertile land due mainly to human activities such as deforestation, overgrazing, and inappropriate agriculture. These activities lead to the break up and erosion of the fertile topsoil and the expansion of deserts. Campaigns to stop or reverse desertification have not been successful everywhere in Jordan. **Location** Archaeological evidence of deforestation is found in a prehistoric human settlement in *Amman* (see *Ain Ghazal*) and in *Finan* (see *Finan Copper Mines*). In the past century, much of Jordan's forests in the *Northern Highlands* were decimated by the Ottomans to build and fuel the Hejaz Railway. Livestock tracks crisscross most of Jordan's barren hills, providing visual evidence of overgrazing. Inappropriate agriculture is widely practiced in critical marginal land.

☐ WATER SHORTAGE

As Jordan's population continues to rise, the increased demand for water is currently met by overdrawing ground water. This unsustainable practice is reducing the quality of water and will drain aquifers in just a few years. Much of the Azraq Oasis has been lost due to the overdrawing of its ground water, greatly impacting indigenous wildlife and migrant birds. Surface freshwater is also increasingly diverted to cities, causing the Dead Sea to shrink rapidly. **Location** The three main aquifers in Jordan are under *Amman*, *Azraq*, and *Disi* (north of *Wadi Rum*).

☐ LITTER & POLLUTION

While one piece of litter may seem harmless, each piece contributes to the gradual degradation of whole habitats and ecosystems. Among other things, litter can trap and kill animals, pollute water, and provide breeding grounds for disease-transmitting insects and rodents. Industrial and agricultural pollution can cause diseases and disorders affecting both humans and wildlife. Worldwide, water pollution is the cause of over 14,000 human deaths each day. With the exception of the Aqaba basin, Jordan's drainage basins have no outlets to other bodies of water, which makes them sensitive to pollution (see *Basins*). Pollution brought in by rainwater is left behind by evaporation, gradually building up in the environment and seeping into underground aquifers. **Location** Littering is common on roadsides and picnic areas in Jordan. Some bodies of water, like the *Zarqa River*, have been polluted by sewage and industrial waste. Sources of air pollution include refineries, mines, vehicles, and dust storms.

☐ URBAN SPRAWL

In addition to the deterioration of city centers, horizontal urban expansion leads to the fragmentation, degradation, and loss of wildlife habitats. This greatly disrupts wildlife migration and breeding, and can even disrupt plant pollination and seed dispersal. **Location** Not too long ago, most busy areas outside of city centers belonged to the countryside. Urban sprawl is evident in areas around *Amman* and most cities in western Jordan. New proposals are under way to expand Amman vertically by developing high-rises.

☐ HUNTING

Hunting with automatic weapons has decimated Jordan's wild animals over the past century. It has led to the local extinction of several species, including the Arabian oryx. Although hunting laws are addressing this problem, many animal species remain endangered due to illegal hunting, indiscriminate killing of carnivores to protect livestock, and the killing of animals for superstitious beliefs. **Location** Hunting is banned east of the Hejaz Railway and regulated elsewhere. Hunting is controlled by the *Royal Society for the Conservation of Nature*.

☐ INTRODUCED SPECIES

Although long-term repercussions are not always obvious, introduced species can suddenly become invasive, unraveling ecosystems that took thousands or millions of years to reach a balance. Introduced species can rob native wildlife of water and nutrients, deny local animals of natural food sources and nesting sites, promote harmful organisms, and increase risks such as wildfires. **Location** Introduced ornamental and agricultural plants are common in urban and agricultural areas. Introduced, fast-growing trees are well established in the *Jordan River Valley*. Introduced fish threaten most native and endemic fish species in river valleys and in *Azraq*. Introduced parakeets and crows are well-established in *Amman* and *Aqaba*. Travel and trade increase the risk of accidental introduction of small organism such as algae and viruses.

Field Etiquette

To enjoy nature and conserve it for future generations:

- Drive and walk on existing paths. Minimize your impact on natural habitats.

- Leave everything as you found it. Take photographs instead of collecting natural objects, plants, and animals.

- Minimize noise. Enjoy natural sounds or the peace and quiet of nature.

- Animals do not want to hurt you. They only hunt their natural prey and will only attack humans in self-defense. Make them notice your presence calmly and then give them a chance to leave you alone.

- Leave nothing behind. Carry litter back with you and dispose of it in trash bins.

☐ THREATENED SPECIES

Habitat destruction in Jordan has led to the local extinction of many animal species over the past several thousand years. Archaeological depictions suggest that Jordan's wildlife once included lions, bears, and even crocodiles. In the past century, over-hunting led to the local extinction of the leopard, cheetah, Arabian ostrich, Arabian oryx, and Persian onager. Many species remain endangered or vulnerable today mainly due to habitat loss, including the Nubian ibex, gray wolf, golden jackal, rock hyrax, striped hyena, dorcas gazelle, Eurasian otter, and long-fingered bat. Waterfowl and migrant birds are rare today due to the recent destruction of the Azraq marshlands.

Parks and Reserves

Founded in 1966, the *Royal Society for the Conservation of Nature* (RSCN) established several reserves in Jordan to protect wildlife and natural habitats. The RSCN is working to establish additional protected areas and to raise environmental public awareness.

☐ **SHOMARI RESERVE**

Established in 1975 to breed locally extinct or endangered wildlife, the *Shomari Reserve* occupies 22 square kilometers of desert grassland. It hosts the Arabian oryx, Persian onager, and other rare animals. It includes an observation tower, a small zoo, a picnic area, and exhibits. **Location** On Highway 5, 10 km south of *Azraq*. For details, contact the *Royal Society for the Conservation of Nature* (RSCN).

☐ **AZRAQ WETLAND RESERVE**

Established in 1977 to protect migratory birds, the *Azraq Wetland Reserve* occupies 12 square kilometers of marshland. It attracts over 300 resident and migratory bird species, and a large variety of invertebrates, fish, amphibians, reptiles, and mammals. It is a habitat for the endemic fish *Aphanius sirhani*. The reserve includes a visitor center, boardwalks, a birding tower, and a nearby eco-lodge. **Location** The city of *Azraq*. For details, contact the *Royal Society for the Conservation of Nature* (RSCN).

☐ **MUJIB NATURE RESERVE**

Established in 1987 to protect the Nubian ibex mountain goat, the *Mujib Nature Reserve* occupies 218 square kilometers of mountains, wadis, and a spectacular gorge. In addition to the Nubian ibex, the reserve protects the habitats of a variety of wildlife, including the mountain gazelle, caracal, striped hyena, wild boar, birds of prey, and fish. The reserve includes hiking trails (river and land), a visitor center, and camping sites. **Location** East of the *Dead Sea*. The visitor center is at the Mujib Bridge where the Mujib River terminates at the *Dead Sea*. For details, contact the *Royal Society for the Conservation of Nature* (RSCN).

☐ AJLOUN WOODLAND RESERVE

Established in 1988 to conserve forests and reintroduce the Roe Deer, the *Ajloun Woodland Reserve* occupies 13 square kilometers of woodlands. It is a habitat for oak, pistachio and strawberry trees, and about 190 floral plants. It also provides habitats for badgers, foxes, wild boars, numerous birds, invertebrates, and reptiles. The reserve includes hiking trails, picnic areas, some archaeological sites and old villages, a visitor center, and a forest lodge. **Location** The *Ajloun* highlands, 40 km northwest of *Amman*. For details, contact the *Royal Society for the Conservation of Nature* (RSCN).

☐ DANA NATURE RESERVE

Established in 1989, the *Dana Nature Reserve* occupies 325 square kilometers of magnificent mountains, wadis, and imposing cliffs. The nature reserve is a habitat for over 700 plant species, as well as numerous animals, including the sand cat, rock hyrax, and crested porcupine. The reserve includes the Dana Village whose roots stretch back 6,000 years, many archaeological sites including Nabatean tombs, the ancient Finan copper mines (see *Finan Copper Mines*), a campsite, hiking trails, a guest house with spectacular views of Wadi Dana, and an eco-lodge. **Location** 50 km north of *Petra*. For details, contact the *Royal Society for the Conservation of Nature* (RSCN).

☐ WADI RUM PROTECTED AREA

The *Wadi Rum Protected Area* was established in 1998 to conserve natural scenery, archaeological sites, and indigenous wildlife. It occupies 560 square kilometers of mountains with spectacular vertical cliffs, and valleys with sandy dunes. It is a habitat for over 180 plant species (some endemic), eagles, reptiles, invertebrates, and other wildlife. *Wadi Rum* includes camping and rock-climbing areas, archaeological sites, prehistoric and Nabatean petroglyphs, and a visitor center. **Location** Highway 15, between *Ma'an* and *Aqaba*. For details, contact the *Royal Society for the Conservation of Nature* (RSCN).

☐ DIBBIN NATURE RESERVE

Established in 2004 to conserve forests, the *Dibbin Nature Reserve* occupies eight square kilometers of woodlands. It is a habitat for oak and pine trees, the tawny owl, Syrian woodpecker, Persian squirrel, and other wildlife. The reserve includes picnic areas and a rest house. **Location** South of *Jerash*. For details, contact the *Royal Society for the Conservation of Nature* (RSCN).

Climate

Jordan's Northern Highlands have a moderate Mediterranean climate, while the east and south have a desert climate. The Northern Highlands receive over 600 mm of rain a year and occasionally snow in the winter, while the driest deserts receive less than 100 mm of rainfall per year.

Average Temperatures in Celsius				
	Spring	**Summer**	**Autumn**	**Winter**
Amman	15-21°	21-32°	15-21°	4-15°
Dead Sea	19-25°	25-38°	19-25°	10-19°
Petra	10-14°	14-28°	10-14°	0-10°
Aqaba	20-26°	26-38°	20-26°	10-20°
Azraq	13-19°	19-37°	13-19°	1-13°
Jafr	15-17°	17-35°	15-17°	1-15°

☐ KHAMSEEN

Khamseen (meaning *fifty* in Arabic) is a dust or sandstorm that typically lasts around 50 days, sweeping across many countries in the region. The storms typically blow over Jordan for only a few of these 50 days. They are caused by strong southerly winds passing over arid deserts. Sandstorms have a solid wall of sand at their leading edge; they are usually confined to a shallow layer below calm skies. Dust storms, on the other hand, lift and diffuse light dust particles higher up in the air. Desertification exposes more sand to the wind, increasing the occurrence of such storms. Khamseen can cause minor structural damage, as well as reduce visibility and coat everything with dust. **Location** Large dust and sandstorms usually traverse a number of Middle Eastern countries and may cover all of Jordan. They typically form in late spring.

☐ FLASH FLOOD

A *flash flood* is the rapid flooding of valleys or low grounds after a rainfall. Flash floods are caused either by heavy rains or moderate rains in deserts with hard soils that do not absorb water quickly. Flash floods often occur without any warning and can be a long distance from the actual rainstorm. Flash floods are extremely dangerous. They can easily sweep away people, and sometimes even heavy vehicles and boulders. **Location** Common in all wadis and in low, flat deserts. They are the reason canyoning is discouraged throughout rainy seasons.

☐ DUST DEVIL

A *dust devil* is a rotating column of air and dust. It forms when hot air near the ground rises quickly through pockets of cooler air. Unlike destructive tornadoes associated with thunderstorms, dust devils form on sunny days and are generally harmless. **Location** Flat, dusty deserts. Common in the *Azraq* region.

Sky & Clouds

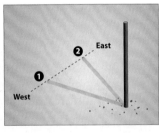

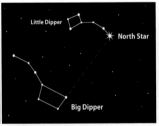

☐ SUN NAVIGATION

To navigate and determine directions by day, plant a stick in the ground and mark the tip of its shadow in the sand. Wait for 15 minutes or more, then mark the tip of the shadow again. Connect the two marks to determine the west-east line (the first mark is west and the second is east). Looking east, north is to your left and south is to your right. This technique works even on cloudy days, but it might be necessary to use a shorter stick to see the shadow, which also requires longer time to produce a clear shadow offset.

☐ STAR NAVIGATION

The North Star (Polaris) always appears over the Earth's north pole and can be used for navigation at night. To locate the North Star, find the Big Dipper and Little Dipper shown in the illustration. They are two groups of bright stars; each forms an easily recognizable spoon shape, but may appear rotated at a different angle than the illustration. The North Star is the brightest and last star in Little Dipper's handle. Looking at the North Star, east is to your right, west is to your left, and south is behind you.

Cloud Identification

Clouds form when warm water vapor rises and condenses into water droplets or ice crystals at cooler altitudes. When the droplets or crystals grow too heavy to remain suspended in the air, they fall back to the ground in the form of rain or in the form of hail and snow in low temperatures.

Cloud Type:

☐ CIRRUS

Cirrus (meaning *curl of hair* in Latin) are high-altitude clouds that form into streaks and indicate wind shear between the air above and below the clouds. Aircraft trails usually turn into cirrus clouds.

☐ CUMULUS

Cumulus (from Latin, *heap*) are puffy, cotton-like clouds with defined edges. They form when warm vapor rises and condenses at cooler altitudes. Cumulus clouds can form at both low and high altitudes, and can even be towering clouds with bases below 2,000 m and tops above 6,000 m.

☐ STRATUS

Stratus (from Latin for *layer* or *blanket*) are continuous clouds with no defined edges that cover large areas of the sky and often obscure the sun. They typically form at low altitudes in cold air saturated with moisture. They form into fog when they are in contact with the ground.

Cloud Altitude:

☐ **HIGH CLOUDS**

Clouds of mostly ice crystals that form in cold air above 6,000 m. High clouds typically cover small patches of the sky; they appear white without gray shadows and never cast shadows on the ground. High clouds are commonly streaked (cirrus), but can also appear in rows or patches of small cloudlets that lack gray shadows (cirrocumulus), or can have large amounts of diffused moisture that produce distant white veils and halos (cirrostratus). Precipitations from high clouds usually evaporate before reaching the ground. An increase in high clouds usually signals a change in the weather or approaching storms.

☐ **MIDDLE CLOUDS**

Clouds between 2,000 and 6,000 meter that cover large areas of the sky, but allow the sun to shine through. Individual middle clouds are generally the size of a finger when pointing to the sky. They appear as patches or sheets of white or light-gray rounded cloudlets (altocumulus), or as a uniform cover that does not fog the horizon (altostratus). Middle clouds either produce precipitation or signal the development of storms.

☐ LOW CLOUDS

Clouds below 2,000 m that typically appear large and white, with shaded, gray bottoms. They either cast shadows on the ground or cover the whole sky. Individual low clouds are the size of a hand or larger when pointing to the sky. They can be cotton-like heaps that form in sunny days and produce no precipitation (cumulus), dark cloud masses that generally bring light precipitation (stratocumulus), formless clouds that generally bring moderate precipitation (nimbostratus), or uniform blankets that obscure the sun and generally bring light precipitation (stratus or fog).

☐ TOWERING CLOUDS

Very large and tall clouds that form in strong up-currents and can have bases below 2,000 m and tops above 6,000 m. They generally have a menacing appearance and produce heavy precipitation and thunderstorms.

Flora

Introduction

L iving things are classified according to their natural evolutionary relationships. Humans, for example, belong to the Animalia kingdom, which includes animals and excludes plants. The Animalia kingdom is further divided into smaller, more closely related groups, down to individual species. Learning the relationships between living things helps to identify and understand them, even when encountered for the first time.

Human Classification		
Kingdom	Animalia	Animals including humans, birds, insects, reptiles, amphibians, etc. Excludes plants, bacteria, etc.
Phylum	Chordata	Animals having backbones or spinal columns including humans, birds, fish, etc. Excludes insects, jellyfish, etc.
Class	Mammalia	Mammals with milk-producing glands including humans, canines, rodents, etc. Excludes fish, birds, reptiles, etc.
Order	Primates	Primates with hand-like feet including humans, monkeys, lemurs, etc. Excludes canines, rodents, etc.
Family	Hominidae	Great apes with similar DNA including humans, chimpanzees, gorillas, etc. Excludes monkeys, lemurs, etc.
Genus	*Homo*	Humans including extinct pre-modern humans such as *Homo erectus* and *Homo habilis*.
Species	*Homo sapiens*	Modern human.

Names

A *species* is a group of living individuals capable of interbreeding. This book generally lists each species with its common English name, followed by its scientific name and the family it belongs to. Common names may differ in other sources and in other countries. Scientific names, on the other hand, follow a standardized system that is used worldwide.

Description

Plant and animal topics generally begin with the subject's typical length (L) and/or height (H), and a description of the subject's physical characteristics. Topics end with the description of the subject's habitat (**Habitat**) and either the plant's flowering time (**Blooms**), or the animal's diet and common behaviors (**Activity**).

Organization

Thousands of living species have been recorded in Jordan. This book lists only the most common or popular. Plants and animals are grouped by *order*, *family*, and *genus*, and arranged generally according to their evolutionary relationships. Closely related species are described collectively when they are too numerous to describe individually. Although *mushrooms* and *algae* are no longer classified under the plant kingdom, they are listed under flora for simplification.

☐ MUSHROOM

Mushrooms belong to the Fungi kingdom, which also includes yeast, mold, and mildew. Mushrooms are generally characterized by a stalk and a cap, which occur in different shapes, sizes, textures, and colors. They acquire food from existing organic matter, unlike plants that synthesize food from carbon dioxide, water, and sunlight. Mushrooms reproduce by releasing single-celled *spores* which grow into new mushrooms. Because it is very difficult to distinguish between edible and poisonous mushrooms, it is not recommended to gather them in the wild. **Habitat** Common in wooded regions, including *Ajloun*, *Jerash*, and *Amman*. Found in wet seasons among fallen leaves. Some species occur in deserts such as *Wadi Rum*.

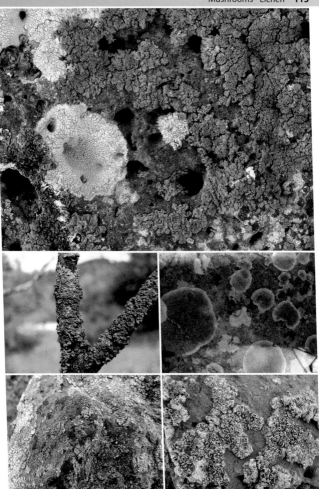

☐ LICHEN

Lichens are symbiotic colonies of *fungi* and *algae*. The fungus surrounds the alga and provides it with minerals and water absorbed from the atmosphere; the alga in turn produces food for both. Lichens grow very slowly (about 1 cm/year) and can live in extreme environments for hundreds or even thousands of years. During droughts, they enter a stasis until water becomes available again. Lichens vary in texture and color depending on the type of fungus they contain and the amount of moisture available. Some fungi grow small but visible mushroom shapes that produce reproductive spores. Lichens are sensitive to pollution, so they are an important indicator of environmental problems. **Habitat** Common on rocks and trees in the *Northern Highlands* and on rocks in the *Basalt Desert*. In some areas of the Basalt Desert, the black basalt rocks are completely covered with contrasting white lichens.

□ PLANT GALL

A plant gall is an abnormal plant growth caused by a parasite such as certain aphids, wasps, and bacteria. Insects produce galls by depositing their eggs in the plant. As the insect larvae grow inside, they irritate the plant tissue and cause it to swell. Parasites tend to favor particular plants, producing galls of identifiable shapes. Pistachio galls are produced by orange aphids; they are harvested as a natural dye. Oak galls are produced by the wasp *Cynips calicis;* they are mixed with iron salts to make high-quality black ink. **Location** Easily identifiable galls are common on pistachio trees (see *Pistachio*) and oak trees (see *Oak*).

□ FASCIATION

Fasciation (or *cresting*) is a rare malformation of plant parts that commonly produces ribbon-like structures from several fused stems, undulating folds in plant tissue, or other growth defects. It can be caused by cell mutation, bacterial infection, insect attack, frost, or any external damage. **Location** Rare and random. The pictured stem fasciation is on a white broom bush (*Retama raetam*) in *Wadi Butum,* near the Amra Palace.

☐ ALGAE

Algae are simple plants that lack roots, stems, leaves, flowers, seeds, and vascular tissue. They are mostly aquatic, but some terrestrial forms survive in dry conditions in a symbiotic relationship with fungi (see *Lichen*). Algae come in different forms such as single-cells, stringed-cells, and even giant sea kelps that can reach up to 80 m in length. Despite their simplicity, algae are essential plants that produce about 80% of Earth's oxygen. About two billion years ago, primitive algae released oxygen into the Earth's atmosphere and set the stage for more complex life forms. As the first plants on Earth, all higher plants evolved from algae. The world's petroleum formed mainly from the remains of prehistoric algae. **Habitat** Widespread in all aquatic habitats, including rivers, reservoirs, irrigation pools, and hot springs. Common in river valleys such as *Wadi Mujib*, *Wadi Hidan*, and *Ma'in*.

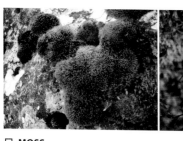

☐ MOSS

Moss is one of the oldest and most primitive plants on Earth. It is a small, green plant that lacks flowers, seeds, and roots. It grows in clusters in moist habitats and reproduces by *spores*. Moss has small but visible stems and leaves, and occasionally grows longer stems that carry spore capsules. **Habitat** Common on the shady, northern side of rocks and tree trunks in damp wooded areas, including *Ajloun* and *Jerash*. Also common in shady areas around streams and water sources.

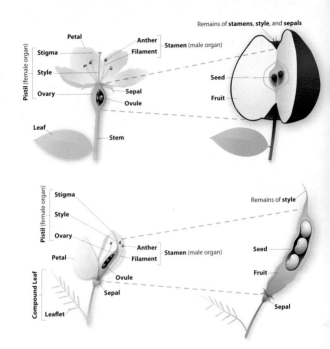

Flower to Fruit

Flowers are reproductive structures of the *flowering plants*, which make up about 90% of the all plants. Showy flowers use color, scent, and food rewards to attract animals that aid in pollination. They typically have both male and female organs (bisexual) and sticky pollen that clings to pollinators.

Other wind-pollinated plants such as grasses, pine, and oak trees typically have smaller, less showy, and separate male and female flowers. Male flowers produce finer, dust-like, wind-dispersed pollen. Female flowers generally have feather-like or sticky stigmas to capture the airborne pollen.

Flowers come in a wide variety of colors, shapes, sizes, adaptations, and number of organs. They generally have one or more pistils (female organs), several stamens (male organs), several petals, and several sepals. Self-fertilization may occur in plants with both sexes, but some plants have ways to prevent it.

After pollination, the ovaries of female flowers develop into seed-bearing fruit. Most plants have small seeds that get disseminated by wind or water. Some fruits have hooked spines that cling to animals. Some seed capsules explode open to eject the seeds away from the parent plant. Most nutritional fruits are eaten and hoarded by animals that disseminate some seeds in the process.

☐ ARUM FAMILY
ARACEAE FAMILY

H 20-60cm. A total of nine arum species have been recorded in Jordan. They are generally characterized by a leaf-like hood (spathe), tiny flowers clustered on a tubular spike (spadix), and reddish berries. Most species in this family produce heat to attract pollinating insects, and some produce a rotten-animal smell for the same purpose. Toxic if ingested. **Habitat** Some species prefer shady areas near water, others prefer open rocky fields. Habitats include *Wadi al-Seer* and semi-deserts such as *Petra*. **Blooms** Winter or spring.

☐ DATE PALM
Phoenix dactylifera
ARECACEAE FAMILY

H 20m. Evergreen tree; slender trunk; new stems and leaves form a crown at the top, while 3-7 year old stems droop or fall off at the bottom; small leaves at the stem base are modified into spines for protection. Female palms produce edible dates, while male palms only produce pollen. In the wild, female palms are pollinated by wind. In farms, they are pollinated manually to insure pollination and reduce the number of male trees. **Habitat** Sunny, hot regions with groundwater such as the *Jordan Valley*, and oases such as *Azraq* and *Ma'an*. **Blooms** Spring. Requires hot, dry climates to produce fruit.

☐ **CARROT & PARSLEY FAMILY**
UMBELLIFERAE FAMILY

About 80 species in the Umbelliferae family have been recorded in Jordan. They are characterized by umbrella-shaped flower clusters (umbels) supported by stems that radiate from a common point. Plants in this family, such as carrot and parsley, have 5-petaled flowers, hallow stems, and fruit that resemble seeds.

☐ **MADONNA FLOWER**
Artedia squamata
UMBELLIFERAE FAMILY

H 50cm. Compound umbel made up of small white flowers at the center, an outer ring of elongated petals, and green bracts below. **Habitat** Sunny hillsides in the *Northern Highlands* and western valleys, including *Amman*. **Blooms** Spring.

☐ **HAIRY-SEEDED CHERVIL**
Chaetosciadium trichospermum
UMBELLIFERAE FAMILY

H 50cm. Parsley-like leaves; pink or white, small flowers clustered on umbrella-shaped umbels. Flowers continue to bloom as the bristly fruit develops at their base. **Habitat** Shrublands and rocky regions in the northern and southern highlands. **Blooms** Spring.

☐ **SYRIAN ERYNGO**
Eryngium creticum
UMBELLIFERAE FAMILY

H 80cm. Long, serrated basal leaves that wilt early; green branches that turn purple-blue; small yellow flowers in domed clusters surrounded by purple-blue, spiny bracts. Young shoots are edible when cooked. **Habitat** Sunny, dry areas in northwestern and western Jordan, including *Irbid*, *Amman*, and *Tafilah*. **Blooms** Late spring and summer.

☐ **FERULA**
Ferula Genus
UMBELLIFERAE FAMILY

H 1-3m. A total of five *Ferula* species have been recorded in Jordan, including the giant fennel (*F. communis*). They are generally characterized by their thick, hollow stems with large basal sheaths; leaves divided into narrow lobes; yellow flowers clustered on umbrella-shaped umbels; and ribbed fruit. **Habitat** Mountains and deserts, including *Amman*, *Shobak*, and *Azraq*. **Blooms** Spring.

☐ **COMMON PARSLEY**
Petroselinum crispum
UMBELLIFERAE FAMILY

H 25cm. Small, yellow flowers; aromatic, lobed leaves used to flavor and garnish foods (effective against garlic smell); rich in vitamine C and minerals. Toxic if ingested in excessive quantities. **Habitat** Rocky areas with dry soils in the *Northern Highlands* and the *Jordan River Valley*. Cultivated commercially in the *Jordan River Valley*. **Blooms** Second summer.

☐ **VENUS-COMB**
Scandix pecten-veneris
UMBELLIFERAE FAMILY

H 40cm. Leaves dissected into many narrow lobes; small, white flowers clustered in umbels; long fruit forming comb-like clusters. Edible stem tops. **Habitat** Sunny, grassy fields in western Jordan, including *Amman*. **Blooms** Spring.

☐ ONION & GARLIC FAMILY
ALLIACEAE FAMILY

A total of 29 species in the Alliaceae family have been recorded in Jordan. Plants in this family include onions, garlics, leeks, and chives. They produce chemicals, such as *cystein sulfoxide*, which give them their onion or garlic odor when crushed. They generally have narrow basal leaves; straight stems; white, yellow, pink, or purple flowers that emerge from papery sheaths and form spherical or hemispherical flower heads; and small seedpods that split open in three sections.

☐ BLACK GARLIC
Allium aschersonianum
ALLIACEAE FAMILY

H 30cm. Wide and long basal leaves; dark-pink, spherical flower head; each flower has six tepals and long, purple stamens. **Habitat** Semi-deserts, including *Mafraq, Karak, Shobak, Azraq,* and some *Eastern Desert* areas. **Blooms** Spring.

☐ NAPLES GARLIC
Allium neapolitanum
ALLIACEAE FAMILY

H 45cm. Long, thin basal leaves; fragrant, white, hemispherical flower head; each flower has six tepals and long stamens. Edible, garlic-tasting leaves. **Habitat** Sunny areas with moist soil in the *Northern Highlands*, including *Ajloun, Amman,* and *Karak*. **Blooms** Spring.

☐ CHINESE SACRED LILY
Narcissus tazetta
AMARYLLIDACEAE FAMILY

H 20cm. Also known as "bunch-flowered narcissus", "cream narcissus", and "joss flower". Bulb plant; scented flowers with six white tepals (3 petals and 3 sepals) and an orange central crown; long, thick, basal leaves. **Habitat** Rocky, sunny fields in the *Salt* region and nearby valleys. **Blooms** Winter.

☐ STERNBERGIA
Sternbergia Genus
AMARYLLIDACEAE FAMILY

H 10-20cm. A total of three *Sternbergia* species have been recorded in Jordan. They have yellow, cup-shaped flowers with a long flowering duration and a large amount of nectar and pollen to ensure pollination. The linear leaves appear late, after the plant spends most of its resources on the flowers. **Habitat** Sunny, dry, rocky mountains and valleys, including *Jerash*, *Karak*, and *Salt*. **Blooms** Autumn. Bloom is triggered by lower temperatures.

☐ ALOE VERA
Aloe vera
ASPHODELACEAE FAMILY

H 90cm. Succulent plant; green, white-spotted, fleshy leaves with serrated margins; orange, tubular flowers clustered on a long spike. Leaf gel is commonly used to treat skin burns and other skin conditions. **Habitat** Introduced to the *Petra* region from North Africa, likely by the Nabateans. **Blooms** Late spring and early summer.

☐ COMMON ASPHODEL
Asphodelus aestivus
ASPHODELACEAE FAMILY

H 100cm. Also known as "tall asphodel". Evergreen herb with long, narrow basal leaves; star-shaped flowers with both male and female organs; and six white tepals (3 petals and 3 sepals) with brown spines. **Habitat** Roadsides and rocky fields in the highlands, including *Amman*, *Irbid*, *Ajloun*, *Karak*, and *Shobak*. **Blooms** Late winter and spring.

☐ YELLOW ASPHODEL
Asphodeline lutea
ASPHODELACEAE FAMILY

H 100cm. Grass-like leaves denser at the base; scented, star-shaped flowers clustered along a tall stem, each flower has six yellow, brown-spined tepals; hard, round, brown seed pods. Edible flowers, young shoots, and cooked roots. **Habitat** Stony areas in the *Northern Highlands* including *Irbid*, *Ajloun*, and *Amman*. **Blooms** Spring.

☐ HYACINTH FAMILY
HYACINTHACEAE FAMILY

A total of 39 species in the Hyacinthaceae family have been recorded in Jordan. They are characterized by underground bulbs, basal leaves, leafless stems, and raceme inflorescence (separate flowers attached to the main stem by short stalks). The lower flowers develop first. The fruit is a 3-chambered capsule.

☐ BELLEVALIA
Bellevalia Genus
HYACINTHACEAE FAMILY

H 5-50cm. A total of 11 *Bellevalia* species have been recorded in Jordan. They are generally characterized by fleshy, curling, basal leaves; leafless stem; and a raceme of white or pale-violet, tubular flowers made up of six fused petals and violet anthers. Flowers turn brown as they age. Distinguished from grape hyacinths by partly-fused petals and longer lobes. **Habitat** Different species occur in habitats ranging from the highlands, including *Amman*, to arid regions such as *Shobak* and *Ma'an*. **Blooms** Winter or spring.

☐ **TASSEL HYACINTH**
Leopoldia bicolor
HYACINTHACEAE FAMILY

☐ **GRAPE HYACINTH**
Muscari neglectum
HYACINTHACEAE FAMILY

H 30cm. Erect stem; narrow, curved basal leaves; tubular, stalked flowers loosely clustered along the length of the stem; top flowers are violet and sterile; lower flowers are greenish and fertile; all flowers have dark, restricted, dentate mouths. **Habitat** Sandy, arid regions, including *Wadi Araba*, *Wadi Dana*, and the *Eastern Desert*. **Blooms** Spring.

H 20cm. Urn-shaped flowers tightly clustered at stem tips (grape-like); top flowers are light-blue and sterile; lower flowers are dark-blue with white-toothed rims; narrow basal leaves longer than stems. Edible flowers. Poisonous bulb. **Habitat** Sunny highlands, including *Irbid, Ajloun, Jerash, Amman, Karak,* and *Tafilah*. **Blooms** Late winter and early spring.

☐ **STAR OF BETHLEHEM**
Ornithogalum Genus
HYACINTHACEAE FAMILY

H 30cm. A total of eight *Ornithogalum* species have been recorded in Jordan. They are generally characterized by star-shaped flowers clustered loosely in some species, and in racemes or spikes in others. Each flower has six white tepals with a green underside and six stamens around an ovary. The leaves are generally basal and grass-like. Toxic if ingested. **Habitat** Grassy fields, roadsides, and woods in the *Northern Highlands*, including *Irbid, Ajloun,* and *Amman*. **Blooms** Spring. Each flower lasts only a couple of days.

☐ **SEA SQUILL**
Urginea maritima
HYACINTHACEAE FAMILY

H 100cm. Also known as "sea onion" and "red squill". White, star-shaped flowers with green centers, clustered along a long stalk. Each flower has six tepals (petals and sepals), six stamens (male organs), and a single pistil (female organ). Flowers develop into round seed pods that split open when dry. Toxic if ingested. **Habitat** Dry, sandy areas and desert margins in western Jordan, including *Irbid*, *Amman*, *Karak*, *Wadi Dana*, *Petra*, and *Wadi Araba*. **Blooms** Basal leaves appear from late autumn to spring and dry up in summer. Leafless, flowering stalks appear in late summer and early autumn.

☐ IRIS FAMILY
IRIDACEAE FAMILY

Plants in the Iridaceae family are herbaceous: the above-ground parts die at the end of the season and new plants grow from underground storage organs such as bulbs and corms. They are characterized by sword-shaped leaves that overlap at the base. They generally produce attractive flowers, each with an inner whorl of three petals, an outer whorl of three sepals, a single compound pistil (female organ) that often resembles three additional petals, and three stamens (male organs). The fruit is a 3-chambered capsule.

☐ VARTAN IRIS
Iris vartanii
IRIDACEAE FAMILY

H 13cm. Light-blue flowers; three reduced, upright petals; three spreading, pointed sepals adorned with lines; yellow, tubular reproductive organs; sword-like, basal leaves with white, spiny tips. **Habitat** Rare in the *Salt* and *Suwaylih* regions. **Blooms** Winter.

☐ GILEAD IRIS
Iris atrofusca
IRIDACEAE FAMILY

H 35cm. Slightly curved leaves; brown-purple flowers, each with three upright petals (standards) and three drooping sepals (falls). Solitary male bees take shelter inside the dark flowers for warmth. **Habitat** Rocky hillsides in the *Northern Highlands*, including *Wadi al-Seer*. **Blooms** Spring.

□ **BLACK IRIS**
Iris nigricans
IRIDACEAE FAMILY

H 30cm. The black iris is the national flower of Jordan and endemic to the country. The black iris has thin, down-curving, basal leaves shorter than stems; dark-purple, glossy, veined flowers with three upright petals (standards) and three drooping sepals (falls); a single compound pistil (female organ) that resembles three additional petals; and three stamens (male organs). Distinguished from the closely-related Petra iris by longer stems and darker flowers that grow in smaller clusters (10 or less). **Habitat** Semi-deserts east of the *Dead Sea*, including *Madaba, Karak, Qatranah*, and *Shobak*. Endangered species. **Blooms** Spring.

☐ **MESOPOTAMIAN IRIS**
Iris mesopotamica
IRIDACEAE FAMILY

H 60cm. Slightly fragrant, violet-blue flowers; long, sword-like basal leaves; stems longer than leaves. Each flower has three upright petals (standards) and three drooping sepals (falls) with a fuzzy, yellow beard running down the middle. Causes allergies in some people. Toxic if ingested. Roots are used to make black dye. Flowers are used to make blue dye. Dried, aged roots are fragrant and commonly used in potpourri. *I. germanica* is a natural hybrid of *I. mesopotamica* and other bearded irises. **Habitat** Rocky and sunny regions in the *Northern Highlands*, including *Amman*, *Jerash*, and *Karak*. **Blooms** Late spring.

☐ **WINTER CROCUS**
Crocus hyemalis
IRIDACEAE FAMILY

H 15cm. Grass-like leaves with white spines; white, cup-shaped flowers with six tepals; yellow flower centers with orange stigmas and black stamens. Grows from corms (swollen underground stems that store nutrients). Closely related to *Crocus sativus*, which produces the saffron spice. **Habitat** Dry soil in the northern woodlands, including *Ajloun* and *Jerash*. **Blooms** Winter.

☐ **SPANISH NUT**
Gynandriris sisyrinchium
IRIDACEAE FAMILY

H 20cm. Grass-like leaves; purple flowers with three upright petals, three spreading sepals that have a white and yellow base, and a single compound pistil (female organ) that resembles additional petals.

Habitat Sunny areas with rich soil in the highlands, including *Amman*, *Salt*, and *Madaba*. **Blooms** Spring. Produces multiple flowers over several days, each opens briefly only on warm afternoons.

☐ **VIOLET GLADIOLUS**
Gladiolus atroviolaceus
IRIDACEAE FAMILY

H 50cm. Narrow sword-shaped basal leaves; violet flowers with six tepals fused together at the base; the lower tepals have white streaks or lighter violet patches; flowers are arranged in one-sided spikes. **Habitat** Fields of the *Northern Highland* including *Irbid*, *Amman*, and *Shobak*. **Blooms** Spring.

☐ **ITALIAN GLADIOLUS**
Gladiolus italicus
IRIDACEAE FAMILY

H 100cm. Narrow, sword-shaped basal leaves; pinkish-purple flowers with six tepals fused together at the base; the lower three tepals have white streaks bordered by dark-purple; flowers are arranged in one-sided spikes. **Habitat** Northwestern Jordan, including *Irbid*, *Ajloun*, and the *Jordan River Valley*. **Blooms** Spring.

☐ **SUNFLOWER FAMILY**
ASTERACEAE FAMILY

Over 90 species in the Asteraceae family have been recorded in Jordan. Plants in this family, such as chamomile and thistle, are characterized by small flowers (florets) that form larger flower heads. Each composite flower head resembles a single flower, but generally contains numerous *disk florets* and an outer ring of *ray florets* in some species.

☐ **MARIGOLD**
Calendula Genus
ASTERACEAE FAMILY

H 15-50cm. A total of four *Calendula* species have been recorded in Jordan. They are generally characterized by composite flower heads made up of brownish, tubular disk florets and an outer ring of orangish ray florets; oblong leaves larger at the base; and claws-like fruit. **Habitat** Different species occur in habitats ranging from the *Northern Highlands,* including *Ajlun* and *Amman,* to arid regions such as *Wadi Araba* and *Azraq.* **Blooms** Late winter or spring.

☐ CHAMOMILE
Anthemis Genus
ASTERACEAE FAMILY

A total of 19 *Anthemis* species have been recorded in Jordan. They are aromatic herbs characterized by composite flower heads made up of tiny yellow disk florets at the center, a white or yellow outer ring of ray florets, and leaves dissected into several narrow lobes. **Habitat** Different *Anthemis* species occur in habitats ranging from the grassy fields of the *Northern Highlands*, including *Jerash* and *Amman*, to dry regions such as *Wadi Rum*, *Petra*, and the *Eastern Desert*. **Blooms** Spring and early summer.

☐ GOLDEN CHAMOMILE
Matricaria aurea
ASTERACEAE FAMILY

H 20cm. Known as "babounij" in Arabic. Composite flower head made up of tiny, tubular, yellow disk florets at the center and an outer ring of white ray florets that fall off early. Leaves are dissected into several narrow lobes. Aromatic and commonly used as herbal tea for stomachaches and insomnia. **Habitat** Rich, silty soils in the *Northern Highlands* and some deserts, including *Amman, Jerash, Mafraq, Azraq, Madaba,* and *Karak*. **Blooms** Spring.

☐ YARROW
Achillea Genus
ASTERACEAE FAMILY

H 20-60cm. A total of seven *Achillea* species have been recorded in Jordan. They are generally characterized by gray-green, hairy, basal stems; gray-green, hairy, aromatic, bitter-tasting leaves; gray, woolly flower buds; and large clusters of yellow flower heads at stem tips. **Habitat** Different species occur in habitats ranging from dry fields in the highlands, including *Mafraq* and *Amman*, to humid soils around flood pools in the *Basalt Desert*. **Blooms** Mostly spring. Some species bloom in summer or autumn.

☐ FLAX-LEAF FLEABANE
Conyza bonariensis
ASTERACEAE FAMILY

H 100cm. Hairy stems; bluish-green, narrow leaves; cup-shaped involucres with purple tips; composite flower heads made up of tiny, yellow disk florets surrounded by taller, whitish bristles (lacks ray florets); feathery, wind-dispersed seeds that form a puffball. **Habitat** Roadsides and wastelands in the *Northern Highlands*, including *Jerash*. **Blooms** Late summer and autumn.

☐ **GOLD COIN**
Asteriscus Genus
ASTERACEAE FAMILY

H 10-50cm. A total of 5 *Asteriscus* species have been recorded in Jordan. They are generally characterized by hairy stems and leaves, and yellow flower heads made up of small disk florets and two outer rings of ray florets, surrounded by a whorl of long bracts. **Habitat** Different *Asteriscus* species occur in habitats ranging from grassy fields in the *Northern Highland,* including *Amman,* to deserts such as the *Eastern Desert.* **Blooms** Spring and early summer.

☐ **DANDELION**
Taraxacum Genus
ASTERACEAE FAMILY

H 10-20cm. Two *Taraxacum* species have been recorded in Jordan. They are characterized by jagged leaves that resemble canine teeth (dandelion is from the French meaning lion's tooth). Leaves form a flattened rosette that directs rainwater to the center of the plant. Stems are unbranched, leafless, and carry solitary flower heads. Composite flower heads are made up of yellow florets, each with five marginal teeth representing five petals; the central florets narrow into tubes. **Habitat** Moist soils in the *Northern Highlands* and the *Dead Sea* region. **Blooms** Spring to autumn.

☐ **AROMATIC INULA**
Dittrichia viscosa
ASTERACEAE FAMILY

H 90cm. Highly-branched shrub. Young branches are covered with green leaves and tipped with yellow flower panicles. Mature branches are brown and woody. Leaves are narrow with serrated edges, pointed tips, and covered with hairs that produce a sticky and aromatic resin. Composite flower heads are made up of yellow disk florets, surrounded by a ring of ray florets, held by a green, cylindrical involucre. Seeds from a wind-dispersed puff ball. Roots produce a yellow dye. **Habitat** River valleys and damp roadsides, including *Ajloun*, *Jerash*, *Amman*, *Salt*, and *Karak*. **Blooms** Late summer and autumn.

☐ **RED EVERLASTING**
Helichrysum sanguineum
ASTERACEAE FAMILY

H 30cm. Basal stems; silver-green, narrow, woolly leaves; small flower heads with showy red bracts and inconspicuous yellow tepals. **Habitat** Woodlands including *Ajloun*, *Jerash*, and *Salt*. **Blooms** Spring.

☐ GOLDY-LOCKS
Varthemia iphionoides
ASTERACEAE FAMILY

H 50cm. Aromatic bush with a minty-thyme scent; woody base; numerous hairy, sticky stems; small leaves; cylindrical composite flower heads with yellow tubular florets, longer yellow styles, and green involucres; feathery, wind-dispersed seeds. Used in herbal teas. **Habitat** Rocky and desert regions including *Ajloun*, *Amman*, the *Jordan Valley*, and *Petra*. **Blooms** Autumn.

☐ WAVE-LEAVED FLEABANE
Pulicaria incisa
ASTERACEAE FAMILY

H 20cm. Many basal stems; wooly leaves with wavy margins; composite flower heads made up of tiny, yellow disk florets at the center and an outer ring of yellow ray florets. The aromatic leaves are used as a tea. **Habitat** Hot, humid regions, including the *Dead Sea*, *Wadi Dana*, and *Aqaba*. **Blooms** Spring.

☐ KOELPINIA
Koelpinia linearis
ASTERACEAE FAMILY

H 20cm. Basal stems; grass-like leaves; small, yellow flowers; distinctive star-shaped seed head with curved, spiny seeds. **Habitat** Diverse habitats, including highlands, semi-deserts, and deserts. **Blooms** Spring.

□ **THISTLE**
ASTERACEAE FAMILY

Over 50 thistle species in 12 genera have been recorded in Jordan. They are successful, hardy plants generally characterized by prickly leaves and stems, and composite flower heads made up of small tubular florets and spiny bracts (modified leaves subtending flowers). The success of thistles derives from their prickles that deter herbivores and their high nectar yield that attracts numerous pollinators. **Habitat** Dry fields and roadsides with high-lime soils in the highlands and deserts. **Blooms** Mostly spring or summer.

☐ **STAR THISTLE**
Centaurea Genus
ASTERACEAE FAMILY

A total of 20 *Centaurea* species thrive in Jordan. They are generally characterized by composite flower heads made up of tubular disk florets, held by an involucre of spiny bracts (modified leaves subtending the flower head). The flowers of most species are yellow. Some are pink, white, or blue. **Habitat** Widespread in cultivated and wild fields all over Jordan, including the highlands and deserts. **Blooms** Spring and summer.

☐ **ERYNGO STAR-THISTLE**
Centaurea eryngioides
ASTERACEAE FAMILY

H 40cm. Long, lobed basal leaves; upright stems; composite flower heads made up of tubular pink florets with purple reproductive organs, held by an involucre of white-fringed, spine-tipped bracts. **Habitat** Rocky, shady areas in western Jordan, including *Karak*, *Wadi Dana*, and *Wadi Rum*. **Blooms** Late spring.

☐ **SYRIAN CORNFLOWER**
Centaurea cyanoides
ASTERACEAE FAMILY

H 50cm. Hairy stems branching from the base; hairy leaves; violet-blue composite flower heads made up of tubular disk florets at the center and an outer ring of fringed ray florets, held by an involucre of fringed bracts. **Habitat** The highlands, including *Amman* and *Salt*. **Blooms** Spring.

☐ **GLOBE THISTLE**
Echinops Genus
ASTERACEAE FAMILY

H 50-125cm. A total of five globe thistle species have been recorded in Jordan. They are characterized by dense, ball-shaped, composite flower heads covered with tubular flowers and spines. Flowers are either white or blue, each with five petals. Globe thistles are drought-resistant. **Habitat** Sunny, dry, rocky areas in the highlands, including *Irbid*, *Jerash*, *Amman*, *Tafilah*, and *Petra*. **Blooms** Late spring and summer.

☐ **COTTON THISTLE**
Onopordum Genus
ASTERACEAE FAMILY

H 20-200cm. Nine *Onopordum* species have been recorded in Jordan. They are characterized by spiny, winged stems; grayish-green, spiny leaves; recurved bracts; and semi-spherical flower heads with purple or pink tubular florets. **Habitat** Fields and arid regions, including *Mafraq*, *Amman*, *Petra*, and the *Eastern Desert*. **Blooms** Spring and Summer.

☐ **CARLINE THISTLE**
Carlina Genus
ASTERACEAE FAMILY

H 10-80cm. Two *Carlina* species have been recorded in Jordan. They are generally characterized by composite flower heads made up of tiny disk florets at the center and an outer ring of ray florets surrounded by spiny bracts. **Habitat** Dry fields and roadsides in the highlands, including *Mafraq*, *Amman*, and *Karak*. **Blooms** Summer and early autumn.

☐ **SYRIAN THISTLE**
Notobasis syriaca
ASTERACEAE FAMILY

H 60cm. Green leaves with conspicuous white veins and spiny margins; basal leaves are larger and less spiny; purple, white-tipped flower bristles, held by an involucre of spiny bracts. **Habitat** Rich soils in the *Northern Highlands* and valleys, including *Amman*, *Irbid*, *Jerash*, *Karak*, and the *Jordan River Valley*. **Blooms** Spring and early summer.

☐ **SOLDIER THISTLE**
Picnomon acarna
ASTERACEAE FAMILY

H 50cm. Densely-branched, winged stems; gray-green, wooly leaves with yellow spines; small composite flower heads made up of tiny, pink-purple florets, surrounded by spiny involucres and longer spiny leaves. **Habitat** Roadsides and rocky fields in the highlands, including *Irbid*, *Jerash*, *Amman*, *Karak*, and *Petra*. **Blooms** Summer.

☐ **MOAB COUSINIA**
Cousinia moabitica
ASTERACEAE FAMILY

H 30cm. Spiny, leathery leaves; composite flower head with a few purple, tubular florets, and short, spiny bracts. **Habitat** Roadsides and wastelands in the *Southern Highlands*, including *Karak*, *Shobak*, and *Ras al-Naqb*. **Blooms** Summer.

☐ **GUNDELIA**
Gundelia tournefortii
ASTERACEAE FAMILY

H 40cm. Spiny, brown flower heads with small, yellow florets; large, veined, lobed leaves with spiny margins; basal branches. Immature flower heads are edible cooked (like artichoke). Roots, seeds, and leaves are also edible when cooked. **Habitat** Fields and roadsides of the *Northern Highlands*, including *Irbid*, *Jerash*, *Amman*, *Karak*, and *Tafilah*. **Blooms** Spring.

☐ **PINK VIPER'S GRASS**
Scorzonera papposa
ASTERACEAE FAMILY

H 40cm. Pink, composite flower heads with only ray florets (disk florets are absent); yellow styles surrounded by brown, tubular anthers; basal branches; narrow, hairy leaves with wavy margins. Edible roots, flowers, and young leaves. **Habitat** Fields and roadsides of western Jordan, including *Mafraq*, *Ajloun*, *Madaba*, and *Tafilah*. **Blooms** Spring.

☐ **GOATSBEARD**
Tragopogon Genus
ASTERACEAE FAMILY

☐ **DWARF CHICORY**
Cichorium pumilum
ASTERACEAE FAMILY

H 20-60cm. Four *Tragopogon* species have been recorded in Jordan. They are characterized by a few upright branches; violet-pink or yellow flower heads with only ray florets (absent disk florets); yellow styles surrounded by brown anthers; generally long bracts; grass-like leaves; milky sap; and a puffball of wind-dispersed seeds. **Habitat** The highlands including *Ajloun, Amman,* and *Shobak.* **Blooms** Spring and early summer.

H 50cm. Dentate basal leaves; blue, composite flower heads with only ray florets (disk florets are absent); blue styles surrounded by darker, tubular anthers; each ray floret has five marginal teeth representing five petals. **Habitat** Fields and roadsides of western Jordan, including *Ajloun, Amman,* the *Jordan River Valley,* the *Dead Sea* region, and *Tafilah.* **Blooms** Spring and summer.

☐ **SPINY COCKLEBUR**
Xanthium spinosum
ASTERACEAE FAMILY

☐ **COMMON COCKLEBUR**
Xanthium strumarium
ASTERACEAE FAMILY

H 100cm. Narrow, triangular, veined leaves with basal lobes; three long spines at the base of each leaf. Male, pollen-producing flowers develop at stem tips. Female, fruit-producing flowers develop lower on stems. Fruit is oval-shaped, covered with hooked spines that cling to animals for dispersal. Each fruit contains two seeds that germinate in different seasons. **Habitat** Warm areas with moist soil in the *Jordan River Valley* and the *Northern Highlands,* including *Jerash* and *Irbid.* **Blooms** Spring or summer.

H 55cm. Heart-shaped, hairy leaves with toothed margins. Male, pollen-producing flowers develop at stem tips. Female, fruit-producing flowers develop lower on stems. Fruit is oval-shaped, covered with hooked spines that cling to animals for dispersal. Each fruit contains two seeds that germinate in different seasons. Highly toxic if ingested. **Habitat** Warm areas with moist soil in the *Jordan River Valley* and the *Northern Highlands,* including *Jerash* and *Irbid.* **Blooms** Spring or summer.

☐ BORAGE FAMILY
BORAGINACEAE FAMILY

A total of 74 species in the Boraginaceae family have been recorded in Jordan. Plants in this family generally have hairy leaves and flowers with five petals fused at the base to form a tubular or funnel-shaped corolla. The flowers of some species in this family turn from pink to blue as they age.

☐ STRIGOSE ALKANET
Alkanna strigosa
BORAGINACEAE FAMILY

H 30cm. Hairy branches and leaves; pink, small flowers that turn blue and violet as they age. What looks like five petals are actually five lobes of a single corolla fused at the base. **Habitat** The highlands of northwestern and western Jordan, including *Irbid*, *Ajloun*, *Amman*, and *Karak*. **Blooms** Spring.

☐ **PRICKLY BUGLOSS**
Anchusa strigosa
BORAGINACEAE FAMILY

H 100cm. Pale-green, spiny leaves, dense at the plant's base; small, pale-blue flowers with a pink-white center. What looks like five petals are actually five lobes of a single corolla fused at the base. **Habitat** The highlands, including *Irbid*, *Amman*, and *Dana*. **Blooms** Spring and summer.

☐ **ITALIAN BUGLOSS**
Anchusa italica
BORAGINACEAE FAMILY

H 60cm. Bristly, green stems, sometimes purple; narrow, bristly leaves; small, blue, 5-petaled flowers with a white center and a narrow tube as long as the calyx. Edible flowers and leaves. **Habitat** Moist, sunny fields of the *Northern Highlands*, including *Irbid*, *Amman*, and *Madaba*. **Blooms** Spring.

☐ **EGYPTIAN BUGLOSS**
Anchusa aegyptiaca
BORAGINACEAE FAMILY

H 25cm. Also known as "Egyptian alkanet". Small, pale-yellow flowers; green, white-spotted, prickly leaves with wavy margins. Edible young leaves. **Habitat** Humid, warm areas in all of Jordan, including the *Jordan River Valley*, the *Dead Sea*, *Wadi Araba*, and the *Eastern Desert*. **Blooms** Spring.

☐ **GERMAN MADWORT**
Asperugo procumbens
BORAGINACEAE FAMILY

H 100cm. Weak stems with backward pointing bristles; bristly leaves; small, violet or blue, 5-petaled flowers 2-3mm long; distinctive, clam-shaped seed pod. **Habitat** Roadsides and fields in the highlands, including *Irbid*, *Amman*, and *Tafilah*. Also occurs near water in northern Jordan, including *Burqu'*. **Blooms** Late winter and spring.

☐ **BLUE HOUND'S TONGUE**
Cynoglossum creticum
BORAGINACEAE FAMILY

H 55cm. Hairy stems; hairy, oblong, up-pointing leaves; small, net-veined flowers with a corolla fused at the base. Flowers turn from lilac to blue as they age. Fruit has four nutlets covered with hooked spines that cling to animals for dispersal. **Habitat** Humid, warm regions in the *Northern Highlands*, including wadis around *Amman*. **Blooms** Spring.

☐ **JUDAEAN BUGLOSS**
Echium judaeum
BORAGINACEAE FAMILY

H 50cm. Also known as "Judaean viper's bugloss". Pink, trumpet-shaped flowers that turn violet and blue as they age; hairy stems and leaves. **Habitat** Common in stony regions and roadsides in western Jordan, including *Amman*, *Jerash*, *Madaba*, the *Jordan River Valley*, and around water sources farther south. **Blooms** Spring.

☐ **GOLDEN DROP**
Podonosma orientalis
BORAGINACEAE FAMILY

☐ **COMFREY**
Symphytum brachycalyx
BORAGINACEAE FAMILY

H 80cm. Woody base; red, hairy, hanging stems; hairy, narrow leaves; violet-blue, tubular flowers with yellow tips and long stamens. **Habitat** Walls and rocky areas in the highlands, including *Ajloun*, *Amman*, and *Petra*. **Blooms** Late winter to early summer.

H 50cm. Rough, hairy leaves; white or violet, hanging, tubular flowers. **Habitat** Shady areas in the *Northern Highlands*, including *Irbid*, *Ajloun*, *Jerash*, *Amman*, and *Salt*. **Blooms** Spring.

☐ **EUROPEAN TURNSOLE**
Heliotropium europaeum
BORAGINACEAE FAMILY

☐ **BOISSIER BORAGE**
Trichodesma boissieri
BORAGINACEAE FAMILY

H 30cm. Hairy stems and leaves; small, white flowers on curved stalks; leaves turn to the sun (*heliotropium* is from the Greek *helios* meaning *sun*, and *tropaios* meaning *turning back*). Toxic if ingested. Foul smelling when crushed. **Habitat** Moist soil in the highlands, including *Amman*. **Blooms** Spring to fall.

H 60cm. Gray, hairy stems, hairy leaves with wavy margins and tapering tips; light-blue, down-pointing flowers with pointed centers and five up-curving petals. **Habitat** The margins of the *Jordan River Valley*. **Blooms** Spring and early summer.

□ **MUSTARD & CABBAGE FAMILY**
BRASSICACEAE FAMILY

A total of 137 species in the Brassicaceae family have been recorded in Jordan. They are characterized by flowers with four petals, four sepals that commonly form a tubular calyx, six stamens (four long and two short), and two fused female organs that produce 2-chambered seed capsules partitioned longitudinally.

□ **BUCKLER MUSTARD**
Biscutella didyma
BRASSICACEAE FAMILY

H 40cm. Also known as "Mediterranean biscutella". Characterized by basal leaves with toothed margins; smaller higher leaves; small, yellow, 4-petaled flowers; and paired disk-shaped seed pods. **Habitat** Grasslands and fields of western Jordan, including *Amman*. **Blooms** Late winter and spring.

□ **WHITETOP**
Cardaria draba
BRASSICACEAE FAMILY

H 50cm. Single or top-branching stems; hairy leaves with toothed margins; white, domed, terminal flower heads; 4-petaled flowers with six stamens and an ovoid ovary; heart-shaped seeds. **Habitat** Fields of western Jordan, including *Irbid*, *Amman*, and *Shobak*. **Blooms** Spring or early summer.

☐ MUSTARD
Brassica & Sinapis Genus
BRASSICACEAE FAMILY

H 15-100cm. A total of five species in the *Brassica* and *Sinapis* genera have been recorded in Jordan. Over 15 similar plants in other genera are also referred to as mustards. They are generally characterized by long stems; mostly basal leaves; yellow or white, 4-petaled flowers about 2 cm in diameter, clustered at stem tips; and narrow seed pods. Edible leaves and seeds. The seeds of some species are ground up to make a pungent mustard condiment. **Habitat** Sunny areas with moist soil in western Jordan. Common on roadsides and around water sources. **Blooms** Late winter and spring.

☐ ARUGULA
Eruca sativa
BRASSICACEAE FAMILY

H 50cm. Also known as "garden rocket" and "jarjeer" in Arabic. Low-growing, drought-tolerant plant in the mustard family. Yellowish, scented flowers with four brown-veined petals; basal branches; lobed, smooth leaves. Edible young leaves with a horseradish flavor. Flowers are used as a garnish with a similar flavor. Seeds produce edible oil and clean-burning lamp oil. **Habitat** Fields and stony slopes in northwestern Jordan, including the *Jordan River Valley*, *Amman*, *Salt*, *Jerash*, and *Mafraq*. **Blooms** Spring and summer.

☐ EGYPTIAN FARSETIA
Farsetia aegyptiaca
BRASSICACEAE FAMILY

H 50cm. Densely branched shrub; small, narrow leaves; yellowish-white, purple-veined, 4-petaled flowers; flat, mid-ribbed seed pods. **Habitat** Arid regions including *Burqu'* and *Petra*. **Blooms** Late winter or spring.

☐ COMMON MALCOLMIA
Malcolmia crenulata
BRASSICACEAE FAMILY

H 15cm. Pink, 4-petaled flowers, 2 cm in diameter, with a yellow center; green leaves with dentate margins. **Habitat** Rich, moist soil in the *Northern Highlands*, including *Irbid*, *Ajloun*, and *Amman*. **Blooms** Late winter and spring.

☐ **STOCK**
Matthiola Genus
BRASSICACEAE FAMILY

H 10-40cm. A total of seven *Matthiola* species have been recorded in Jordan. They are generally characterized by basal branches and leaves; pink, sweet-scented, 4-petaled flowers with pale centers; petals have wavy margins and overlapping bases. **Habitat** Diverse habitats including the *Northern Highlands*, the *Jordan Valley*, and the *Eastern Desert*. **Blooms** Spring.

☐ **ZILLA**
Zilla spinosa
BRASSICACEAE FAMILY

H 60cm. Dense, spiny shrub with a few small leaves; pink-violet flowers with four veined petals, a whitish center, and yellow stamens; round seed pods with a pointed tip. Source of food for camels. **Habitat** Deserts and hot regions, including the *Dead Sea*, *Wadi Araba*, and the *Eastern Desert*. **Blooms** Spring.

☐ **BELLFLOWER FAMILY**
CAMPANULACEAE FAMILY

A total of 15 species in the Campanulaceae family have been recorded in Jordan. They are characterized by bell-shaped flowers (which give them their name), a milky sap, and ovaries below the petals (inferior ovaries). Flowers are violet-blue (most common), white, or yellow generally with streaked corollas, five lobes, white centers, and hairy bracts.

☐ CAPER
Capparis Genus
CAPPARACEAE FAMILY

A total of six caper species have been recorded in Jordan. They are generally spiny shrubs with rounded leaves and pinkish-white flowers that open at dawn and close before sunset. They are well-adapted to poor soil, saline soil, and low moisture. Immature flower buds and caperberries have a strong flavor and aroma. They are salted or pickled to use as condiments. Immature leaves and shoots can be eaten as vegetables. **Habitat** Dry and sunny regions in western Jordan, including the *Jordan Valley*, *Jerash*, *Amman*, *Tafilah*, and *Petra*. Occurs in well-drained soils, rock crevices, and on stone walls. *Capparis leucophylla* is found around water sources in the *Eastern Desert*. **Blooms** Spring and summer.

□ **BEN TREE**
Moringa peregrina
MORINGACEAE FAMILY

H 10m. Drought resistant; gray or brown bark; compound, tripinnate leaves made up of long axes and small, spaced leaflet pairs that fall off early to conserve water; fragrant, pinkish-white flowers with ten tepals; hanging, ribbed seed pods up to 30 cm long, which split open lengthwise in three parts. Seeds are used to produce the non-drying ben oil. **Habitat** Dry and rocky regions, including the *Dead Sea* and *Wadi Finan*. Endangered by grazing and harvesting. **Blooms** Spring.

□ **TAILY WEED**
Ochradenus baccatus
RESEDACEAE FAMILY

H 150cm. Shrub with numerous, green, slender branches; linear leaves that fall off early to conserve water; small, yellowish-green flowers with prominent ovaries and reduced petals clustered in terminal racemes; white or red, fleshy, round, edible fruit. **Habitat** Arid regions including *Wadi Mujib*, *Wadi Araba*, and *Wadi Rum*. **Blooms** Winter and spring.

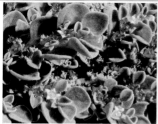

☐ **PURSLANE-LEAVED AIZOON**
Aizoon canariense
AIZOACEAE FAMILY

☐ **SLENDER-LEAVED ICEPLANT**
Mesembryanthemum nodiflorum
AIZOACEAE FAMILY

H 15cm. Spreading, succulent plant; woody stems; yellowish-green, small, fleshy, hairy, concave leaves that store water; small, yellow, 5-petaled flowers. Edible leaves. **Habitat** Deserts and hot regions, including the *Dead Sea*, *Wadi Araba*, *Wadi Rum*, and *Eastern Desert* areas with some moisture. **Blooms** Spring.

H 20cm. Introduced, succulent plant native to South Africa. Cylindrical, green leaves with bladder cells that store moisture and give the plant its glistening appearance and name. Leaves turn reddish with stress. Flowers have small, yellow petals surrounded by larger, white sepals. **Habitat** Saline soils, including the *Dead Sea* region and *Azraq*. **Blooms** Spring.

☐ **PRICKLY PEAR**
Opuntia ficus
CACTACEAE FAMILY

H 4m. Introduced to Jordan from North America. Evergreen, drought-tolerant, succulent tree; waxy cactus pads (modified branches) covered with spines (modified leaves); yellow, cup-shaped flowers with both male and female organs; orange or red fruit with fleshy pulp. Edible fruit-pulp and cooked pads. Used as a fence. **Habitat** Domesticated in sunny regions with dry soil. **Blooms** Spring.

☐ **CARNATIONS & PINKS**
Dianthus Genus
CARYOPHYLLACEAE FAMILY

H 10-75cm. A total of ten *Dianthus* species know as "carnations" or "pinks" have been recorded in Jordan. They are generally characterized by jointed stems with swollen nodes; simple, narrow leaves; pink or white, fragrant flowers; five petals with dented or feathered margins; cylindrical calyxes with short, scaly bracts. **Habitat** Different habitats including *Ajloun, Amman, Dab'a,* and *Tafilah.* **Blooms** Spring, summer, or autumn.

☐ **ARABIC BABY'S BREATH**
Gypsophila arabica
CARYOPHYLLACEAE FAMILY

H 50cm. Branching, slender, jointed stems; small, narrow leaves that fall off early to conserve water; delicate, white, dark-striped, 5-petaled flowers with ten stamens. **Habitat** *Gypsophila* is Latin for *chalk lover.* The *Gypsophila* genus occurs in chalky and limestone woodlands, shrublands, and deserts, including *Amman, Salt,* and *Shobak.* **Blooms** Spring to autumn.

☐ **SANDWORT**
Minuartia picta
CARYOPHYLLACEAE FAMILY

H 15cm. Slender, branched, jointed stems; narrow, grass-like leaves; small, pink or white, 5-petaled flowers with purple stamens. **Habitat** Highlands and arid regions including *Tafilah* and *Shobak.* **Blooms** Late winter or spring.

☐ **ALGERIAN TEA**
Paronychia argentea
CARYOPHYLLACEAE FAMILY

H 10cm. Also known as "silvery whitlow-wort". Ground-covering stems that develop new roots as they spread; minute flowers surrounded by dense, translucent bracts. Flowers are used as tea. **Habitat** Well-drained highlands in northwestern and western Jordan, including *Irbid, Mafraq, Ajloun, Amman, Karak,* and *Tafilah.* **Blooms** Spring.

☐ **CATCHFLY**
Silene Genus
CARYOPHYLLACEAE FAMILY

H 5-40cm. A total of 30 *Silene* species have been recorded in Jordan. They are generally characterized by pale-green, red-veined, balloon-like calyx; white or pink flowers with five forked petals (appearing like 10 in some species); hairy, delicate, jointed stems; and a pair of leaves at each node. Small insects can become trapped in the sticky hairs of some catchfly species, which gives them their name. **Habitat** Mainly fields and roadsides of the *Northern Highlands,* including *Irbid, Ajlun, Amman,* and *Salt.* **Blooms** Spring to autumn.

☐ **COW BASIL**
Vaccaria pyramidata
CARYOPHYLLACEAE FAMILY

H 50cm. Slender, top-branching, jointed stems; a pair of leaves at each node; pink, 5-petaled flowers with a white, green-ribbed calyx. **Habitat** Moist, sunny fields in western Jordan, including *Wadi al-Seer* and *Shobak*. **Blooms** Late winter or spring.

☐ **JOINTED ANABASIS**
Anabasis articulata
CHENOPODIACEAE FAMILY

H 50cm. Bushy plant with woody old branches and green jointed stems; tiny leaves and flowers at stem joints; membranous, pink-winged fruit. Absorbs and stores water rapidly in fleshy stems. Prevents water loss with reduced leaves. Source of food for camels and rodents. **Habitat** Stony, limestone deserts and arid valleys, including *Wadi Rum, Dead Sea, Eastern Desert*, and *Wadi Araba*. **Blooms** Late summer and autumn.

☐ **SYRIAN ANABASIS**
Anabasis syriaca
CHENOPODIACEAE FAMILY

H 50cm. Dense shrub with a woody base; fleshy, jointed stems; tiny, triangular leaves; yellow flowers at stem joints; and membranous, yellow-winged fruit. **Habitat** Loose, alluvial soil in dry areas, including *Mafraq, Amman, Madaba, Tafilah, Ma'an*, and *Wadi Rum*. **Blooms** Late summer and autumn.

☐ **HALOTHAMNUS**
Halothamnus hierochuntica
CHENOPODIACEAE FAMILY

H 20cm. Gray-green branches; small, fleshy, pointed leaves; membranous fruit resembling flowers with yellow petals. **Habitat** Dry regions and deserts, including *Wadi Hidan* and the *Eastern Desert*. **Blooms** Summer and early autumn.

☐ **THORNY SALTWORT**
Noaea mucronata
CHENOPODIACEAE FAMILY

H 50cm. Spiny bush; woody base; green young branches; small leaves; green, succulent outer flowers; reddish-pink seed membranes. **Habitat** Arid regions and deserts, including the *Dead Sea*, *Wadi Araba*, *Shobak*, and the *Eastern Desert*. **Blooms** Late summer or autumn.

☐ **NETTLELEAF GOOSEFOOT**
Chenopodium murale
CHENOPODIACEAE FAMILY

H 60cm. Reddish, erect stems; triangular, dentate leaves; greenish, spherical flower buds that develop into fruit while enclosed by the sepals. Edible leaves and young shoots. **Habitat** Light soils and dunes in diverse habitats, including river valleys and deserts. **Blooms** All year.

☐ **COMMON PURSLANE**
Portulaca oleracea
PORTULACACEAE FAMILY

H 40cm. Succulent and drought-resistant; red, fleshy stems; smooth, green leaves clustered at stem joints and tips; yellow flowers in the middle of leaf clusters. Leaves are edible raw or cooked as a spinach substitute. They are rich in omega-3 fatty acids, vitamins, minerals, and antioxidants. **Habitat** Sunny, dry areas in the highlands and valleys of northwestern Jordan, including *Amman* and *Wadi Hidan*. **Blooms** From spring to autumn. Flowers open only for a few hours on sunny days.

☐ **SYRIAN BRYONY**
Bryonia syriaca
CUCURBITACEAE FAMILY

H cm. Climbing vine with springlike tendrils that twine around any support; heart-shaped leaves with serrated margins; greenish-yellow flowers with five petals; small fruit 1 cm in diameter. Developing fruit resembles its close relative, the green watermelon. It turns red when ripe. **Habitat** The *Northern Highlands*, including *Amman* and the *Ajlun* woodlands. **Blooms** Winter and early spring.

☐ **COLOCYNTH**
Citrullus colocynthis
CUCURBITACEAE FAMILY

L 3m. Also known as "bitter cucumber" and "vine of Sodom". Long, spreading stems; triangular leaves with wavy teeth; yellow male and female flowers that develop on the same plant; round, lemon-size fruit that resembles its close relative, the green watermelon. The fruit turns yellow when ripe. It has an extremely bitter pulp used as a laxative. **Habitat** Common in semi-deserts, including the *Dead Sea*, *Wadi Araba*, and *Wadi Rum*. **Blooms** Summer.

☐ **SQUIRTING CUCUMBER**
Ecballium elaterium
CUCURBITACEAE FAMILY

L 3m. Thick, low plant with spreading branches and bristly, wrinkled leaves. Yellow male and female flowers develop on the same plant. Fruit is green, bristly, and oblong. It explodes and squirts out seeds when ripe, which gives the plant its name. Pulp is used to induce vomiting. **Habitat** Highlands of northwestern and western Jordan, including *Amman*, *Ajloun*, and *Karak*. **Blooms** Summer.

☐ SEDGE
Cyperus Genus
CYPERACEAE FAMILY

H 50-100cm. A total of eight sedge species in the *Cyperus* genus have been recorded in Jordan. They are aquatic plants closely related to papyrus, they have triangular stems in cross-section, and grass-like leaves that occur in whorls at the base of the plant and around green flower clusters. **Habitat** Around slow-moving or still water in river valleys, including *Wadi al-Seer*, *Wadi Hidan*, and *Wadi Mujib*. **Blooms** From spring to autumn.

☐ PINCUSHION FLOWER
Scabiosa Genus
DIPSACACEAE FAMILY

H 15-60cm. Six *Scabiosa* species have been recorded in Jordan. They generally have long, hairy leaves; and white, pink, or lavender flower heads made up of crowded florets with pin-like stamens in the center, surrounded by looser florets with long petals. Seeds generally have cup-shaped membranes, collectively forming a distinctive, ball-shaped seed head. **Habitat** Grassy fields and semi-deserts in western Jordan, including *Wadi al-Seer* and *Petra*. **Blooms** Spring.

☐ ITALIAN HONEYSUCKLE
Lonicera etrusca
CAPRIFOLIACEAE FAMILY

H 5m. Much-branched climbing shrub; oval leaves; pink flower buds; yellowish-white, tubular, fragrant flowers that produce edible nectar; red fruit. **Habitat** Woodlands and shrublands including *Irbid*, *Ajloun*, *Amman*, and *Tafilah*. **Blooms** Spring.

☐ **STORAX TREE**
Styrax officinalis
STYRACACEAE FAMILY

H 5m. Much-branched tree with dark stems; ovate leaves; white, pendulous, scented flowers; rounded fruit. Branches produce a balsamic gum used as a condiment. **Habitat** Rocky woodlands including *Ajloun*, *Jerash*, *Amman*, and *Salt*. **Blooms** Spring and early summer.

☐ **STRAWBERRY TREE**
Arbutus Genus
ERICACEAE FAMILY

H 2-8m. Two strawberry tree species have been recorded in Jordan: *Arbutus andrachne* and *Arbutus unedo*. They are evergreen shrubs or trees with red bark; leathery leaves; clustered, whitish, bell-shaped flowers; and rough, reddish fruits that resemble strawberries, which give the trees their name. Edible but flavorless fruit. **Habitat** Woodlands in the *Northern Highlands*, including *Irbid*, *Ajloun*, and *Amman*. **Blooms** Spring.

□ **SPURGE**
Euphorbia Genus
EUPHORBIACEAE FAMILY

H 15-90cm. A total of 29 *Euphorbia* species have been recorded in Jordan. They are generally characterized by leaves arranged in whorls; leaf-like bracts; reduced male flowers and one female flower grouped in cup-shaped involucres that resemble single flowers (cyathia); 3-chambered seed capsules that split open explosively to eject seeds; poisonous milky sap. **Habitat** Different species occur in habitats ranging from the *Northern Highlands* to the *Eastern Desert*. **Blooms** Spring. Some species bloom in summer or autumn

□ **CASTOR OIL PLANT**
Ricinus communis
EUPHORBIACEAE FAMILY

H 12m. Fast-growing tree; reddish-green, star-shaped leaves with toothed margins; yellowish-green flowers clustered in spikes; spiny, reddish seed pods. Male flowers have long, yellow stamens. Female flowers, located at spike tips, have red stigmas. Seeds and other plant parts are toxic if ingested. Seeds are pressed to produce caster oil, valued industrially for maintaining fluidity at extreme temperatures. **Habitat** Warm, rocky hillsides in regions such as the *Dead Sea*. Used in urban areas as an ornamental tree. **Blooms** Spring.

☐ LEGUME & BEAN FAMILY
FABACEAE FAMILY

Over 260 species in the Fabaceae family have been recorded in Jordan. They are generally characterized by legume fruits (long, one-chambered seed pods that open lengthwise), composite leaves (pinnate, trifoliate, or palmate), and flowers with five overlapping petals.

☐ APPLE-RING ACACIA
Acacia albida
FABACEAE FAMILY

H 20m; the largest of the *Acacia* trees. Rounded crown; hairy leaves; small dot gland at the base of leaves; 2 cm spines at leaf nodes; fragrant, yellow flower-spikes that produce spiral pods. Carries leaves only in dry seasons. Provides shade and food for wildlife in summer. Sap is used as *gum arabic*. **Habitat** Semi-arid regions with sandy soil and underground water such as the river valleys of western Jordan. **Blooms** Early summer.

☐ **UMBRELLA THORN ACACIA**
Acacia tortilis
FABACEAE FAMILY

H 2-4m. Evergreen tree or shrub branching from the base, often with a flat top; compound leaves made up of small leaflets to conserve water; 5 cm spines for protection; fragrant, yellowish-white flowers in spherical clusters; hairy, spiral pods. Sap is used as *gum arabic*. Acacias are essential food for wild gazelles and the only trees found in some deserts. **Habitat** Dry regions with sandy soil, including *Wadi Araba* and the *Dead Sea*. **Blooms** Spring and summer.

☐ **SPIRALED ACACIA**
Acacia raddiana
FABACEAE FAMILY

H 4-6m. Evergreen tree, generally with 1-3 trunks and a rounded crown; compound leaves made up of small leaflets to conserve water; 5 cm spines for protection; fragrant, yellowish-white flowers in spherical clusters; smooth seed pods. Sap is used as *gum arabic*. Acacias are essential food for wild gazelles and the only trees found in some deserts. **Habitat** Dry regions with sandy soil, including *Wadi Araba* and the *Dead Sea*. **Blooms** Early summer.

☐ **CAMELTHORN**
Alhagi maurorum
FABACEAE FAMILY

H 100cm. Also known as "Caspian manna". Spiny shrub with deep and wide-spreading roots; green branches; small, pointed leaves; small, pink flowers that develop into brown pea pods. **Habitat** Dry regions with moist soil, including the *Dead Sea* region and river valleys. **Blooms** From spring to autumn.

☐ **BEAN CLOVER**
Anagyris foetida
FABACEAE FAMILY

H 2m. Also known as "bean trefoil", "stinking wood", and "stinking bean trefoil". Shrub with woody stems; trifoliate leaves; clustered, yellow flowers that develop into seed pods. Leaves fall off in summer. Leaves and seeds emit a foul odor when crushed. Seeds are toxic. **Habitat** The *Northern Highlands*, including *Amman*, *Irbid*, *Ajloun*, and *Salt*. **Blooms** Late winter and spring.

☐ **MILK-VETCH**
Astragalus Genus
FABACEAE FAMILY

H 15-70cm. A total of 55 *Astragalus* species have been recorded in Jordan. They are mostly low shrubs with hairy, compound, odd-pinnate leaves (paired leaflets and one terminal leaflet); pink, yellow, or white flowers with a banner petal that slightly curves back; and inflated pea pods that rattle when dry. Most *Astragalus* species are toxic. **Habitat** Different species occur in habitats ranging from the highlands including *Jerash*, *Amman*, *Salt*, and *Shobak*, to deserts such as *Wadi Araba* and the *Eastern Desert*. **Blooms** Late winter or spring.

☐ **SPINY MILK-VETCH**
Astragalus spinosus
FABACEAE FAMILY

H 50cm. Spiny shrub; compound leaves of four or five leaflet pairs; flowers develop into pinkish or purplish, paper-like seed pods. **Habitat** Rocky, dry areas in the *Dead Sea* region and the *Eastern Desert*, including *Azraq*, *Madaba*, and *Ma'an*. **Blooms** Spring.

☐ **SPINY BROOM**
Calycotome villosa
FABACEAE FAMILY

H 125cm. Spiny, woody shrub; fragrant, yellow flowers; trifoliate leaves shed annually. **Habitat** Sunny, dry, stony slopes in northwestern Jordan, including *Amman*, *Ajloun*, *Jerash* and *Salt*. **Blooms** Winter.

□ **CAROB**
Ceratonia siliqua
FABACEAE FAMILY

H 10m. Also known as "St. John's bread". Evergreen, drought-tolerant tree with a thick, rough trunk and leathery, green oval leaves. Small, clustered, red flowers that lack petals. Long, brown seed-pods that ripen in late summer. They are rich in sugar and protein, and constitute main food source for Bedouins during famine. Fruit is eaten raw or ground to use as a sweetener and chocolate substitute. Seeds are roasted as a coffee substitute and used for medicinal purposes as a laxative. Carob trees are male, female, or hermaphrodite (both sexes). Only female trees produce fruit. **Habitat** Rocky regions in the highlands, including *Amman* and *Ajloun.* **Blooms** Autumn.

□ **COMMON HORSESHOE VETCH**
Hippocrepis unisiliquosa
FABACEAE FAMILY

H 35cm. Composite leaves made up of 7-15 leaflets with blunt tips; small, yellow, 5-petaled flowers; seed pod with horseshoe-shaped segments. **Habitat** Fields and semi-deserts in western Jordan, including *Amman* and *Wadi Dana.* **Blooms** From late winter to early summer.

☐ **SWEET PEA**
Lathyrus Genus
FABACEAE FAMILY

H 30-200cm. A total of 13 species in the *Lathyrus* genus have been recorded in Jordan. They are generally characterized by bushy or climbing plants; linear leaves; 5-lobed calyx; sweet-smelling flowers that come in red, pink, white, yellow, blue, or purple. Used as ornamental garden plants. Seeds are toxic if ingested in excessive quantities. **Habitat** Fields and roadsides in the highlands, including *Irbid*, *Amman*, and *Karak*. **Blooms** Spring.

☐ **YELLOW RESTHARROW**
Ononis natrix
FABACEAE FAMILY

H 50cm. Also known as "sticky restharrow". Dense, sticky branches and small leaves; yellow flowers with red veins. **Habitat** Common on roadsides in the highlands, including *Amman*, *Irbid*, *Ajloun*, *Karak*, and *Ma'an*. **Blooms** Throughout warm seasons.

☐ **SPINY RESTHARROW**
Ononis spinosa
FABACEAE FAMILY

H 60cm. Spiny stems; small, serrated leaves; pinkish-violet flowers. Edible flowers, roots, and young leaves. Flowers are used for food decoration. Roots have a licorice flavor. **Habitat** Well-drained, limy soil in sunny areas of the *Northern Highlands*, including *Irbid*, *Ajloun*, *Amman*, and *Tafilah*. **Blooms** Spring and summer.

☐ DWARF MESQUITE
Prosopis farcta
FABACEAE FAMILY

☐ STAR TRIGONEL
Trigonella stellata
FABACEAE FAMILY

H 100cm. Low, bushy tree; whitish, spiny stems; compound, bipinnate leaves; yellow flower spikes; pinkish, wrinkled, pleasant-smelling seed pods that turn black when dry. **Habitat** The *Jordan River Valley*. **Blooms** Spring and summer.

H 5cm. Aromatic, flattened herb; trifoliate, oval leaves; small, yellow, clustered flowers. Produces ribbed pea pods about 1 cm long. **Habitat** Arid regions, including *Wadi Araba*, *Petra*, *Wadi Rum*, and the *Eastern Desert*. **Blooms** Spring.

☐ WHITE BROOM
Retama raetam
FABACEAE FAMILY

H 2m. Also known as "white weeping broom" and "juniper bush". Dense shrub with a woody stem; slender, green, hanging branches; small leaves; fragrant, white flowers with red-brown sepals; single-seed pods with a pointed end. Well adapted to dry conditions, the leaves fall early to minimize evaporation, while the green branches continue to function like leaves. **Habitat** Semi-arid and arid regions, including the *Jordan River Valley*, *Wadi Araba*, *Irbid*, *Madaba*, *Aqaba*, and the *Eastern Desert*. **Blooms** Spring.

☐ **PINK CLOVER**
Trifolium resupinatum
FABACEAE FAMILY

H 30cm. Also known as "Persian clover" and "pink trefoil". Elliptical, trifoliate leaves with serrated margins; fragrant, pink flower head; inflated, net-veined fruit. **Habitat** Fields and roadsides of northwestern Jordan, including *Irbid*, *Ajloun*, *Jerash*, and *Amman*. **Blooms** Spring.

☐ **PURPLE CLOVER**
Trifolium purpureum
FABACEAE FAMILY

H 30cm. Stiff, hairy stems; narrow, trifoliate leaves; pink-purple flowers clustered on terminal racemes; hairy calyces. **Habitat** Shady areas in the *Northern Highlands*, including *Irbid*, *Ajloun*, and *Salt*. **Blooms** Spring. Lower flowers bloom first.

☐ **STARRY CLOVER**
Trifolium stellatum
FABACEAE FAMILY

H 25cm. Hairy, upright stems; hairy, trifoliate leaves; round flower heads made up of small, pinkish-white flowers surrounded by pointed calyces. As the fruit develops, the red calyces open up and form distinctive, hairy star shapes. **Habitat** Rocky hillsides of western Jordan, including *Amman*. **Blooms** Spring.

Valonia Oak acorn at actual size.

☐ VALONIA OAK
Quercus ithaburensis
FAGACEAE FAMILY

H 7m. Also known as the "deciduous
oak", the valonia oak is the national
tree of Jordan. Woody tree with strong
branches; serrated leaves; small flowers
clustered in separate male and female
drooping spikes. Female flowers are
pollinated by wind. They produce
large acorns 4-6 cm long with cups
covered by long, leathery strips. Seeds
are edible when leached or cooked.
Bark damaged by the wasp *Cynips
calicis* produces galls (see *Plant Gall*).
Acorn cups and galls are used to make
black ink. **Habitat** Woodlands of
the *Northern Highlands*, including
Irbid, *Ajloun*, *Jerash*, *Salt*, and
Wadi al-Seer. **Blooms** Spring.
Sheds its leaves every autumn.

☐ KERMES OAK
Quercus coccifera
FAGACEAE FAMILY

H 5m. Evergreen shrub or small tree; serrated, leathery leaves; small flowers clustered in separate male and female drooping spikes. Female flowers are pollinated by wind. They produce small acorns 1-3 cm long with small cups covered by short scales. Kermes oak is closely related to the Palestine oak (*Quercus calliprinos*), which is distinguished by its larger size and larger acorns. **Habitat** Woodlands of the *Northern Highlands*, including *Jerash*, *Ajloun*, *Amman*, *Tafilah*, and *Shobak*. **Blooms** Spring.

☐ OLEANDER
Nerium oleander
APOCYNACEAE FAMILY

H 3m. Evergreen, thick, fast-growing shrub; dark-green leaves; pink or white, funnel-shaped flowers clustered at branch tips. Flowers develop into long pods that split open when mature to drop the seeds. Despite its beauty and popularity, all parts of the oleander are poisonous if ingested. **Habitat** Warm regions with wet soil. Common in the river valleys of western Jordan. Used in urban areas as an ornamental plant. **Blooms** From spring to autumn.

☐ **CARALLUMA**
Caralluma europaea
ASCLEPIADACEAE FAMILY

H 15cm. Succulent, cactus-like plant; grayish-green stems with red spots; yellow, star-shaped, fleshy flowers with purple stripes and hairy margins; paired, gray, thin seed capsules. **Habitat** Rocky regions, including *Petra*. **Blooms** Spring or summer.

☐ **GIANT MILKWEED**
Calotropis procera
ASCLEPIADACEAE FAMILY

H 3m. Also known as "Sodom apple". Large, aggressive, evergreen shrub; large leaves with pointed tips; fragrant, white flowers with five purple-tipped petals; green, inflated fruit that explodes open when pressed, releasing seeds embedded in white fiber. Secretes a poisonous, milky sap when cut, which protects the plant against goats and camels. Used in skin medicines. Source of strong fiber and gunpowder ash. **Habitat** Hot areas with well-drained soil in *Wadi Araba* and the *Dead Sea* region. **Blooms** From late spring to autumn.

□ **SINAI MILKWEED**
Gomphocarpus sinaicus
ASCLEPIADACEAE FAMILY

H 100cm. Basal stems; two narrow, pointed leaves per node; attractive flowers with five white petals and five yellow sepals that curve back; inflated, bristly, ovoid fruit with a tapering tip; seeds embedded in white fiber; milky sap. **Habitat** Deserts and arid valleys including *Tafilah* and *Petra.* **Blooms** Late winter or spring.

□ **BLUE WOODRUFF**
Asperula arvensis
RUBIACEAE FAMILY

H 40cm. Narrow leaves with pointed tips, three or more per node, hairy when young; blue flowers clustered in terminal heads surrounded by leaf-like bracts; each flower has a long tubular corolla tipped by shorter four lobes. **Habitat** Highland fields, including *Ajloun, Amman,* and *Wadi Dana.* **Blooms** Spring.

□ **CLEAVERS**
Galium aparine
RUBIACEAE FAMILY

H 150cm. Sprawling, hollow, 4-angled stems; whorls of 6-8 leaves covered with tiny, velcro-like bristles; small, white, 4-petaled flowers; bristly, round fruit that clings to animals for dispersal. Edible young shoots. Seeds are a coffee substitute. **Habitat** Shady woodlands and river valleys, including *Ajloun* and *Wadi al-Seer.* **Blooms** Spring.

□ **BRISTLY CROSSWORT**
Valantia hispida
RUBIACEAE FAMILY

H 25cm. Basal stems; whorls of three or four oval leaves that sag when mature; small, yellowish-green, 4-petaled flowers at each node ; bristly fruit. **Habitat** Rocky woodlands and shrublands, including *Ajloun, Amman,* and *Shobak.* **Blooms** Spring.

☐ **CRANESBILL**
GERANIACEAE FAMILY

A total of 23 cranesbill species in the *Erodium* and *Geranium* genera have been recorded in Jordan. They are characterized by long fruit resembling bird bills. When dry, the seeds split and spiral into corkscrews. When moistened by rain, they unscrew, driving the seed heads into the soil. Most cranesbills have pink or purple flowers with five petals. In some species, the petals are forked so deeply that there appear to be ten. Erodiums are distinguished by flowers with five stamens, while geraniums have ten. **Habitat** Western Jordan, including *Ajloun*, *Amman* and *Karak*. **Blooms** Spring.

☐ **SOFT FAGONIA**
Fagonia mollis
ZYGOPHYLLACEAE FAMILY

H 20cm. Compound, trifoliate leaves; spines at the base of leaf stalk; pink flowers with five petals and ten yellow stamens. Used by Bedouins as an antibiotic and to relieve pains. **Habitat** Warm, humid regions, including the *Dead Sea*, *Aqaba*, and *Wadi Rum*. **Blooms** Spring.

□ **HARMAL**
Peganum harmala
ZYGOPHYLLACEAE FAMILY

H 40cm. Green, fleshy leaves divided into narrow lobes that turn grayish with age; white, 5-petaled flowers with yellow centers; brown seed capsules with three chambers that split open when mature. Seeds contain hallucinogenic alkaloids. **Habitat** Widespread in all grasslands and deserts, including *Wadi Finan, Azraq,* and the *Eastern Desert.* **Blooms** Spring.

□ **BUSHY BEAN-CAPER**
Zygophyllum dumosum
ZYGOPHYLLACEAE FAMILY

H 30cm. Desert shrub with woody stems and succulent leaves. Flowers have five white petals that appear in between five greenish sepals. Fruit has five winged seeds with wavy margins. **Habitat** Deserts including *Wadi Araba* and *Wadi Rum.* **Blooms** Spring.

□ **COMMON WALNUT**
Juglans regia
JUGLANDACEAE FAMILY

H 30m. Composite leaves made up of 5-9 leaflets; male flowers clustered in drooping spikes; female flowers clustered in groups of 2-9; fruit has a thin, green, outer flesh and a hard inner shell covering the familiar walnut. Edible nuts. **Habitat** Sunny areas with moist soil in western Jordan, including *Amman.* **Blooms** Early summer.

☐ **SYRIAN BEAR'S BREECH**
Acanthus syriacus
ACANTHACEAE FAMILY

H 50cm. Spiny plant; long leaves with many deep lobes; yellowish-white flowers clustered on spikes; each flower is protected above by an enlarged purple sepal and supported below by a spiny bract. **Habitat** Stony fields in the *Northern Highlands*, including *Irbid, Ajloun, Jerash, Amman,* and *Madaba*. **Blooms** Spring.

☐ **EYELASH PLANT**
Blepharis ciliaris
ACANTHACEAE FAMILY

H 30cm. Small, spiny plant; 2-3 cm, purple, tubular flowers; each flower has 3-lobed, veined corolla limb supported by a long, spiny bract. Seeds are shot in the air when heavy rains wet the seed capsule. Root ashes are mixed with other ingredients to make the *kohl* mascara. **Habitat** Hot regions including the *Dead Sea, Wadi Araba, Wadi Rum,* and *Aqaba.* **Blooms** From late spring to autumn.

☐ MINT FAMILY
LAMIACEAE FAMILY

Over 100 species in the Lamiaceae family have been recorded in Jordan. Plants in this family are mostly aromatic and include mint, basil, sage, rosemary, thyme, and lavender. They are generally characterized by flowers with five fused petals that form a 2-lobed upper lip and a 3-lobed lower lip. Leaves are arranged in whorls around stem nodes. Flowers are arranged in two opposite clusters at each stem node (often appearing like whorls). Stems are generally square in cross section.

☐ CHIAN BUGLE
Ajuga chia
LAMIACEAE FAMILY

H 20cm. Soft, purple stems; hairy, slender, 3-lobed leaves; yellow flowers with purple spots. **Habitat** Rocky areas in the highlands, including *Irbid*, *Amman*, and *Shobak*. **Blooms** Winter and spring.

☐ EASTERN BUGLE
Ajuga orientalis
LAMIACEAE FAMILY

H 30cm. Woolly stems curving up from the base; hairy, dentate leaves; blue-violet, tubular flower with yellowish base and long calyx. **Habitat** Humid soil in the *Northern Highlands*, including *Ajloun*, *Salt*, and *Amman*. **Blooms** Spring.

☐ **COMMON BLACK HOREHOUND**
Ballota undulata
LAMIACEAE FAMILY

H 50cm. Woody base; hairy, basal stems; dark-green, wrinkled leaves, smelly when rubbed; small, white flowers with a light-green, saucer-shaped, protective calyx. **Habitat** Roadsides and fields of the *Northern Highlands*, including *Irbid*, *Jerash*, *Amman*, and *Karak*. **Blooms** Spring and summer.

☐ **WHITE HOREHOUND**
Marrubium vulgare
LAMIACEAE FAMILY

H 40cm. Hairy, basal stems; hairy, gray-green, wrinkled leaves, smelly when rubbed; small, white flowers in round clusters at each stem node; star-like calyx. **Habitat** Roadsides and fields in the highlands, including *Wadi al-Seer* and *Petra*. **Blooms** From late winter to early summer.

☐ **JAGGED-LEAVED PHLOMIS**
Eremostachys laciniata
LAMIACEAE FAMILY

H 100cm. Hairy, gray stems; two opposite serrated leaves on each stem node; flowers have hairy, whitish upper lip and yellow-orange lower lip; flowers occur in two clusters at each stem node. **Habitat** Roadsides and fields in the *Northern Highlands*, including *Amman*, *Irbid*, *Jerash*, and *Karak*. **Blooms** Spring.

☐ **HENBIT DEADNETTLE**
Lamium amplexicaule
LAMIACEAE FAMILY

H 20cm. Also known as "common henbit" and "giraffe head". Hairy, square stems; paired, lobed leaves forming spaced nodes on stem; pink, tubular flowers clustered at stem-end. Leaves are edible as herbs. **Habitat** Nutrient-rich, moist to dry soil in the *Northern Highlands*, including *Amman*, and semi-deserts. **Blooms** Winter and early spring.

☐ **MUSK DEADNETTLE**
Lamium moschatum
LAMIACEAE FAMILY

H 30cm. Basal stems; two opposite, serrated leaves on each stem node; white patterns on top leaves; white flowers arranged in two opposite clusters at each stem node. **Habitat** Shady areas in the *Northern Highlands* including *Ajloun*, *Amman*, and *Salt*. **Blooms** Late winter and spring.

☐ **HORSE MINT**
Mentha sylvestris
LAMIACEAE FAMILY

H 100cm. Also known as "wild mint", and "habag" in Arabic. Hairy stems; stalkless, pointed leaves with toothed margins; pink-purple flowers clustered on tapering, terminal spikes. The aromatic leaves are edible as tea and food flavoring. **Habitat** Moist soil near water, including *Wadi Hidan*, *Wadi al-Seer*, and *Wadi Finan*. **Blooms** Summer and early autumn.

☐ PHLOMIS
Phlomis Genus
LAMIACEAE FAMILY

H 30-150cm. A total of ten *Phlomis* species have been recorded in Jordan. They are generally sticky and hairy shrubs with thick, rough leaves. Flowers are yellow or pink, arranged in two opposite clusters at each stem node, each flower has a hood-shaped upper lip and a 3-lobed lower lip. **Habitat** The *Northern Highlands* including *Irbid*, *Jerash*, and *Amman*. Some species occur in the *Eastern Desert*. **Blooms** Spring and summer.

☐ SAGE
Salvia Genus
LAMIACEAE FAMILY

A total of 20 *Salvia* species have been recorded in Jordan. They are characterized by flowers with two stamens (male organs), each functions as a lever. The stamens pivot down and deposit pollen onto pollinators as they collect nectar. Sage varieties were widely used in ancient times for numerous medicinal purposes. The name *Salvia* derives from the Latin verb *to save*.

☐ **DOMINICA SAGE**
Salvia dominica
LAMIACEAE FAMILY

☐ **JERUSALEM SAGE**
Salvia hierosolymitana
LAMIACEAE FAMILY

H 70cm. White flowers with yellow lower lip clustered on hairy basal stems. Hairy, aromatic leaves with round-toothed margins. **Habitat** Rocky areas in the *Northern Highlands*, including *Amman, Irbid, Ajloun, Jerash, Karak,* and *Tafilah*. **Blooms** Spring and early summer.

H 50cm. Basal stems with a square cross-section; long, rough, basal leaves; purple-red flowers with paler lower lips; flowers are arranged in two opposite clusters at each stem node. **Habitat** Rocky fields of the *Northern Highlands*, including *Ajloun, Amman,* and *Karak*. **Blooms** Spring and early summer.

☐ **TURNIP-LEAVED SAGE**
Salvia napifolia
LAMIACEAE FAMILY

☐ **ANNUAL SAGE**
Salvia viridis
LAMIACEAE FAMILY

H 60cm. Blue-violet flower spikes with two opposite flower clusters at each stem node. Hairy leaves at the base of the plant. **Habitat** Well-drained soil in the highlands, including *Amman, Ajloun,* and *Karak*. **Blooms** Spring.

H 30cm. Purple flower spike, topped by more showy purple bracts. Rough, aromatic, edible basal leaves. **Habitat** Warm, dry, limestone hills and roadsides in western Jordan, including roads that lead to the *Jordan River Valley*. **Blooms** Late winter and spring.

☐ **FELTY GERMANDER**
Teucrium polium
LAMIACEAE FAMILY

H 30cm. Fuzzy, aromatic leaves with toothed margins; small, white or pink flowers in woolly clusters. Drought-resistant. Edible leaves used in herbal remedies for stomachaches and colds. **Habitat** Stony and semi-desert habitats, including *Wadi Hidan* and *Petra*. **Blooms** Late spring and summer.

☐ **BROOMRAPE FAMILY**
OROBANCHACEAE FAMILY

H 15-40cm. A total of 13 broomrape species have been recorded in Jordan. They are parasitic plants that lack chlorophyll, cannot produce their own nutrients, and rob water and nutrients from the roots of neighboring plants. They are characterized by a thick, succulent stem; reduced, scaly leaves that are never green (green leaves around a broomrape belong to the host plant); and blue, white, or yellow tubular flowers that spiral around the stem. **Habitat** Dry regions, including *Wadi Mujib*, *Wadi Araba*, *Azraq*, and *Wadi Rum*. **Blooms** Spring.

☐ PLANTAINS
Plantago Genus
PLANTAGINACEAE FAMILY

H 5-35cm. A total of 20 species in the *Plantago* genus have been recorded in Jordan. They are generally characterized by a rosette of basal leaves, several stalks, and spikes of small, 4-petaled flowers. Flowers bloom in sequence from the base to the apex of each spike, and the long stamens of newly developed flowers commonly form a ring around the spike. **Habitat** Different *plantain* species occur in habitats ranging from humid highlands, including *Ajloun* and *Jerash*, to deserts such as the *Eastern Desert*. **Blooms** Mostly spring and summer.

☐ FIGWORT
Scrophularia Genus
SCROPHULARIACEAE FAMILY

H 40-70cm. A total of 11 *Scrophularia* species have been recorded in Jordan. They are characterized by square stems; opposite leaf pairs; red or green, small, two-lipped, curling flowers arranged in branching clusters and attached to the main stem by short stalks (panicled cymes). **Habitat** The highlands, including *Ajlun*, *Amman*,

and *Petra*. Some species occur in deserts. **Blooms** Spring and summer.

☐ MULLEIN
Verbascum Genus
SCROPHULARIACEAE FAMILY

H 30-150cm. A total of 18 mullein species have been recorded in Jordan. They generally produce small rosettes of hairy leaves in their first year. Adult plants over a year old produce large, hairy, basal leaves with wavy margins and densely branched crowns with yellow flowers. The flowers of most species have red centers. Mulleins are a source of food for numerous insects such as moth caterpillars and ants. **Habitat** Stony mountains and valleys of western Jordan, including *Amman, Karak, Tafilah,* and *Shobak.* **Blooms** Late spring and summer.

☐ **SPEEDWELL**
Veronica Genus
PLANTAGINACEAE FAMILY

H 15-50cm. A total of 12 *Veronica* species have been recorded in Jordan. They are generally small shrubs with violet or white flowers. Each flower has four striped, unequal lobes (smaller bottom lobe), white or yellow center, and two stamens. The fruit is a capsule with numerous seeds. Edible leaves and stems. **Habitat** Sunny fields with moist soils in the *Northern Highlands*, including *Irbid, Ajloun,* and *Wadi al-Seer.* **Blooms** From spring to autumn.

☐ **COMMON VERBENA**
Verbena officinalis
VERBENACEAE FAMILY

H 75cm. Aromatic leaves with toothed margins; delicate spikes of pale purple or pink flowers. Edible leaves used in herbal teas to treat headaches, fevers, insomnia, and other medical conditions. **Habitat** Limestone hills and roadsides in western Jordan, including *Amman.* **Blooms** Late spring and summer.

☐ **COLCHICUM**
Colchicum Genus
COLCHICACEAE FAMILY

A total of nine *Colchicum* species have been recorded in Jordan. They are characterized by pink or white flowers without stems, and long female organs that extend below ground where the ovaries are. Each flower has six stamens (male organs) and three styles (female organs). Toxic if ingested. **Habitat** Different *Colchicum* species occur in habitats ranging from the humid *Northern Highlands*, including *Jerash* and *Amman*, to desert regions such as *Wadi Araba, Azraq, Petra,* and *Wadi Rum*. **Blooms** Most *Colchicum* species flower in winter and produce leaves later in spring. A few species flower and produce leaves in spring.

☐ **ANDROCYMBIUM**
Androcymbium palaestinum
COLCHICACEAE FAMILY

H 5cm. Basal rosette of leaves with thick bases tapering to narrow tips. White flowers with purple veins. **Habitat** Sandy, lime-free, warm areas, including the *Jordan River Valley*, the *Dead Sea* region, *Wadi Araba*, and *Wadi Rum*. **Blooms** Winter.

☐ **PERSIAN BELLS**
Fritillaria *persica*
LILIACEAE FAMILY

H 60cm. Single stem; grayish-green leaves arranged spirally halfway up the stem; green, purple-veined, hanging, bell-shaped flowers on the top half of the stem. **Habitat** Woodlands and humid areas, including *Jerash*, *Amman*, and *Petra*. **Blooms** Late winter or spring.

☐ **GAGEA**
Gagea Genus
LILIACEAE FAMILY

H 5-15cm. A total of five *Gagea* species have been recorded in Jordan. They are generally characterized by basal rosettes of narrow leaves and yellow, star-shaped flowers with six pointed tepals (3 petals and 3 sepals). **Habitat** Different species occur in habitats ranging from the humid highlands including *Ajloun*, to the *Eastern Desert* and *Wadi Araba*. **Blooms** Late winter and spring.

☐ **EYED TULIP**
Tulipa *agenensis*
LILIACEAE FAMILY

H 25cm. Basal leaves with wavy margins; straight stem; red or orange, solitary, bowl-shaped flower with a black, yellow-fringed spot near the base of each tepal; yellow reproductive organs. **Habitat** Woodlands and shrublands in the *Northern Highlands*, including *Ajloun*, *Amman*, and *Tafilah*. **Blooms** Spring.

☐ **SARSAPARILLA**
Smilax *aspera*
SMILACACEAE FAMILY

Climbing, evergreen shrub with spiny stems; glossy, heart-shaped leaves; greenish-white, small, scented flowers; and red, spherical fruit that turns black when dry. Edible leaves and roots. **Habitat** Bushy fields and woodlands in the *Northern Highlands*, including *Ajloun* and *Amman*. **Blooms** Autumn or winter.

□ **HAIRY PINK FLAX**
Linum pubescens
LINACEAE FAMILY

H 30cm. Pink flowers with blue centers; high-branching stems; thin, hairy leaves. Closely related to the common flax used to produce linen. **Habitat** Woodlands and shrublands in the *Northern Highlands*, including *Amman*, *Irbid*, *Ajloun*, *Jerash*, and *Karak*. **Blooms** Spring.

□ **BERMUDA-BUTTERCUP**
Oxalis pes-caprae
OXALIDACEAE FAMILY

H 25cm. Invasive weed of South African origin, also known as "soursob". Trifoliate leaves with three heart-shaped, green leaflets, often speckled with purple spots. Yellow, 5-petaled flowers clustered on a slender, leafless stem. Edible, sour-tasting stems and leaves. Roots are edible when cooked. **Habitat** Woodlands and shrublands in the *Northern Highlands*, including *Amman, Irbid, Ajloun, Jerash,* and *Karak.* **Blooms** Late winter and early spring.

☐ **ROCK ROSE**
CISTACEAE FAMILY

A total of 18 species in the Cistaceae family have been recorded in Jordan. They are generally characterized by yellow, pink, or white flowers with five, wrinkled, short-lived petals and numerous stamens. Each flower has five sepals, the outer two are narrow and look like small bracts (modified leaves subtending flowers). Most species have red, thin, branching stems.

☐ **HOARY ROCK ROSE**
Cistus creticus
CISTACEAE FAMILY

H 60cm. Evergreen; hairy, thick, rough leaves with wavy margins; pink flowers with five wrinkled petals and yellow centers; hairy seed capsules that split open into five parts when mature. The aromatic leaves are used as a tea and condiment. **Habitat** The *Northern Highlands*, including *Irbid*, *Ajloun*, and *Amman*. **Blooms** Late spring and early summer.

☐ **PINK SUNROSE**
Helianthemum vesicarium
CISTACEAE FAMILY

H 25cm. Evergreen, spreading plant with grayish branches; hairy, narrow leaves; pink, 5-petaled flowers with orange stamens and three hairy, red-veined sepals. **Habitat** Rocky areas in the highlands, including *Jerash*, *Amman*, and *Shobak*. **Blooms** Late winter and spring.

☐ **HOLLYHOCK**
Alcea Genus
MALVACEAE FAMILY

H 1-3 m. A total of nine hollyhock species have been recorded in Jordan. They are generally characterized by basal stems; hairy, round, lobed leaves; white, yellow, pink, or red flowers; and fused yellow stamens that form a tubular center. Drought-resistant. **Habitat** Different species occur in habitats ranging from the *Northern Highlands* including *Amman*, to deserts such as the *Basalt Desert*. Common, ornamental plant in urban gardens. **Blooms** Spring and early summer.

☐ **COMMON MALLOW**
Malva sylvestris
MALVACEAE FAMILY

H 75cm. Pink flowers; five veined petals with slightly forked tips; hairy, heart-shaped, shallowly-lobed leaves with toothed, wavy margins. The wheel-shaped fruit is edible when immature. Young leaves and flowers are edible raw. Mature leaves are edible when cooked. **Habitat** Fields and roadsides in the highlands, including *Irbid*, *Mafraq*, *Jerash*, *Amman*, and *Tafilah*. **Blooms** Spring and early summer.

☐ **SAGO PONDWEED**
Potamogeton pectinatus
POTAMOGETONACEAE FAMILY

Aquatic plant; slender, branching stems; submersed, thread-like leaves, up to 20 cm long; leaf-like appendages (stipules) fused to leaves at the base; flower spikes pollinated by water; brown, egg-shaped fruit with a curved beak. Provides habitat and food for aquatic animals and waterfowl. **Habitat** Permanent sedimentary ponds, reservoirs, and rivers in the *Northern Highlands* and the *Jordan River Valley*. **Blooms** From spring to autumn.

☐ **WILD OLIVE**
Olea europaea
OLEACEAE FAMILY

H 11m. One of the earliest cultivated trees by humans. Evergreen; oblong, pointed, green-gray leaves with paler, hairy undersides; small, fragrant, white flowers. Raw olives are inedible. Unripe olives are cured and often fermented to produce edible green olives. Ripe olives are cured to produce black olives or pressed to extract oil. Pollen causes allergies in some people. Olive trees may live over 1,000 years. Olive branches symbolize peace. **Habitat** Sunny, limestone areas in the *Northern Highlands*, including *Jerash*, *Ajloun*, *Amman*, and *Madaba*. **Blooms** Spring.

Orchid Family
ORCHIDACEAE FAMILY

Orchids are the most diverse flowering plants with over 25,000 species worldwide. A total of 24 have been recorded in Jordan. They are generally characterized by flowers with three petals, three sepals, and a tubular back projection containing nectar (spur). The lower petal (labellum) is enlarged into a landing platform for pollinating insects. The upper sepal is modified into a protective hood.

☐ **BEE ORCHID**
Ophrys Genus
ORCHIDACEAE FAMILY

H 10-60cm. Nine orchids in the *Ophrys* genus have been recorded in Jordan. They are generally characterized by three outer sepals and three furry inner petals that resemble a bee. In addition to the visual mimicry, bee orchids generally release pheromones that mimic the scent of female bees. As a male bee attempts to mate with the flower, detachable anthers adhere to the bee to be carried to another flower. **Habitat** Semi-dry, limestone, open woodlands in the *Northern Highlands*, including *Ajloun* and *Amman*. **Blooms** Spring.

☐ **SWORD-LEAVED HELLEBORINE**
Cephalanthera longifolia
ORCHIDACEAE FAMILY

H 40cm. Narrow, sword-shaped leaves halfway up the stem, which give the plant its name. White, bell-shaped flowers with an orange lower petal on the top half of the stem. **Habitat** Woodlands of the *Northern Highlands*, including *Dibbin* and *Salt*. **Blooms** Spring.

☐ **FAN-LIPPED ORCHID**
Orchis collina
ORCHIDACEAE FAMILY

H 30cm. Basal leaves; single, brown stem; brown-purple flower spike; each flower has a large, fan-shaped lower petal (labellum) and a white, shallow spur (tubular back projection containing nectar). **Habitat** The highlands, including *Ajloun*, *Amman*, and *Salt*. **Blooms** Spring.

☐ **ANATOLIAN ORCHID**
Orchis anatolica
ORCHIDACEAE FAMILY

H 30cm. Green, brown-spotted basal leaves; pink flower spike; each flower has a long spur (tubular back projection) containing nectar and a large, lobbed central petal (labellum) with a white, violet-dotted central patch. **Habitat** Wooded areas in the *Northern Highlands*, including *Ajloun*, *Amman*, and *Salt*. **Blooms** Spring.

☐ **PINK BUTTERFLY ORCHID**
Orchis papilionacea
ORCHIDACEAE FAMILY

H 25cm. Basal leaves shorter than stem; pink flower spike; each flower has veined petals and sepals, a large lower petal (labellum) with a paler central patch and wavy margins, and a drooping spur (tubular back projection containing nectar). **Habitat** Wooded areas in the *Northern Highlands*, including *Ajloun*, *Amman*, and *Salt*. **Blooms** Spring.

☐ **POPPY**
Papaver Genus
PAPAVERACEAE FAMILY

A total of nine species in the *Papaver* genus have been recorded in Jordan. They are characterized by droopy stems that turn upright as the flower bud opens to free the crumpled petals inside. Flowers are mostly red with 4-6 petals, some with a black basal spot that is occasionally white-rimmed. The ovary (female organ) is pot-shaped, surrounded by dense stamens (male organs). At maturity, the stamens and petals fall off, leaving only the seed capsule. All plants in the Papaveraceae family secrete a bitter milky sap when cut, which protects them against herbivores. **Habitat** Fields and roadsides in the highlands, including *Irbid*, *Jerash*, *Amman*, *Karak*, and *Shobak*. Some species extend into the *Eastern Desert*. **Blooms** Spring and early summer.

☐ HORNED POPPY
Glaucium Genus
PAPAVERACEAE FAMILY

A total of four horned poppy species have been recorded in Jordan. They have red (most common), orange, or yellow flowers; and four petals, generally with a black basal spot. Easily distinguished from other poppies by pointed, horn-like flower buds, and 5-15 cm cylindrical seed pods. **Habitat** Fields and roadsides of the highlands, including *Irbid*, *Ajloun*, *Jerash*, *Amman*, *Karak*, and *Shobak*. **Blooms** Spring and early summer.

☐ COMMON FUMITORY
Fumaria officinalis
FUMARIACEAE FAMILY

H 50cm. Pink, 4-petaled flowers with dark tips clustered on spikes. Flowers have spoon-shaped lower petal and both male and female organs. Roots emit an odor when first exposed. Used to make yellow dye and in several medicinal remedies such as the treatment of acne. **Habitat** Fields and roadsides in the *Northern Highlands*, including *Irbid*, *Ajloun*, and *Karak*. **Blooms** Mainly in spring and occasionally in autumn.

☐ SICKLEFRUIT HYPECOUM
Hypecoum imberbe
PAPAVERACEAE FAMILY

H 30cm. Also known as "Persian poppy". Parsley-like basal leaves; yellow flowers with two distinctive, 3-lobed outer petals and smaller inner petals; sickle-like fruit. **Habitat** Fields and roadsides of western Jordan, including *Amman*. **Blooms** Late winter and spring.

☐ ROEMERIA
Roemeria hybrida
PAPAVERACEAE FAMILY

H 20cm. Thin, hairy branches; leaves dissected into narrow lobes; violet flowers with blue pollen. **Habitat** Highlands and desert margins, including *Irbid*, *Mafraq*, *Jerash*, *Amman*, *Karak*, *Tafilah*, and *Ma'an*. **Blooms** Spring.

☐ **CROWN ANEMONE**
Anemone coronaria
RANUNCULACEAE FAMILY

H 30cm. Parsley-like basal leaves; flowers are red (most common), pale-violet, or white; 5-8 tepals (undifferentiated petals and sepals) often with a white base; violet-blue stigmas (female organs) surrounded by dense stamens (male organs). Distinguished from poppy and buttercup by a whorl of parsley-like leaves below the flower. At maturity, stamens and tepals fall off, leaving a wind-dispersed seed spike. **Habitat** Hillsides and roadsides in the *Northern Highlands*, including *Irbid, Jerash, Amman,* and *Karak*. **Blooms** Early spring.

☐ **ASIAN BUTTERCUP**
Ranunculus asiaticus
RANUNCULACEAE FAMILY

H 20cm. Hairy stem and leaves; lobed basal leaves; dissected upper leaves; mostly red or orange flowers; five or more petals (without white patches or dark spots); dark stigmas (female organs) surrounded by dense stamens (male organs). Distinguished from poppy and anemone flowers by five green sepals subtending the petals. At maturity, stamens and petals fall off, leaving a round seed spike. **Habitat** Mountains and hillsides of western Jordan. **Blooms** Late winter and spring.

☐ **PHEASANT'S-EYE**
Adonis Genus
RANUNCULACEAE FAMILY

H 5-30cm. A total of six *Adonis* species
have been recorded in Jordan. They are
characterized by finely dissected leaves;
and red, orange, or yellow flowers with
5-30 petals and generally dark centers.
Habitat The *Northern Highlands*,
including *Irbid*, *Jerash*, *Amman*,
Karak, and *Tafilah*. **Blooms** Spring.

☐ **LARKSPUR**
Delphinium Genus
RANUNCULACEAE FAMILY

H 10-100cm. A total of three
Delphinium species have been recorded
in Jordan. They are characterized by
lobed and toothed leaves; upright stems;
dolphin-shaped buds; and purple, blue,
or white 5-petaled flowers with a back
projection (spur). **Habitat** Chalky soils
in the *Northern Highlands*, including
Jerash. **Blooms** Late spring and summer.

☐ **WHITE WATER-BUTTERCUP**
Ranunculus aquatilis
RANUNCULACEAE FAMILY

Aquatic plant; slender stems; thread-
like underwater leaves; fan-shaped
floater leaves that develop only when
the plant requires extra buoyancy;
white, 5-petaled flowers with yellow
centers. **Habitat** Ponds, reservoirs,
and river banks in the *Northern
Highlands*, including *Ajlun*. **Blooms**
Late winter, spring, or summer.

☐ **JERUSALEM BUTTERCUP**
Ranunculus millefolius
RANUNCULACEAE FAMILY

H 25cm. Hairy stems; dissected
leaves; flowers with 5-8 yellow tepals,
dense yellow stamens (male organs),
and yellow stigmas (female organs)
that produce a green seed spike.
Habitat Woodlands and shrublands
in the *Northern Highlands*, including
Ajloun and *Amman*. **Blooms** Spring.

☐ **MEDITERRANEAN CYPRESS**
Cupressus sempervirens
CUPRESSACEAE FAMILY

H 25m. Evergreen, upright, slender tree; gray trunk; level branches; scaly, dark-green leaves. The same tree carries separate, tiny male and female flowers. Female flowers develop into round, brown seed cones. Drought-tolerant and may live over 1,000 years. **Habitat** Sunny regions in the *Northern Highlands*, including *Jerash*, *Ajloun*, and *Amman*. Common ornamental tree in urban gardens and parks. **Blooms** Early in the year.

☐ **PHOENICIAN JUNIPER**
Juniperus phoenicea
CUPRESSACEAE FAMILY

H 2-10m. Dense, evergreen tree or shrub with scale-like mature leaves and needle-like young leaves. Seed cones are composed of several fused scales forming reddish-brown spheres. Seeds mature and get released about 18 months after pollination. Aromatic. Lives up to 1,000 years. **Habitat** Rocky *Southern Highlands*, including *Wadi Dana*, *Petra*, and *Wadi Rum*. **Blooms** Spring.

☐ **ALEPPO PINE**
Pinus halepensis
PINACEAE FAMILY

H 20m. Evergreen tree with thick, scaly, orange bark; green, needle-shaped leaves that grow in pairs; tiny male and female flowers clustered separately at branch-tips; egg-shaped seed cones that mature and open in two years or when heated by fire. **Habitat** Sunny areas in the *Northern Highlands*, including *Jerash* and *Ajloun*. Common ornamental tree in urban gardens and parks. **Blooms** Spring.

☐ GRASS FAMILY
POACEAE FAMILY

There are over 9,000 grass species worldwide and around 200 have been recorded in Jordan. Grasses are characterized by hollow stems with spaced nodes, sharp-edged leaves (blades) with a lower segment that hugs the stem (sheath), small flowers clustered in spikes, and simple dry fruit known as *grain*. Grass blades grow at their base, which enables them to continue growing even after being grazed by animals. In addition to their importance for grazing animals, some domesticated grasses produce edible grains essential to humans such as rice and wheat. Other grasses are also very useful to humans such as reed and bamboo. Remains of wheat and barley in early stages of domestication from wild grasses were found in prehistoric human settlements in *Beida*, north of *Petra*. **Habitat** Widespread in all habitats. **Blooms** Mainly in spring.

☐ **COMMON REED**
Phragmites australis
POACEAE FAMILY

H 6m. Large grass with erect, jointed stems; broad, tapering leaves; small flowers clustered in purple, feathery, nodding panicles that turn gray or brown in fruit. Reed is used for thatching and water treatment, and to make baskets, brooms, paper, and many other products. **Habitat** Damp soil in river valleys and wetlands, including the *Jordan River Valley*, *Wadi Hidan*, *Wadi Finan*, and *Azraq*. **Blooms** Autumn and winter.

☐ **EGYPTIAN SEA-LAVENDER**
Limonium lobatum
PLUMBAGINACEAE FAMILY

H 30cm. Basal rosette of lobed leaves; winged stems; yellowish-white flowers on branched stem tips, each flower has five petals with thinly-lobed tips. **Habitat** Hot regions, including the *Jordan River Valley*, *Dead Sea*, *Wadi Araba*, and *Wadi Rum*. **Blooms** Spring.

☐ **KNOTWEED**
Rumex cyprius
POLYGONACEAE FAMILY

H 30cm. Triangular leaves; small, green flowers; red fruit with sheet-like, veined wings. Edible leaves. **Habitat** Shrublands and deserts in all of Jordan, including the *Jordan River Valley*, *Jerash*, *Dead Sea*, *Karak*, *Wadi Araba*, and *Wadi Rum*. **Blooms** Late winter and spring.

□ **CYCLAMEN**
Cyclamen persicum
PRIMULACEAE FAMILY

H 5cm. Pink flowers with five petals pointing upwards; slender stems; thick, heart-shaped leaves with finely serrated margins; leaves are green with white patterns above and purple below. Poisonous if ingested. **Habitat** Shady, wooded areas in the *Northern Highlands*, including *Amman, Ajloun, Irbid, Karak*, and *Tafilah*. **Blooms** Winter and spring.

□ **PIMPERNEL**
Anagallis arvensis
PRIMULACEAE FAMILY

H 15cm. Square stems; heart-shaped leaves with smooth margins; blue or orange flowers with five petals, white and purple centers, and five yellow stamens. Edible leaves. Slightly poisonous seeds. **Habitat** Roadsides and sandy fields of western Jordan, including *Mafraq, Ajloun, Amman, Karak*, and *Ma'an*. **Blooms** Early spring.

□ **BLACK MAIDENHAIR FERN**
Adiantum capillus-veneris
ADIANTACEAE FAMILY

H 50cm. Evergreen fern with bright green, fan-like leaves (fronds). Like all primitive ferns, the black maidenhair has no flowers or seeds. It reproduces by spores clustered in black spots at leaf margins. **Habitat** Moist soil along shady river valleys and springs, including *Wadi al-Seer* and *Petra*. **Blooms** Produces spores in summer.

☐ JUJUBE
Ziziphus Genus
RHAMNACEAE FAMILY

H 2-10m. A total of four jujube species have been recorded in Jordan. They are drought-resistant shrubs or trees generally characterized by spiny branches; shiny leaves with three basal veins; and small, yellowish, scented, honey-filled flowers. Fruit is round, red, and sweet when ripe; tastes and feels like dates; and a source of food for Bedouins during famine. Leaves are a source of food for camels. **Habitat** *Ziziphus spina-christi* is found mainly in alluvial plains in *Wadi Araba*. Other species are found in limestone slopes in valleys of western Jordan, including *Wadi al-Seer* and *Wadi Hidan*. **Blooms** Throughout the year, mostly in late summer.

☐ **ALMOND**
Amygdalus communis
ROSACEAE FAMILY

H 2-9m. Brown branches that turn grayish with age; light-green leaves with finely serrated margins; pinkish-white flowers with five petals and long stamens; fruit has thin outer flesh and a hard inner shell that protect the familiar almond nut. Almonds have a toxin that gives them their distinctive bitter flavor, which is removed by roasting or leaching. Among the cultivated varieties is the Jordan almond that produces sweeter almonds with smaller toxin amounts. **Habitat** Woodlands and shrublands in the highlands, including *Irbid, Amman,* and *Wadi Dana.* **Blooms** Late winter and early spring. Flowers appear before leaves.

☐ **HAWTHORN**
Crataegus Genus
ROSACEAE FAMILY

H 2-6m. Four hawthorn species have been recorded in Jordan. They are shrubs or trees generally characterized by 3-5 lobbed leaves covered with tiny hairs; clustered, pinkish-white flowers with a green center and brown anthers; edible, yellow or red, round fruit 1-2 cm in diameter. **Habitat** Woodlands of western Jordan, including *Irbid, Ajloun, Amman, Tafilah,* and *Ma'an.* **Blooms** Spring.

☐ SYRIAN PEAR
Pyrus syriaca
ROSACEAE FAMILY

H 5m. Green, oblong, pointed leaves with serrated edges; small, white flowers with both male and female organs; yellow fruit, edible raw or cooked. Closely related to apples. Pollution tolerant. **Habitat** Sunny, dry, rocky regions in the *Northern Highlands*, including *Amman*, *Ajloun*, and *Salt*. **Blooms** Spring.

☐ BLACKBERRY
Rubus sanguineus
ROSACEAE FAMILY

H 2m. Shrub with backward-pointing prickles; dark-green, serrated leaves; and pink flowers. Ripe seed-fruit is bluish-purple, edible, and commonly used to make purple dye. **Habitat** Moist, well-drained soil in the *Northern Highlands*, close to water sources. **Blooms** Spring and summer.

☐ THORNY BURNET
Sarcopoterium spinosum
ROSACEAE FAMILY

H 50cm. Spiny bush; dense, woody branches that terminate with thorns; small pinnate leaves. Produces small, round, red-brown fruit. Used as a hedge, fire starter, tranquilizer, and pain reliever for such ailments as stomachaches and toothaches. **Habitat** The *Northern Highlands*, including *Amman*, *Ajloun*, *Jerash*, *Madaba*, and *Karak*. **Blooms** Spring.

☐ WHITE POPLAR
Populus alba
SALICACEAE FAMILY

H 20m. Fast-growing shade tree; smooth, white-green bark; green, 5-lobed leaves with white undersides, giving the tree a glittery appearance. Seeds are carried by wind in small fiber balls. Aggressive roots that can damage nearby structures. Drought, salt, and pollution tolerant. **Habitat** Sunny, moist areas such as riverbanks. Common ornamental tree in urban areas. **Blooms** Spring. Flowers develop before the tree grows leaves.

☐ FIRAT POPLAR
Populus euphratica
SALICACEAE FAMILY

H 15m. Yellowish-gray young stems; grayish old bark; variable leaves generally elongated on young trees, and ovate and dentate on older trees; small flowers in drooping catkins; female trees produce greenish fruit capsules that contain small seeds with feathery hairs for wind dispersal. **Habitat** Rich, damp soils in sunny river valleys, including *Wadi Finan*. **Blooms** Early spring.

☐ **BLACK POPLAR**
Populus nigra
SALICACEAE FAMILY

H 30m. Upright tree with grayish-green bark that darkens and cracks with age; triangular, finely-serrated leaves, bright-green on both sides; reddish flower catkins. Leaves turn yellow before dropping in autumn. **Habitat** Sunny river valleys including *Wadi al-Seer*. **Blooms** Early spring.

☐ **ACACIA STRAP FLOWER**
Plicosepalus acaciae
LORANTHACEAE FAMILY

Also known as "mistletoe". Parasitic plant that grows to other trees. Leathery, dark-green leaves; red flowers with long, red stamens and green corollas; red fruit. **Habitat** Grows on trees such as *Acacia* and *Ziziphus* in the *Jordan River Valley*, the *Dead Sea* region, *Wadi Araba*, and *Wadi Rum*. **Blooms** All year, except in winter.

☐ **WHITE OSYRIS**
Osyris alba
SANTALACEAE FAMILY

H 100cm. Parasitic shrub that robs nutrients from the roots of neighboring plants. It has numerous, 3-ridged, upright stems; small, narrow leaves; yellowish-green, small, cup-shaped, 3-tepaled flowers at stem ends; and red fruit 1 cm in diameter with a ring-shaped end. **Habitat** Moist shrublands in the *Northern Highlands* and the *Jordan River Valley*. **Blooms** Spring and summer.

☐ PISTACHIO
Pistacia Genus
ANACARDIACEAE FAMILY

H 3-7m. Four pistachio species have been recorded in Jordan. Wild pistachios produce edible seeds known as *butum* in Arabic, which are smaller than the familiar commercial pistachios. Pistachio trees have compound leaves with 7-11 leaflets (odd pinnate). Female trees produce red, brown, or blue fruit. The terebinth (*Pistacia palaestina*) produces a resin distilled into turpentine. The evergreen pistachio (*Pistacia lentiscus*) produces a chewable *mastic* resin, also used in varnishes, glues, and other products. **Habitat** Sunny highlands and desert margins, including *Irbid*, *Amman*, *Petra*, and *Wadi Butum*. *Wadi Butum*, named after this tree, terminates near the Amra Palace west of *Azraq*, at the GPS coordinates: 31.8000°, 36.5883°. **Blooms** Spring.

☐ COMMON PENNYWORT
Umbilicus intermedius
CRASSULACEAE FAMILY

H 25cm. Round, succulent leaves with wavy margins and a central depression that resembles a navel. Pinkish-green, bell-shaped flowers arranged on spikes. **Habitat** Woodlands and shrublands in the *Northern Highland*. Grows in the shade among rocks that pool some rainwater. **Blooms** Late spring.

☐ **RED STONECROP**
Sedum rubens
CRASSULACEAE FAMILY

H 10cm. Reddish-green, cylindrical, succulent leaves; pinkish-white flowers with five, mid-ribbed petals (occasionally four or six), and usually twice as many stamens. **Habitat** Rocky areas in the highlands and deserts, including *Ajloun* and *Jerash*. **Blooms** Spring.

☐ **SMALL-FRUITED STONECROP**
Sedum microcarpum
CRASSULACEAE FAMILY

H 20cm. Low shrub with red stems; green or red, succulent leaves; white, tiny flowers. **Habitat** Woodlands and shrublands in the *Northern Highland*, including *Amman*. Grows among rocks that pool some rainwater. **Blooms** Late winter and spring.

☐ **BINDWEED**
Convolvulus Genus
CONVULVULACEAE FAMILY

H 20-300cm. A total of 20 *Convolvulus* species have been recorded in Jordan. They are climbing plants generally characterized by narrow stems that spiral around other plants or spread on the ground. They have white, pink, blue, or violet, funnel-shaped flowers. **Habitat** Different species occur in habitats ranging from the highlands including *Amman*, to deserts such as *Wadi Araba*. **Blooms** From spring to autumn.

☐ **NIGHTSHADE & POTATO FAMILY**
SOLANACEAE FAMILY

A total of 27 species in the Solanaceae family have been recorded in Jordan. Plants in this family include several non-native, agricultural plants such as potato, tomato, eggplant, and chilli pepper. It also includes many toxic plants such as nightshade and mandrake. They are generally characterized by trumpet-shaped flowers with five fused petals, often hairy or sticky leaves, and berry or capsule fruit.

☐ **ANGEL'S-TRUMPET**
Datura innoxia
SOLANACEAE FAMILY

H 1m. Also known as "thorn-apple", "sacred datura", and various other names. Reddish stems and large, green leaves covered with short, white hairs; white, trumpet-shaped flowers with 10 margin teeth; spiny, round fruit that clings to animals for dispersal. The fruit splits open when ripe to release its seeds. The plant's juices are very toxic and foul-smelling. **Habitat** Regions with rich, moist soil in western Jordan. **Blooms** Summer and fall.

☐ **GOLDEN HENBANE**
Hyoscyamus aureus
SOLANACEAE FAMILY

☐ **EGYPTIAN HENBANE**
Hyoscyamus reticulatus
SOLANACEAE FAMILY

H 60cm. Basal stems; hairy, lobed leaves with wavy margins; yellow flowers with purple throats and smaller lower petals. Very toxic if ingested. Henbane was used in the first Arab hospitals as an anesthetic. **Habitat** Shaded rocky areas in diverse habitats, including *Irbid*, *Amman*, *Petra*, and the *Eastern Desert*. **Blooms** From spring to autumn.

H 50cm. Hairy and sticky stems and leaves; violet flowers with five veined petals and an unpleasant smell. Highly toxic if ingested. Henbane was used in the first Arab hospitals as an anesthetic. **Habitat** Fields of the highlands, including *Irbid*, *Jerash*, *Amman*, *Karak*, and *Tafilah*. **Blooms** Spring.

☐ **ARABIAN BOXTHORN**
Lycium shawii
SOLANACEAE FAMILY

☐ **AUTUMN MANDRAKE**
Mandragora autumnalis
SOLANACEAE FAMILY

H 180cm. Much-branched, thorny shrub; narrow leaves arranged in groups of 2-6; purple or white, trumpet-shaped, 5-petaled flowers; orange, fleshy, spherical fruit. **Habitat** Saline soils and deserts including the *Dead Sea* region, *Wadi Araba*, and *Azraq*. **Blooms** All year, except hot summer and autumn months.

H 30cm. Large rosette of dark-green, wrinkled leaves; purple, bell-shaped, 5-petaled flowers with five stamens; orange, spherical fruit with a sweet scent when ripe. The twisted and swollen roots often resemble a human body. Toxic if ingested. **Habitat** Rich soils in the *Northern Highlands*, including *Ajloun*, *Amman*, and *Salt*. **Blooms** Winter and early spring.

☐ **TREE TOBACCO**
Nicotiana glauca
SOLANACEAE FAMILY

H 5m. Native to South America; naturalized in Jordan. Evergreen tree or shrub with multiple stems; tubular, yellow flowers; and thick, rubbery leaves with a powdery surface. Related to *tobacco*. Poisonous if ingested. **Habitat** Sunny areas with rich soil, including *Jerash* and the *Jordan River Valley*. **Blooms** All warm seasons.

☐ **SILVERLEAF NIGHTSHADE**
Solanum elaeagnifolium
SOLANACEAE FAMILY

H 100cm. Aggressive, invasive weed introduced from North America. Pale-purple, star-like flowers with five petals, five yellow stamens, and one pistil; thin, hairy, grayish-green leaves with wavy margins; hairy, grayish-green stems with short spines; red berries. Toxic if ingested. **Habitat** The *Jordan River Valley*. **Blooms** From early spring to summer.

☐ **HAIRY NIGHTSHADE**
Solanum villosum
SOLANACEAE FAMILY

H 50cm. Hairy stems and leaves; musky scent; small, drooping clusters of white, star-shaped flowers with yellow centers; green, round, 5 mm fruit that turns yellow or red when ripe. Edible fruit. **Habitat** Moist, nutrient-rich soils of western Jordan, including *Amman* and *Salt*. **Blooms** Spring and summer.

☐ **BLACK NIGHTSHADE**
Solanum nigrum
SOLANACEAE FAMILY

H 75cm. Leaves narrow at both ends; small, drooping clusters of white, star-shaped flowers with yellow centers; round, green fruit that turns black when ripe. Edible, young leaves. Fruit is toxic if ingested raw in large amounts, but edible when cooked as in jam. **Habitat** Moist, well-drained soils of western Jordan, including *Wadi al-Seer*. **Blooms** All seasons.

☐ TAMARIX
Tamarix Genus
TAMARICACEAE FAMILY

H 1-5m. A total of ten *Tamarix* species have been recorded in Jordan. Tamarix is an evergreen shrub or small tree with slender stems, red when young; gray-green, scaly leaves that resemble cypress; and white or pink flowers clustered on terminal spikes. Tamarix can be distinguished from cypress by its slimmer leaves, larger flowers, and lack of seed cones. Most tamarix species are salt-tolerant that extract salt from water and expel it through the leaves. **Habitat** Saline deserts and river valleys, including *Azraq*, the *Jordan River Valley*, *Wadi Araba*, *Wadi Hidan*, and *Wadi Finan*. **Blooms** From spring to early autumn. Some species also bloom in winter.

☐ **LINEAR-LEAVED DAPHNE**
Daphne linearifolia
THYMELAEACEAE FAMILY

H 150cm. Evergreen shrub with dense branches; long, linear leaves with curly tips; fragrant, yellowish-white flowers; and red fruit. **Habitat** Rocky semi-deserts in the *Petra* region. **Blooms** Summer and autumn.

☐ **SPUR FLAX**
Thymelaea hirsuta
THYMELAEACEAE FAMILY

H 100cm. Shrub with a woody stem and hanging branches; small, yellow flowers; and small, fleshy, overlapping, scale-like leaves, green on the exposed side and hairy white on the other side. Each shrub is either male or female. Branch strips are twisted together by Bedouins to make ropes. **Habitat** Dry, stony soils in western valleys and the *Eastern Desert*. **Blooms** Spring and summer.

☐ CATTAIL
Typha Genus
TYPHACEAE FAMILY

H 2m. Two cattail species have been recorded in Jordan. They have long stems; long, thin basal leaves; tiny female flowers clustered in brown, cylindrical spikes; and male flowers clustered in thinner, yellow spikes above the female spikes. Male spikes become bare after shedding their pollen. Mature seeds embedded in downy fibers are dispersed by wind. Green flower stalks are edible boiled (like corn on the cob). Roots are edible raw or cooked. Stems and leaves are used to make paper or woven into mats. Seed fibers are used for kindling, insulation, and mattress stuffing. **Habitat** Sunny wetlands and riverbanks, including *Azraq*, the *Jordan River*, *Wadi Mujib*, and *Wadi al-Seer*. **Blooms** Spring or summer.

☐ ROMAN NETTLE
Urtica pilulifera
URTICACEAE FAMILY

H 60cm. Herb plant with stinging, irritant hairs; serrated leaves; small, independent male and female flowers; female flowers develop into round fruit. Young leaves are edible when cooked; they are rich in vitamins and minerals. **Habitat** Shady areas in western Jordan, including the *Jordan River Valley*, *Jerash*, *Amman*, *Karak*, and *Tafilah*. **Blooms** Spring.

□ **COMMON FIG**
Ficus carica
MORACEAE FAMILY

H 7m. One of the earliest domesticated trees; domesticated over 10,000 years ago in the *Jordan Valley*. Fig trees have large, veined leaves with three or five lobes. They produce green fruit that turns purple when ripe. Fig fruit is actually a container holding hundreds of small fleshy flowers; each develops into a small seed. Fruit is edible raw, dried, or in jams. Fig trees are drought tolerant. **Habitat** Sunny regions in the *Jordan River Valley* and the highlands including *Ajloun*, *Amman*, and *Petra*. **Blooms** Produces a crop in spring and another in late summer. Leaves fall off after the second crop.

□ **MULBERRY**
Morus Genus
MORACEAE FAMILY

H 15m. Two mulberry species were recorded in Jordan: white mulberry (*M. alba*) and black mulberry (*M. nigra*). They have heart-shaped leaves with serrated margins and small, greenish-yellow flowers that produce edible, 3 cm long berries. Cultivated white mulberry produces white fruit, while wild varieties produce purple fruit. Black mulberry produces dark-purple fruit. White mulberry holds the speed record in observed biology: the bent stamens spring out of flower buds at more than half the speed of sound, ejecting pollen into the air long distances. **Habitat** Cultivated in urban gardens and orchards. Wild varieties occur in warm, sunny regions, including *Jerash* and *Salt*. **Blooms** Spring.

□ **SWEET VIOLET**
Viola odorata
VIOLACEAE FAMILY

H 10cm. Evergreen herb with heart-shaped leaves and violet, fragrant, 5-petaled flowers. Spreads horizontally with above-ground stems (stolons) that produce new clones. Edible flowers and young leaves. Used to produce scented oils. **Habitat** Fields and woodlands in the *Northern Highlands*, including *Amman*. Common ornamental plant in urban gardens. **Blooms** Early spring.

Fauna

Invertebrates

Invertebrates are animals that lack backbones. They make up over 97% of all animals and include microscopic organisms, worms, mollusks, crustaceans, spiders, and insects. The animals that do not belong to this group are fish, amphibians, reptiles, birds, and mammals.

Invertebrates are cold-blooded. They regulate their body temperature mainly through external means and become dormant or die at low or high temperatures. They are generally active in warm seasons.

☐ **EARTHWORMS**
CLITELLATA CLASS

☐ **LEECHES**
CLITELLATA CLASS

L 12-15cm. Earthworms have reddish, legless, cylindrical bodies with about 150 segments and both male and female organs. Most earthworm species have some ability to regenerate lost body segments. Earthworms feed on decaying vegetation. They benefit the soil by aerating it and by breaking down organic matter into nutrients. **Habitat** Moist soil with vegetation, including grasslands, woodlands, and urban gardens. **Activity** Spends most of its time burrowing and feeding underground. Ventures to the surface after heavy rains. After mating, a ring-shaped cocoon forms around the front part of the worm, which eventually slips off and develops into a new earthworm.

L 5cm. Leeches are closely related to earthworms. They have a dark-brown legless body with 34 segments and a clinging sucker at each end. Leeches feed on worms, crustaceans, and snails. Some leech species also feed on the blood of humans and animals such as fish, birds, and amphibians. The bite of bloodsucking leeches is not dangerous. Leeches are used medicinally to prevent blood clots after some surgeries. **Habitat** River valleys of western Jordan, including *Wadi Hidan*. **Activity** Swims with a wavelike motion. Found mainly among vegetation near the bottom of shallow, slow-flowing water.

☐ FRESHWATER SNAILS
GASTROPODA CLASS

L 5-22mm. A total of 17 freshwater snail species have been recorded in Jordan. They have smooth coiled shells, some with colorful patterns. Shells are built by adding new larger sections as the snails grow larger. Snails have a pair of upper tentacles with light sensors and another lower pair of feelers. **Habitat** Common in permanent freshwater bodies, including the *Jordan River*, the *Yarmouk River*, *Wadi Hidan*, *Wadi al-Seer*, *Azraq*, and irrigation canals in the *Jordan River Valley*. **Activity** Snails move slowly by repeatedly stretching and contracting their body. They retract into their shell when disturbed.

☐ LAND SNAILS
GASTROPODA CLASS

A total of 39 land snail species have been recorded in Jordan. They have coiled shells, built by adding new larger sections as the snails grow larger. Snails have a pair of upper tentacles with light sensors and another lower pair of feelers. Land snails produce mucus that keeps them moist, protects their delicate skin, acts as an adhesive on vertical surfaces, and serves as a repellent to predators. Snails feed mostly on vegetation. **Habitat** Near water sources, mostly in the *Northern Highlands*. **Activity** Moves slowly by repeatedly stretching and contracting its body. Retracts into the shell when disturbed. Some snail species seal themselves inside their shells to hibernate in winter or during dry conditions.

☐ LAND SLUGS
GASTROPODA CLASS

Slugs are closely related to snails. Some have reduced shells and most lack them entirely. They have worm-like bodies covered with slimy mucus that keeps them moist, protects their delicate skin, acts as an adhesive on vertical surfaces, and serves as a repellent to predators. Slugs have a pair of upper tentacles with light sensors and another lower pair for smell. Most species feed on vegetation. Some feed on dead animals and prey on worms. **Habitat** Moist soil in wooded areas in the *Northern Highlands* and in urban gardens. **Activity** Moves slowly by repeatedly stretching and contracting its body. Retracts its tentacles and contracts its body when disturbed.

☐ PILL BUGS
ARMADILLIDIIDAE FAMILY

L 15mm. Gray-brown segmented shells; 14 legs; two antennae. Although pill bugs live on land, they are related to sea crustaceans such as crabs and lobsters. They still breathe through gills and require moist habitats. They feed on moss, tree bark, algae, and animal remains, producing pungent ammonia in the process. They benefit their habitats by recycling decaying organic matter. **Habitat** Moist soil with decomposing organic matter. Found in dark crevices under organic debris or stones. Burrows deeper into soil in dry seasons. **Activity** Mostly nocturnal. Rolls into a ball when threatened or to prevent moisture loss. Sheds its outgrown shell. Female carries its eggs under its body until they hatch.

☐ WOODLICE
PORCELLIONIDAE FAMILY

L 25mm. Reddish-brown, segmented shell; 14 legs; two antennae. Closely related to pill bugs with similar characteristics and behaviors, but cannot roll into a ball. See *Pill Bugs*.

☐ CRABS
DECAPODA ORDER

L 10cm. Hard outer shell (exoskeleton) that protects internal organs and provides support; 10 legs, the first pair modified into claws; flattened thorax which hides the abdomen underneath; two antennae. Breathes underwater with gills located under the upper shell. Feeds on fish, snails, other small animals, and decaying vegetation. **Habitat** Wadis of western Jordan, including *Wadi Hidan*, *Wadi Mujib*, and *Zarqa River*. **Activity** Walks sideways. Sheds its outgrown shell.

☐ MILLIPEDES
Archispirostreptus Syriacus
SPIROSTREPTIDAE FAMILY

L 18cm. Millipede is from the Latin *mille,* meaning *thousand*, and *ped,* meaning *foot.* Millipedes have long, black, cylindrical, segmented bodies with four legs on each segment. They are blind and feel their way with antennae. They feed on vegetation and benefit their habitats by recycling decaying organic matter. Millipedes differ from centipedes in that they have two pairs of legs on each body segment, while centipedes have one; millipedes are non-venomous, while some centipedes are mildly venomous; millipedes are slow, while centipedes are fast; and millipedes feed on vegetation, while centipedes feed on insects. **Habitat** Humid soil in the *Northern Highlands*, including *Jerash* and *Amman.* **Activity** Slow. Curls into a spiral when threatened. Digs underground tunnels.

☐ CENTIPEDES
CHILOPODA CLASS

L 5-20cm. A total of 22 centipede species have been recorded in Jordan. Centipede is from the Latin *centum* meaning *hundred*, and *ped* meaning *foot.* Centipedes have a reddish-brown, flattened, segmented body; a pair of antennae; and a pair of mandibles. The first pair of legs after the head has mildly venomous claws used to paralyze its prey. The last pair of legs resembles antennas to confuse predators. Despite their alarming appearance, centipedes are beneficial for feeding on insects. Millipedes differ from centipedes in that they have two pairs of legs on each body segment, while centipedes have one; millipedes are non-venomous, while some centipedes are mildly venomous; millipedes are slow, while centipedes are fast; and millipedes feed on vegetation, while centipedes feed on insects. **Habitat** Moist microhabitats under rocks, decaying vegetation, or burrows. **Activity** Mainly nocturnal. Raises its rear end when threatened.

☐ HOUSE CENTIPEDE
Scutigera coleoptrata
SCUTIGERIDAE FAMILY

L 5cm. Gray-yellow body with three, dark, longitudinal stripes; 15 pairs of long, banded legs; long antennae; compound eyes. Venomous to its prey, but beneficial to humans. Feeds on cockroaches, termites, spiders, and other invertebrates. **Habitat** Damp microhabitats under rocks or plant

debris. Also common in damp places indoors. **Activity** Mainly nocturnal and difficult to detect in homes. Fast runner.

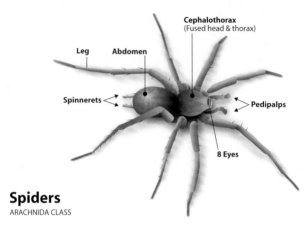

Spiders
ARACHNIDA CLASS

Spiders are not insects. They are distinguished from insects by having eight, instead of six legs. They are characterized by a fused head and thorax (cephalothorax), eight eyes, a pair of sensory pedipalps, and 2-6 silk-producing spinnerets at the tip of the abdomen. Most spiders are venomous to their prey, but generally harmless to humans. Large spiders may bite defensively, inflicting minor pain. Most spiders are predators that hunt and feed on insects, and some feed on vegetation.

☐ ORB-WEAVER SPIDERS
ARANEIDAE FAMILY

L 6-25mm. There are over 3,000 orb-weaver species worldwide. They are generally characterized by bright colors or striking patterns, banded legs, and bulging or spiny abdomens. They build the type of webs that are commonly associated with spiders: radial spokes filled with a spiral, generally built vertically between plants. Some species in the *Argiope* genus stabilize their webs with zigzag bands (stablimentum). **Habitat** Widespread in urban gardens, fields, and woodlands. **Activity** Timid. Mainly nocturnal. Females rest head down in the center of the web. Males are smaller and often on the move in search of females.

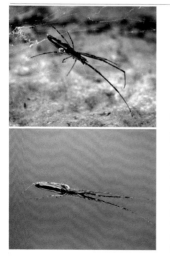

☐ LONG-JAWED ORB WEAVERS
Tetragnatha Genus
TETRAGNATHIDAE FAMILY

L 5-25mm. Long-jawed orb weavers are characterized by their long jaws and abdomens and can easily camouflage as twigs. They generally build near-horizontal webs with open centers. They feed on insects. **Habitat** Near or over water in the river valleys and reservoirs of western Jordan, including *Amman* and *Wadi Hidan*. **Activity** Keeps its legs on the web to detect motion. Retreats quickly if disturbed. Reconstructs its web daily and often found on an incomplete web.

☐ WOLF SPIDERS
LYCOSIDAE FAMILY

A total of seven wolf spider species have been recorded in Jordan. They have a large cephalothorax (fused head and thorax), an abdomen slightly larger than cephalothorax, body and legs sparsely covered with hair, and eyes arranged in three rows. Despite having eight eyes and good eyesight, wolf spiders heavily rely on vibrations to detect their prey. Males are generally smaller than females and have more vivid patterns. Wolf spiders are venomous to their prey, but harmless to humans. **Habitat** Common in diverse habitats, including *Amman* and *Aqaba*. **Activity** Solitary and mainly nocturnal. Hibernates in winter inside burrows. Hunts by rushing and biting its prey. Does not build web traps. After mating, females produce egg sacs that they drag behind everywhere they go. Hatched spiders ride on their mother's back for a few weeks before dispersing.

☐ DADDY LONG-LEGS SPIDERS
PHOLCIDAE FAMILY

L 2-10 mm. Also known as "house spiders", "cellar spiders", and "vibrating spiders". They are characterized by small bodies, cylindrical abdomens, and very long, fragile, legs up to 50 mm long. They feed on insects and other spiders, and resort to cannibalism when necessary. Venomous to their prey, but harmless to humans. **Habitat** Damp dark places in crevices, caves, and urban structures. **Activity** Builds non-adhesive, messy webs that trap insects with their irregular structures. Usually hangs upside down in the web. Vibrates its web or hangs from a strand and spins rapidly when threatened, which makes it almost invisible. Vibrates webs of other spiders to draw them out and eat them.

☐ FISHING SPIDERS
Dolomedes Genus
PISAURIDAE FAMILY

Also known as "dock spiders". They are so called for ambushing their prey on the surface of water. They usually anchor their back legs on a rock or plant, and then use their front legs to feel water vibrations. Fishing spiders feed on insects. **Habitat** Streams, rivers, and ponds in most of Jordan, including *Wadi Mujib*, *Wadi al-Seer*, and *Azraq*. **Activity** Ambushes insects on the surface of water. Some species dive under water when threatened. Females carry their egg sac with their fangs.

☐ JUMPING SPIDERS
SALTICIDAE FAMILY

L 4-10mm. There are over 5,000 jumping spider species worldwide, 22 have been recorded in Jordan. They are so named for their ability to jump tethered by a silk lifeline. They have eight eyes characteristically spread out over their head for excellent stereoscopic, telescopic, and wide vision. Some species have colorful patterns that aid in camouflage. Males are generally more colorful for visual courtship. Jumping spiders feed on insects; some species feed on nectar or vegetation. **Habitat** Widespread in diverse habitats including deserts. **Activity** Hunts by jumping on prey. Weaves tent-like webs for shelter. Appears curious and does not immediately flee when approached. Males perform a complex courtship dance to attract a female.

☐ CRAB SPIDERS
THOMISIDAE FAMILY

L 4-10mm. Nine crab spider species have been recorded in Jordan. They are so called for resembling crabs when walking sideways or holding their front legs up to catch prey. They are generally well camouflaged with colors that match their hunting spots. Some species change colors over several days to match their new surroundings.

Crab spiders feed on insects such as flies. They are venomous to their prey and harmless to humans. **Habitat** Although difficult to spot, crab spiders are common in meadows and urban gardens. **Activity** Ambushes and catches prey without a web. Often hides on flowers of the same color. Some hunt on the ground.

☐ FALSE WIDOW SPIDERS
Steatoda Genus
THERIDIIDAE FAMILY

L 7-15mm. Resembles the black widow spider. Distinguished by a crescent band around the front of its shiny, round abdomen. Feeds on insects and other spiders. May bite defensively, inflicting minor pain to humans. **Habitat** Common in fields and urban areas. Occurs in undisturbed places under rocks, plant debris, or furniture. **Activity** Builds irregular, very sticky webs. Females often eat the smaller males after mating.

☐ WOODLOUSE SPIDER
Dysdera crocata
DYSDERIDAE FAMILY

L 12mm. Dark-red legs and cephalothorax (fused head and thorax); cream-brown abdomen; large fangs. Male is slightly smaller than the female. Feeds exclusively on woodlice, which give it its name. **Habitat** Damp, dark places under plant debris in warm regions. **Activity** Mostly nocturnal. Hunts without a web. Pierces woodlice with its fangs. Bites if provoked; mildly venomous to humans.

☐ SUN SPIDER
SOLIFUGID ORDER

L 4cm. Distinctive, fang-like mouth parts (chelicerae); long pedipalps that look like an extra pair of legs; lacks silk glands. The pedipalps are used for sensing and have adhesive tips used for climbing smooth surfaces. Despite its alarming appearance and ability to bite in self defense, the sun spider is non-venomous and considered to be beneficial for feeding on pesky insects such as mites and ticks. It is a myth that it kills or hurts camels. **Habitat** Arid regions and deserts. **Activity** Mainly nocturnal. Seeks shade during the day.

☐ MITES
ACARI SUBCLASS

L 1-3mm. Mites are either very small or microscopic, which enables them to thrive unnoticed by larger animals. They are closely related to spiders and have eight legs with a distinct gap between the second and third pair. Mites feed on mold, pollen, plant cells, and animal skin or blood. **Habitat** Widespread in all habitats. Many species live in the soil or water. Parasitic mites live on plants, animals, and even humans. **Activity** Mites that feed on pollens gather on flowers in spring. Most mites go unnoticed due to their small size.

☐ HARVESTMEN
OPILIONES ORDER

Also known as "opiliones". There are about 1,900 harvestman species worldwide. Harvestmen have eight long legs, the second pair used as antennae is the longest. Despite their resemblance, harvestmen are not spiders. Their body sections are fused into one compact structure, while spiders have two body sections (cephalothorax and abdomen); they have two eyes, while spiders have 8; and they lack silk and venom glands. Harvestmen feed on small insects, vegetation, dung, fungi,

and dead animals. **Habitat** Wooded or bushy areas in northwestern Jordan and semi-arid regions near water and vegetation. **Activity** Mainly nocturnal. Harmless to humans. Has a foul-smelling chemical defense.

☐ SCORPIONS
SCORPIONES ORDER

L 10cm. Scorpions are closely related to spiders. They have eight legs, a pair of pedipalps tipped with pincers, and a sting at the end of a segmented tail. A total of 14 scorpion species have been recorded in Jordan, 11 belong to the generally venomous Buthidae family characterized by thick tails relative to their thin pincers. The most dangerous is the deathstalker (*Leiurus quinquestriatus*) pictured in the first photo. Scorpions feed on insects, spiders, and small animals including other scorpions. Highly venomous scorpions also kill and feed on rodents and reptiles. **Habitat** Widespread, but most common in arid areas. Scorpions that carry their tails over their backs live in burrows, while those that carry their tails to one side live under rocks. **Activity** Mainly nocturnal. Timid. Attacks humans only in self-defense. Females carry newly hatched scorpions on their backs. Juveniles undergo several molts as they grow.

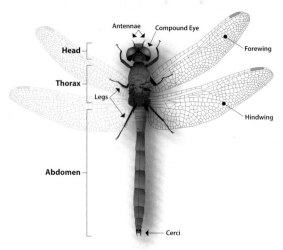

Head
Thorax
Legs
Abdomen

Antennae
Compound Eye
Forewing
Hindwing
Cerci

Insects

INSECTA CLASS

Insects are the most numerous and diverse animals on Earth and constitute about 80% of all described animals. They are generally characterized by six legs, four wings, and bodies divided into head, thorax, and abdomen. They include dragonflies, cockroaches, grasshoppers, bugs, beetles, flies, butterflies, ants, and bees. They perform essential roles in all ecosystems, including pollinating most flowering plants and recycling organic matter.

☐ EYES & OCELLI

Most insects have two large compound eyes on the sides of the head, each with up to thousands of independent lenses. They enable a wide angle view and fast motion detection. In addition to their compound eyes, most insects have three small eyes called *ocelli*, each with a single lens. Ocelli are most noticeable on wasps where they form a triangle on the top of the head, but they are also present on most invertebrates. Crickets have only two ocelli. Some insects and larvae have 2-12 lateral ocelli on the sides of the head. In general, ocelli are simple remnants of

evolution that barely detect light. In some insects such as dragonflies, ocelli serve as horizon detectors to maintain stability in flight. In desert ants, ocelli function like a compass, reading information from the sky to detect direction (see *Desert Ant*).

☐ LARVA

A *larva* is the young form of animals such as insects, amphibians, and jellyfish. It looks completely different than the adult and in most insects, it is worm-like with six true legs and several leg-like, fleshy structures known as *prolegs*. The larvae of different animals have different names such as *caterpillar* for butterflies, *grub* for beetles, and *maggot* for flies. Larvae spend most of their time feeding to store energy for their next stage of life.

☐ PUPA

P*upa* is a stage between larva and adult in the life of some insects such as butterflies, beetles, flies, ants, and bees. Depending on the species, the inactive pupa is protected by a hard shell, silk cocoon, camouflage, or other means. Pupae undergo a complete metamorphosis and emerge as adults within days in most species. The pupal stage of butterflies (chrysalis) occurs on trees, which makes it the most familiar. However, most insects pupate in underground cells.

☐ WINGS, HALTERES, & ELYTRA

Insects come from a common ancestor that possessed two pairs of wings. Most insects today still have two pairs of wings used in flight, however some have wings modified through evolution to serve other functions. The hindwings of flies and mosquitoes were modified into small balancers (halteres) that vibrate to maintain stability in flight. The forewings of beetles were modified into hard cases (elytra) for protection. Some insects such as grasshoppers develop wings only at maturity, while others such as female scale insects lose them at maturity. In some insect species, such as ants and some bagworm moths, only mating adults or only one gender has wings.

☐ DRAGONFLIES
ODONATA ORDER

L 6cm. A total of 31 dragonfly species have been recorded in Jordan. Dragonflies have large compound eyes that see in nearly all directions. They have four independent wings that make them the fastest flying insects and enable them to fly backwards. Their legs are attached behind their head, making them useful to hold onto prey, but impossible to walk on. They feed mainly on insects such as mosquitoes and flies. **Habitat** Common around permanent freshwater sources such as the river valleys of western Jordan and around irrigation pools all over Jordan. **Activity** Spends most of its several-year lifespan in a larval stage underwater. Crawls out of the water and sheds its nymphal case only in its last months of life to breed. Flies low over water following the same path, perching repeatedly on the same spot.

☐ DAMSELFLIES
ODONATA ORDER

L 35mm. A total of 15 damselfly species have been recorded in Jordan. Damselflies look very similar to and are often confused with dragonflies. However, damselflies are smaller; weaker fliers; have separated eyes that bulge outside of their head, while most dragonflies have connected eyes above their head; at rest, damselflies hold their wings together along their body, while dragonflies stretch them out on the sides; damselflies have four similar wings, while dragonflies have hindwings that are broader at the base. **Habitat** Common around permanent, freshwater sources such as the river valleys of western Jordan and around irrigation pools all over Jordan. **Activity** Perches with its wings held together along the body.

☐ EGYPTIAN DESERT ROACH
Polyphaga aegyptiaca
POLYPHAGIDAE FAMILY

L 30mm. Female has a brown, segmented, wingless, dome-shaped body; long hind legs; and shovel-shaped forelegs for digging. Male is darker, smaller, and has veined leathery wings with round tips. Well-adapted to desert conditions. **Habitat** Damp, dark places in arid areas, including the *Madaba* region and *Wadi Finan*. Also found indoors in some urban areas. **Activity** Mainly nocturnal.

☐ COMMON EARWIG
Forficula auricularia
FORFICULIDAE FAMILY

L 12mm. Dark-brown body; yellowish legs and wings; long flexible abdomen tipped with forceps-like cerci; short, leathery forewings which protect folded hindwings. Male has more curved and stronger forceps than female. Forceps are used for feeding, mating, and occasionally for defense. Feeds on insects, plants, and decaying matter. **Habitat** Common in dark, humid places under rocks and plant debris. **Activity** Mostly nocturnal. Rarely flies.

☐ TERMITES
ISOPTERA ORDER

L 1cm. Although termites resemble ants in many ways, including social behavior, they are more primitive than ants and more closely related to cockroaches. Wingless termites have a white body and a brownish head. Winged termites (alates) are dark with two pairs of long, white wings; they emerge in spring to start new colonies. Termites feed on the fiber of dead wood and grasses, and play an important role in recycling organic matter. **Habitat**

Widespread in all habitats, including deserts with some vegetation. Builds dark, underground nests. Often found under rocks or plant debris. **Activity** Spends most of its time in dark places. Emerges to explore new food sources and to build new nests.

☐ PRAYING MANTISES
MANTODEA ORDER

Despite their difference in appearance, praying mantises are closely related to cockroaches. Praying mantises are characterized by forelegs usually held in a position reminiscent of praying, which gives them their name. The two forelegs are specialized to grasp prey, leaving only four of the six legs for walking. Praying mantises have small, rotating heads with bulging eyes and excellent eyesight. They feed on insects and other small animals. **Habitat** Dry areas with vegetation, including valleys in the *Amman* region. **Activity** Ambushes its prey by blending with its surroundings and by rocking back and forth to mimic the swaying of plant parts. When threatened, it stands taller and stretches out its wings and forelegs to look larger. Most praying mantises feed during the day and fly at night. They only hear ultrasonic sounds (frequencies above the human hearing range), which allows them to hear and evade bats that hunt by echolocation. Females lay many eggs in a foamy substance, which hardens into an egg case called *ootheca*. Adults then die in winter, while the eggs remain protected and hatch the following spring.

☐ BOXER MANTISES
EREMIAPHILIDAE FAMILY

L 2-3cm. Mantises in this family are often mistaken for either grasshoppers because of their appearance or ants because of the way they run. On closer examination, they are clearly identifiable as mantises by their characteristic forelegs held in a praying position. Unlike other mantises, they have short thoraxes and heads that do not rotate as freely. **Habitat** Deserts

and semi-arid regions, including *Wadi Dana* and *Karak*. **Activity** Fast runner. Does not climb on vegetation.

☐ GRASSHOPPERS
ORTHOPTERA ORDER

Grasshoppers are distinguished from crickets and katydids by antennae shorter than their bodies and their short ovipositor (needle-like organ for laying eggs at the tip of the female's abdomen). Grasshoppers have long hind legs used for leaping. Adults have two pairs of wings, only the hindwings are used in flight. Males are smaller than females. Among grasshoppers are *locusts*, which occasionally group in large swarms, causing extensive crop damage. **Habitat** Widespread in all habitats, including deserts. **Activity** Mostly males make noise to attract females. Depending on the species, they make noise by rubbing their hind legs or wings against each other or against other body parts, and some make noise in flight by vibrating their forewings. Females lay eggs in sand or crevices to hatch the following spring.

☐ **CRICKETS**
ORTHOPTERA ORDER

Crickets are related to grasshoppers, but are more closely to katydids. They are distinguished by their flattened bodies and antennae that are about the length of their body. Crickets have long hind legs used for leaping and a long pair of hair-like appendages at the tip of their abdomen (cerci). In addition, females have a long, needle-like organ for laying eggs (ovipositor) between the cerci. Adults have two pairs of wings. Crickets feed on vegetation and scavenge dead animals. **Habitat** Widespread in all habitats, including deserts. Lives in damp places under rocks or plant debris. **Activity** Mostly nocturnal. Males make chirping mating calls by rubbing their wings together. Females lay eggs in the sand.

☐ **KATYDIDS**
ORTHOPTERA ORDER

Katydids look similar to grasshoppers, but are more closely related to crickets. They are distinguished from grasshoppers by antennae longer than their bodies and from crickets by short cerci. Most katydids resemble plant parts for camouflage. Katydids feed on vegetation. Some prey on small animals and occasionally resort to cannibalism. **Habitat** Widespread in all habitats. Most common in the *Northern Highlands*. **Activity** Spends most of its time among vegetation.

Bugs
HEMIPTERA ORDER

Many insects are mistakenly referred to as bugs. True bugs are generally characterized by hard forewings with soft, membranous tips. They include about 40,000 species worldwide.

☐ **SHIELD & STINK BUGS**
PENTATOMOIDEA SUPERFAMILY

L 1-14mm. Shield bugs are characterized by a body that generally looks like a shield and needle-like mouthpart for piercing plants. Some species are known as "stink bugs" for having a foul-smelling chemical defense. Most species feed on plant sap and some feed on insects. **Habitat** Fields of northern and western Jordan, including the *Amman* region and the *Jordan River Valley*. **Activity** Wingless nymphs spend most of their time feeding on the plants they hatch on. They disperse for mating after developing wings. Shield bugs occasionally gather in large groups, causing significant crop damage. The *sunn pest* can cause heavy wheat and barley losses.

☐ FIREBUGS
PYRRHOCORIDAE FAMILY

L 8-11mm. Oval, flat, red body with black head and legs. Each species has distinct, black wings-markings. Most adults have short wings and are unable to fly. Nymphs are mostly red with black dots on the abdomen; they develop wings and adult markings as they mature. Firebugs feed on seeds. **Habitat** Grassy and agricultural fields of western Jordan. **Activity** Active in warm seasons. Hibernates in winter. Often clusters to mate or feed on fallen seeds.

☐ SEED BUGS
Lygaeus pandurus
LYGAEIDAE FAMILY

L 4-20mm. The seed bug family includes over 4,000 species worldwide. They are characterized by forewings with 4-5 veins; flat, oval, bodies; and 4-segmented antennae. Most seed bug species feed on seeds. Some feed on insects, plant sap, or blood. **Habitat** Grassy and agricultural fields of western Jordan. **Activity** Occasionally gather in large numbers, causing crop damage.

☐ CAPSID BUGS
MIRIDAE FAMILY

L 4-12mm. Capsid bugs are the largest of the true bug families with over 10,000 species worldwide. They are characterized by small, elongated or oval bodies and long antennae. They are best known for being agricultural pests, piercing plants to feed on their sap. **Habitat** Wild and agricultural fields in western Jordan. **Activity** Common in spring around young plant shoots.

☐ ASSASSIN BUGS
REDUVIIDAE FAMILY

L 4-30mm. There are about 7,000 assassin bug species worldwide. They are characterized by a long head, narrow neck, long legs, and a 3-segmented beak for stabbing prey. They feed on insects, larvae, and eggs. **Habitat** Fields with insects to prey on. **Activity** Injects its prey with lethal and digestive saliva and then sucks out the liquefied insides. May bite and cause an allergic reaction in humans if handled.

☐ **BACKSWIMMERS**
NOTONECTIDAE FAMILY

☐ **WATER STRIDERS**
GERRIDAE FAMILY

L 1-2cm. Aquatic insects that swim upside down on their back. They tuck their four front legs in, while using the fringed hind legs for paddling. Backswimmers hunt and feed on insects, tadpoles, and small fish. **Habitat** Still water and slow streams in reservoirs and wadis, including *Wadi Finan*. **Activity** Flies to explore new habitats. Dives underwater with an air bubble in search of prey. Hangs on bottom vegetation to stay under water. May bite if handled.

L 1-2cm. Slender, brown body; six legs with microscopic hairs that trap air for floating on water; the two short front legs are held forward to catch prey; the middle legs are used for propelling; the hind legs are used for steering. Feeds on insects. **Habitat** The surface of still water such as ponds, marshes, reservoirs, and river margins. **Activity** Skates on water in fast bursts without breaking the water's surface tension. Occasionally flies.

☐ **CICADAS**
CICADIDAE FAMILY

L 2-5cm. Cicadas include about 2,500 species worldwide. They are characterized by a stout body; veined wings; short antennae; and two compound eyes wide apart. Adults feed on plant sap. **Habitat** Warm regions and deserts with trees in western Jordan. **Activity** Males produce the loudest mating songs of all insects.

Females lay eggs in tree bark. Hatched nymphs drop to the ground and burrow to feed on root juices. Nymphs appear in the summer, shed their skin to emerge as adults, mate, and then die. Some cicada species have a long nymphal stage of up to 17 years, preventing predators from adapting to their life cycles.

□ HOPPERS
AUCHENORRHYNCHA SUBORDER

L 2-12mm. Hoppers include several insect groups such as froghoppers, leafhoppers, and treehoppers. They are generally characterized by small bodies with wings usually held like a sloping tent over the abdomen. They feed on plant sap. **Habitat** Widespread in grasslands and woodlands, including *Ajloun* and *Amman*. **Activity** Hoppers leap from plant to plant and rarely fly. The nymphs of froghoppers (spittlebugs) produce a frothy substance (cuckoo spit) for protection against predators and the elements. Some ants provide protection to hoppers in exchange for the honeydew they excrete as waste. Most hoppers go unnoticed due to their small size, but their sticky waste is evident on cars parked under trees.

□ SCALE INSECTS
COCCIDAE FAMILY

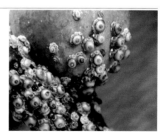

L 1-5mm. Also known as "tortoise scales", there are over 1,100 species in this family worldwide. They begin their lives looking like very small insects. Then, females develop protective, shell-like, waxy plates; their external organs shrink; and they become immobile. Males remain small and winged, but they live only for a few days. Most scale insects are plant parasites that feed on tree juices. **Habitat** The pictured *Ceroplastes rusci* species is common on fig trees. **Activity** Scale insects excrete honeydew as they feed. Ants harvest the honeydew and defend the insects in exchange.

Net-winged
NEUROPTERA ORDER

The order of net-winged insects includes over 6,000 species worldwide. They are characterized by membranous, net-veined wings.

☐ ANTLIONS
MYRMELEONTIDAE FAMILY

There are over 2,000 antlion species worldwide. They are characterized by slender abdomens; long, net-veined wings; hairy legs and bodies; and antennae with curved, clubbed tips. The antlion spends 2-3 years in its larval stage and only about one month in its adult stage. The antlion's larva is smaller and has a rounded body with protruding neck, head, and jaws. Adults feed on pollen and nectar. Larvae feed mainly on ants, some other insects, spiders, and even adult antlions. **Habitat** Arid, sandy areas including *Karak*, *Madaba*, *Amman*, and the *Azraq* region. **Activity** Adults flutter about in search of mates mainly in the evening; they are attracted to light. After mating, females lay eggs in the sand. A hatched larva sets off in search of a suitable location to build a sand trap, leaving a distinct winding trail behind that gives it its *doodlebug* nickname. Once the location is found, the larva builds a sand pit and buries itself in the middle to capture insects trapped by the pit's loose sand. Carcasses of consumed insects are usually found discarded around the pit. Fully grown larvae enclose themselves in sand and silk cocoons, and then emerge later as adult antlions.

☐ THREAD-WINGED ANTLIONS
NEMOPTERIDAE FAMILY

L 25cm. Also known as "spoonwings", and "ribbon-winged lacewings". They are characterized by their slender bodies, net-veined forewings, and very long hindwings. In some species, the hindwings have conspicuous, feather-like tips. Adults feed on nectar and pollen. Larvae feed on insects. **Habitat** Open grasslands with sandy soil, including the *Pella* region. **Activity** Adults are slow fliers and mainly active in late spring. Males attract females by dispersing chemical pheromones. Females lay eggs in the sand.

☐ MANTID LACEWINGS
MANTISPIDAE FAMILY

L 2-4cm. Although they resemble mantises, they are not closely related. Mantid lacewings are characterized by two forelegs specialized to grasp prey, and net-veined wings that are longer than their body. Adults prey on insects and other small invertebrates. Larvae are parasites that feed on spider eggs and insect larvae, eventually killing their hosts. **Habitat** Fields of the *Northern Highlands*, including *Wadi al-Seer*. **Activity** Hunts in shrubs. Females lay clustered, stalked eggs on leaves.

☐ GREEN LACEWINGS
CHRYSOPIDAE FAMILY

Green lacewings are characterized by pale-green bodies that turn yellow-brown in autumn; transparent, net-veined wings that are longer than their body; shiny eyes; and long antennae. Adults feed on honeydew, nectar, and pollen. Adults of some species are predators. Larvae feed on insects and their eggs. They are known as "aphid lions" for their ferocious appetite for aphids. **Habitat** Common in grassy and wooded areas in western Jordan. **Activity** Communicates by surface vibrations. Females lay eggs on the undersides of leaves.

Beetles
COLEOPTERA ORDER

Beetles are the most diverse animal order with over five million species worldwide that constitute 25% of all described animals. They are generally characterized by hard forewings (elytra) that protect the soft hindwings used in flight. Some beetle species have fused elytra for extra protection, making them flightless.

□ **SEVEN-SPOT LADYBUG**
Coccinella septempunctata
COCCINELLIDAE FAMILY

L 7mm. Rounded body; black head with two small, white spots; black thorax with two, larger, white spots; red wing cases (elytra) with three, black spots on each and a seventh spot in the middle at the base. Larvae are worm-like with black segmented bodies, orange spots, and six legs. They pupate to metamorphose into adults. Both adults and larvae feed on aphids (plant lice), making them beneficial to agriculture. **Habitat** Common among wild vegetation, crops, and urban gardens. **Activity** Active in warm seasons. Adults huddle and hibernate in large groups in winter.

☐ BLISTER BEETLES
MELOIDAE FAMILY

L 20mm. The blister beetle family includes about 2,500 species worldwide, at least 20 occur in Jordan. They have a chemical defense that causes temporary skin blisters, which gives them their name. They generally are characterized by elongated abdomens, narrow and visible necks, square heads bending downwards, and long mouthparts for nectar feeding. Different species vary in color, patterns, size, and shape. Adults feed on nectar, pollen, and leaves. Larvae feed mainly on grasshopper eggs and immature bees. **Habitat** Fields and desert margins in western Jordan, including *Amman*. **Activity** Adults are attracted to light at night. Females lay eggs in the sand. Larvae crawl into crevices in search of grasshopper eggs, or find their way into bee nests to feed on immature bees and bee provisions. Blister beetles have four larval stages that last a whole year. Adults live about three months.

☐ CHECKERED BEETLES
CLERIDAE FAMILY

L 3-13mm. The checkered beetle family includes about 3,000 species worldwide. They are characterized by colorful bands across their backs. Adults feed on beetles. Larvae feed on immature wood-boring beetles. **Habitat** Wooded areas and orchards in the *Northern Highlands*. **Activity** Adults are very active in warm seasons. Females lay eggs in trees infested by borer and bark beetles.

☐ SOLDIER BEETLES
CANTHARIDAE FAMILY

L 1-15mm. This family includes about 3,500 species worldwide. They are so called because of their cloth-like wing cases, which in some species are red and reminiscent of military uniforms. They have soft, flat bodies. They can be distinguished from blister beetles by their rounder heads, covered necks, and a diet that does not include leaves. Adults and larvae feed on insect eggs and soft-bodied insects such as aphids and caterpillars. Adults also feed on nectar and pollen. **Habitat** Fields and urban gardens in western Jordan, including *Amman*. **Activity** Hunts for insects on the top of flowers. Females lay eggs in the soil.

☐ JEWEL BEETLES
BUPRESTIDAE FAMILY

L 2-40mm. Most jewel beetles have an iridescent gloss, which gives them their name. The iridescence is produced by the way they reflect light, not by pigments. Jewel beetles generally have elongated bodies that narrow toward the rear, often with color patterns. Adults feed on nectar and leaves. Larvae feed on roots, stems, and leaves. **Habitat** Sunny and warm areas with fruit orchards and shrubs, including *Irbid*, *Ajloun*, *Amman*, *Shobak*, *Qatranah*, and *Azraq*. **Activity** The legless, blind larvae bore into tree branches and roots. Adults emerge mainly in spring. They are fast flyers and occasionally land on the ground and plants.

☐ LONGHORN BEETLES
CERAMBYCIDAE FAMILY

L 2-60mm. Also known as "timber beetles" and "goat beetles", this family includes about 20,000 species worldwide. They are characterized by antennae typically longer than their body. They feed on flowers and other plant parts. **Habitat** Wooded areas and orchards in northwestern Jordan. **Activity** Larvae bore into wood, causing damage to trees and wooden urban structures.

☐ LEAF CHAFERS
Rutelinae Subfamily
SCARABAEIDAE FAMILY

L 2-62mm. Also known as "shining leaf chafers". There are around 4,100 leaf chafer species worldwide; some are metallic or brightly colored. Beetles from the Scarabaeidae family, which includes flower beetles, are characterized by antennae with clubbed tips that fan out like leaves, used for smelling. Leaf chafers have two claws of unequal length at the tip of each leg. Adults feed on leaves and flowers. The C-shaped larvae feed on roots and decomposing vegetation.

Habitat Woodlands, fields, and urban areas in northwestern Jordan, including *Amman*. **Activity** Females lay eggs in the soil next to tree roots. Adults emerge simultaneously in spring after the soil is softened by rain.

☐ **FLOWER BEETLES**
Cetoniinae Subfamily
SCARABAEIDAE FAMILY

L 2-62mm. There are around 4,000 flower beetle species worldwide, also known as "flower scarabs" and "flower chafers". Beetles from the Scarabaeidae family, which includes leaf chafers, are characterized by antennae with clubbed tips that fan out like leaves, used for smelling. Some flower beetle species have strikingly brilliant metallic colors. Pollen feeders are hairy. Adults feed on pollen, nectar, and ripe fruits. The C-shaped larvae feed on roots and decomposing vegetation. **Habitat** Woodlands, fields, and urban areas in northwestern Jordan, including *Amman*. **Activity** Most common in spring and early summer. Flies without lifting up its wing cases (elytra). Lands on flowers to feed during the day. Females lay eggs in the soil next to tree roots.

☐ BUMBLE BEE SCARAB BEETLES
GLAPHYRIDAE FAMILY

L 6-20mm. This family includes about 80 species worldwide. They are generally characterized by bodies covered in dense hair, down-curving head, and u-shaped wing cases (elytra) shorter than their abdomen and have divergent tips. Adults are pollinators that feed on pollen and nectar. Larvae feed on decaying matter. **Habitat** Open fields near water in western Jordan, including *Amman*, *Ajloun*, and

Jerash. **Activity** Feeds inside flowers, often in groups of several beetles. Females lay eggs in sandy river banks.

☐ LEAF BEETLES
CHRYSOMELIDAE FAMILY

L 1-16mm. There are over 35,000 leaf beetle species worldwide. They generally have domed bodies, often with bright or metallic colors, and antennae shorter than the length of their body. Adults feed on leaves and other plant parts. Larvae feed on leaves and roots. **Habitat** Woodlands, fields, and urban areas with trees and shrubs. **Activity** Females with enlarged abdomens lay egg clusters on the underside of leaves in spring.

☐ SNOUT BEETLES
CURCULIONIDAE FAMILY

L 1-35mm. Also known as "weevils" and "curculio", there are over 60,000 species in this family worldwide. They are characterized by long, down-curving snout and elbowed antennae that emerge from the side of the snout. Adults feed on soft vegetation. Larvae feed on roots, seeds, or other plant parts. **Habitat** Wooded areas in the *Northern Highlands*. **Activity** Adults often play dead when threatened.

☐ DARKLING BEETLES
TENEBRIONIDAE FAMILY

L 10-80mm. The darkling beetle family includes around 18,000 species worldwide, over 100 occur in Jordan. Darkling beetles are mostly black, they have a characteristic eye notch covering the antenna-base, and the first three plates on the underside of their abdomen are fused. Most species have fused wing cases (elytra), making them flightless. Some have chemical defenses, making them distasteful to predators. Darkling beetles feed on dung, fresh and decaying vegetation, and scavenge dead animals. **Habitat** Widespread, but mainly in dry regions, including *Azraq*, *Wadi Dana*, and *Wadi Rum*. **Activity** Found under stones, decaying vegetation, and around dung.

☐ ROVE BEETLES
STAPHYLINIDAE FAMILY

L 1-25mm. Rove beetles are characterized by short wing cases (elytra) and exposed lower abdomens. They have slender, elongated bodies and flexible abdomens. They feed on decaying animals and prey on small insects such as fleas. **Habitat** Common in humid soil near water sources, including *Amman*. Found under stones or plant debris. **Activity** Mainly nocturnal. One of the first insects to appear on decaying animals.

☐ GROUND BEETLES
CARABIDAE FAMILY

L 3-35mm. The ground beetle family includes over 22,000 species worldwide, most are shiny black with narrow heads, ridged wing cases (elytra), and a spike on the forth segment of each leg. Most ground beetles feed on insects and small animals, some feed on pollen and seeds. **Habitat** Found under logs and rocks in humid fields and urban gardens. **Activity** Most ground beetles hunt on the ground at night.

☐ TIGER BEETLES
CARABIDAE FAMILY

L 10-20mm. Tiger beetles are a subfamily of ground beetles. They are generally characterized by a head wider than their thorax, bulging eyes, and large mandibles. Some species are brightly colored. Tiger beetles are ferocious insect and spider hunters. **Habitat** Sandy or clay soil near water. Common on the dam banks of western Jordan. **Activity** Unlike other ground beetles, tiger beetles are active during the day. Adults are fast runners and hunt by chasing their prey. Larvae ambush their prey by hiding in vertical burrows. Males ride on females' backs during copulation.

Mosquitoes & Flies
DIPTERA ORDER

Mosquitoes and flies differ from other flying insects in that they have only one pair of wings. The second pair has been modified into small balancers (halteres), which vibrate to maintain stability in flight.

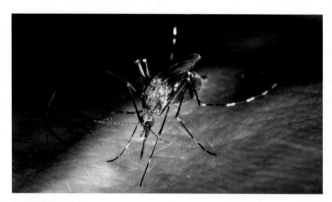

☐ MOSQUITOES
CULICIDAE FAMILY

L 5-15mm. Slender body; long legs; scaled wing-veins. Mosquitoes feed mainly on nectar. Only females require blood-protein for reproduction and have a piercing proboscis (needle-like mouthpart). **Habitat** Widespread around large animals and in urban areas. Breeds in small pools of standing water. **Activity** Mainly nocturnal. Active in warm seasons. Females bite and suck the blood of humans and animals, and may transmit diseases in the process. Females lay eggs in standing water. Larvae are aquatic.

☐ CRANE FLIES
TIPULIDAE FAMILY

Also known as "mosquito eaters", although they do not eat mosquitoes. Distinguished from mosquitoes by their larger bodies, longer legs (twice the length of their body), weaker flight, a v-shaped structure on their thorax, and lack of scales on wing veins. Adults feed on nectar. Larvae feed on vegetation. **Habitat** Grassy areas near water. Breeds in wet soil. **Activity** Does not bite humans. Adults live only to mate and often die before ever feeding. Active in spring. Wings often stretched out at rest.

☐ BLOW FLIES
CALLIPHORIDAE FAMILY

L 1cm. Metallic, green, blue, or black body; big, red compound eyes; black cross-grooves on abdomen. Feeds on both the decaying flesh of dead animals and on nectar. Larvae are scavengers that feed on decaying flesh and dung, and occasionally used to feed on infected human wounds. **Habitat** Common in warm areas with damp soil such as the river valleys of western Jordan. **Activity** First insect to detect and gather around dead animals. Females lay rice-like eggs in decaying flesh. Hatched larvae feed on the flesh and then burrow into damp soil before emerging as adults. Forensic science uses the predictable life-cycle of blow fly larvae to determine the age of corpses.

☐ FLESH FLIES
SARCOPHAGIDAE FAMILY

L 12mm. Gray thorax with black longitudinal stripes; gray and black checker pattern on the abdomen; red compound eyes. Flesh flies are beneficial for consuming dead animals, but can carry diseases. **Habitat** Common in all of Jordan. **Activity** Detects dead animals after blow flies, but competes by laying already hatched larvae that also feed on the younger larvae of other insects. Females lay their larvae on decaying flesh, garbage, dung, and even open mammal wounds. Larvae feed, grow, and then burrow into soil before emerging as adults.

☐ LESSER HOUSE FLIES
FANNIIDAE FAMILY

L 9mm. Gray thorax with four longitudinal dark lines; gray abdomen with dark cross-grooves; dark-red compound eyes. Distinguished from flesh flies by their smaller bodies and lack of checker pattern on the abdomen. Adults feed on nectar and pollen. Larvae feed on decaying organic matter. **Habitat** Mainly woodlands, including *Ajloun* and *Amman*. **Activity** Males often swarm beneath trees. Females are attracted to human refuse or decaying matter where they deposit their eggs.

☐ ROOT-MAGGOT FLY
Anthomyia pluvialis
ANTHOMYIIDAE FAMILY

L 8mm. Gray, black-spotted body; cross-grooved abdomen; dark-red compound eyes. Adults feed on nectar and pollen. Larvae feed on plant shoots and roots, which gives the fly its name. **Habitat** Moist fields and woodlands of western Jordan, including *Amman*. **Activity** Lingers around flowers.

☐ ROBBER FLIES
ASILIDAE FAMILY

L 3cm. Hairy body and bearded face; humped back; slender, tapered abdomen; long legs for holding onto prey; two large compound eyes. Male has grabbing pincers at the tip of its abdomen used during mating. Female has pointy ovipositor used to lay eggs in the sand or decaying wood. Feeds on insects such as flies, spiders, moths, bees, and grasshoppers. **Habitat** Warm regions with vegetation and insects, including *Ajloun*, *Amman* and *Petra*. **Activity** Active in warm seasons. Perches waiting for prey, catches it in midair, and then injects it with paralyzing and digesting enzymes to suck out the liquefied insides.

☐ **HORSE FLIES**
TABANIDAE FAMILY

L 8-25mm. A total of 23 horse fly species have been recorded in Jordan. They are generally characterized by large compound eyes and veins that form a 'Y' at the tip of the wings. Males are distinguished from females by their eyes which meet at the top of the head. Adults are pollinators that feed on nectar. The females of most horse fly species also feed on blood. Larvae feed on insects, worms, and snails. **Habitat** Common in warm regions near water, including the river valleys of western Jordan and the *Azraq* region. The larvae of most horse fly species are aquatic. **Activity** The females of most horse fly species bite humans and animals to feed on blood.

☐ **DEER FLY**
Chrysops flavipes
TABANIDAE FAMILY

The deer fly belongs to the same family as the horse fly. They share common characteristics and behaviors (see *Horse Flies*). The deer fly, however, has a smaller body, wings with dark patches, and spotted eyes.

☐ **FLOWER FLIES**
SYRPHIDAE FAMILY

L 4-25mm. Also known as "hoverflies". They generally look like bees, which protects them against fly predators. Males are distinguishable from females by eyes that meet at the top of the head. Adults are important pollinators that feed on nectar. The larvae of some species feed on insects such as aphids. The larvae of other species feed on decaying matter. **Habitat** Meadows, agricultural land, and urban gardens of western Jordan. **Activity** Darts from one flower to another and then hovers in one place to feed. Basks in the sun to gain warmth. Adults mate in midair.

☐ BEE FLIES
BOMBYLIIDAE FAMILY

L 1-20mm. A total of 138 bee fly species have been recorded in Jordan. They are generally characterized by round, hairy bodies that resemble bumble bees. Adults are flower pollinators that feed on nectar. Larvae are parasites that feed on the eggs and larvae of other insects. Both the adults and larvae are beneficial to agriculture. **Habitat** Common in Jordan, particularly in semi-arid regions. **Activity** Hovers above flowers and uses its long proboscis to feed on nectar. Darts off when approached. Seeks warmth by flying over or landing on hot surfaces. Females deposit eggs near colonies of host insects for the larvae to feed on.

☐ MOTH FLIES
PSYCHODIDAE FAMILY

L 5mm. Small, gray, hairy body with a moth-like appearance; leaf-shaped wings with parallel veins; feathery antennae. Adults feed on decaying matter and nectar. Larvae feed on decaying matter. **Habitat** Damp soils or polluted water. Common in septic tanks and bathrooms. **Activity**

Nocturnal. Females often lay eggs in bathroom sinks and drains, which gives them their "drain fly" nickname.

Butterflies
LEPIDOPTERA ORDER

After hatching from eggs, butterfly larvae (caterpillars) spend most of their time feeding on vegetation to store energy. When ready, they shed their larval skin and start their next pupal stage inside a hardened shell where they undergo a metamorphosis. They later emerge as full adults with six legs and four wings covered with tiny, colorful scales.

Adult butterflies consume liquids through a tubular and flexible mouth part (proboscis). They feed mainly on nectar for energy and require minerals for reproduction, which they get from wet sand, dung, and even human sweat.

☐ SKIPPER BUTTERFLIES
HESPERIIDAE FAMILY

L 2-3cm. A total of 16 skipper species have been recorded in Jordan. They are so called for their darting flight pattern. They are characterized by stout bodies and antennae with backward-hooked tips. Adults feed on nectar. **Habitat** Occurs near water in river valleys including the *Jordan River Valley*, *Wadi Zarqa*, *Wadi al-Seer*, and *Wadi Hidan*. **Activity** Darts off if disturbed.

☐ SWALLOWTAIL BUTTERFLIES
PAPILIONIDAE FAMILY

L 5cm. Five butterfly species in this family have been recorded in Jordan. They are generally very colorful and have wing tails that resemble the forked tail of swallows. Adults feed on nectar. Larvae feed on vegetation. **Habitat** The *Jordan Valley* and the highlands, including *Wadi Zarqa*, *Wadi al-Seer*, and *Salt*. **Activity** Caterpillars emit a foul-smelling substance if threatened.

☐ FOUR-FOOTED BUTTERFLIES
NYMPHALIDAE FAMILY

L 35mm. A total of 25 species in this family have been recorded in Jordan. They are characterized by reduced, frequently hairy forelegs that are kept folded (only four legs are used). They have orange, brown, or blue wings. Adults feed on nectar, rotting fruit, and dung. Larvae feed on vegetation. **Habitat** Most four-footed butterflies are migrant species that occur in the *Jordan Valley*, the highlands, and some locations in the *Eastern Desert*, including *Jerash*, *Wadi Dana*, and *Azraq*. **Activity** Most species are fast fliers.

☐ **GOSSAMER-WINGED BUTTERFLIES**
LYCAENIDAE FAMILY

L 1-2cm. A total of 27 species in this family have been recorded in Jordan. They are generally characterized by blue, brown, or orange wings with delicate, streaked markings. Some species have antenna-like wing tails and glossy, eye-like rear spots to confuse predators. Adults feed on nectar. The larvae of some species feed on aphids and ant larvae. **Habitat** Semi-arid regions including the *Jordan Valley*, *Jerash*, *Karak*, and *Aqaba*. **Activity** Some species deposit their eggs near ants. The ants protect the larvae in exchange for honeydew milked from their nectary gland.

☐ **WHITES & SULPHURS**
PIERIDAE FAMILY

L 1-3cm. A total of 24 butterfly species in this family have been recorded in Jordan. They are generally characterized by white, yellow, or orange wings, frequently with black or greenish markings. The word *butterfly* may have originated from some butter-colored species in this family. Caterpillars are mostly green. Adults feed on nectar. Larvae feed on vegetation. **Habitat** Different species occur in all habitats except for extreme deserts. **Activity** Often swarms around wet sand to take in diluted salts.

Moths
LEPIDOPTERA ORDER

Moths are closely related to butterflies. They differ in that moth caterpillars spin silk cocoons for their pupal stage, while butterfly caterpillars only molt; moths can fold their wings backwards, while butterflies keep their wings stretched; and moths fly day and night, while butterflies fly only during the day. Most moths do not have mouths and never eat as adults. Other moths feed mainly on nectar and plant sap. Larvae feed mainly on vegetation, and some feed on fabrics made of natural fibers.

☐ **WOOLLY BEARS**
ARCTIIDAE FAMILY

☐ **TENT CATERPILLAR**
LASIOCAMPIDAE FAMILY

L 1-4cm. Wooly bears are hairy moth caterpillars that belong mainly to the Arctiidae and Lymantriidae families. They generally have orange and black bands. Their hair keeps them warm, aids in camouflage, and stings in some species. Some caterpillars in the Lymantriidae family incorporate their hairs into the cocoons before they pupate. Some adult moths use the hairs to camouflage their eggs. Woolly bears feed on vegetation. **Habitat** The *Northern Highlands*, including *Ajloun* and *Amman*. **Activity** Rolls into a spiral if disturbed.

L 1-4cm. Tent caterpillars are moth larvae in the Lasiocampidae family. They gather in large social groups and build silken tents or mats for protection, to regulate their body temperatures in sunny or shady compartments, and to mark gathering and feeding sites. Tent caterpillars feed on vegetation. **Habitat** The *Northern Highlands*, including *Ajloun* and *Amman*. **Activity** The caterpillars leave the tent more frequently as they grow. They use scent trails, like ants, to find their way back after foraging.

☐ **BURNET MOTHS**
ZYGAENIDAE FAMILY

L 2-3cm. Moths in this family generally have bright colors with a metallic gloss. The striking colors serve as a warning to predators that the moth contains a distasteful poison. Larvae feed on vegetation. **Habitat** The *Northern Highlands*, including *Amman*, *Salt*, and *Wadi Mujib*. **Activity** Active around flowers, mainly during the day. Slow flyer.

☐ CRIMSON-SPECKLED FLUNKEY
Utetheisa pulchella
ARCTIIDAE FAMILY

L 3cm. White forewings with red and black spots; white hindwings with irregular black margins; looks white in flight. Larvae feed on vegetation. **Habitat** The *Northern Highlands*, including *Ajloun* and *Amman*. **Activity** Produces ultrasonic sounds from a tymbal organ on the thorax during mating and to defend against predators. Females lay a row of pale green eggs on leaf tips.

☐ PLUME MOTHS
PTEROPHORIDAE FAMILY

Plume moths have unusual wings divided into segments that stack on top of each other to form narrow structures disguised as twigs. Some species have feathery wing margins that give this family its name. At rest, the stacked wings are held horizontally, giving the moths their characteristic T-shape. **Habitat** Grasslands and urban gardens in semi-arid areas, including *Amman*. **Activity** Difficult to spot among grasses.

☐ BAGWORM MOTHS
PSYCHIDAE FAMILY

Moth larvae in this family build protective cases unique to each species, using silk and materials such as wood or sand. Larvae feed on lichen and tree leaves, often killing the host tree. **Habitat** The highlands, including *Amman* and *Madaba*. **Activity** Carries its case as it forages. Attaches its case to a rock or tree to pupate. In some species, adult females lack wings and continue to live inside their cases, while males leave their cases in search of mates.

Ants, Bees, and Wasps
HYMENOPTERA ORDER

Ants, bees, and wasps are closely related. They share narrow waists and other physical and behavioral characteristics. Bees, wasps, and winged ants have two pairs of wings, just like most flying insects. Each pair, however, is hooked together, making them appear as one. The females of some species have long ovipositors for laying eggs, often modified into stingers to defend their nest. Bees are distinguishable from wasps by a pollen sack on their hind legs and more hair.

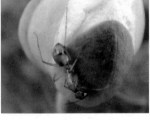

☐ ANTS
FORMICIDAE FAMILY

Ants are characterized by elbowed antennae and a restricted abdomen segment. In most ant species, males and breeding females are winged and mate in flight. Only females survive to start new colonies. Ants communicate with scents picked up by their antennae. **Habitat** Widespread in all habitats, including deserts. They build complex nests either in soil or wood. **Activity** Ants live in social colonies comprised of one or more female queens that lay eggs; male drones that mate with breeding females; and sterile female workers that build and protect the nest, gather and store food, and tend the larvae.

☐ DESERT ANT
Cataglyphis fortis
FORMICIDAE FAMILY

L 25mm. Black body; raised abdomen to avoid the hot sand; long legs to run and forage quickly under the hot sun. Unlike most ant species, the desert ant is a solitary forager. It finds its way back to the nest without scent trails, even in the absence of landmarks. After foraging in random patterns, it returns to its nest in a straight line. It orients itself with the sky's light patterns and determines distances by counting its steps. **Habitat** Desert and dry regions

with some vegetation, including *Wadi Mujib*, *Wadi Dana*, and *Wadi Araba*. **Activity** Avoids the hot sand by running. Stops on cooler rocks or in shady spots. Jumps off tall plants after foraging, controlling its fall and landing.

☐ **HONEY BEE**
Apis mellifera
APIDAE FAMILY

L 2cm. Fuzzy yellow abdomen with dark stripes that increase in thickness towards the tip. Two large compound eyes on the sides of the head and three small ocelli on the forehead that form a triangle (see *Ocelli*). The hind legs have sacks used to transport pollen. The abdomen tip has a stinger used to defend the beehive. Bees feed on pollen and nectar, pollinating flowers in the process. **Habitat** Mostly domesticated to produce honey and wax. Wild bees are found in open fields and urban gardens. They build beehives on trees and buildings. **Activity** Bees live in social colonies comprised of one female queen that lays eggs; male drones that mate with the queen; and sterile female workers that build and protect the hive, gather and store food, and tend the larvae. Only the queen survives the winter to start a new colony the following spring.

☐ **CARPENTER BEE**
Xylocopa pubescens
APIDAE FAMILY

L 25mm. Large bee with black head and legs; shiny, black abdomen; yellow thorax with a black, central stripe; and dark wings with a blue-violet sheen. Feeds on nectar and pollen, pollinating flowers in the process. **Habitat** Open fields and urban gardens in western Jordan. Builds nests by burrowing shallow tunnels in dead wood, usually without causing structural damage

(does not feed on wood). **Activity** Lives in solitary or small social nests with one alpha female. Does not sting humans unless provoked.

☐ **EUROPEAN PAPER WASP**
Polistes dominulus
VESPIDAE FAMILY

☐ **MAMMOTH WASP**
Megascolia Genus
SCOLIIDAE FAMILY

L 3cm. Black body with a contrasting yellow pattern on its face, back, and abdomen; orange antennae; narrow waist; two large compound eyes on the sides of the head; three small ocelli on the forehead that form a triangle (see *Ocelli*). Feeds mainly on caterpillars and some other insects. **Habitat** Urban areas and dry regions with water sources such as river valleys. **Activity** Non-aggressive, except when defending its nest. Only reproductive females winter in crevices and survive to form new colonies the following spring.

L 5cm. Large wasp with black body, orange head, an orange spot on the thorax, and four yellow spots on the abdomen. The wings are reddish with a blue gloss. Females are larger than males. Adults feed on nectar. Larvae feed on grubs. **Habitat** Fields near water in western Jordan, including *Wadi Finan*. **Activity** Solitary; slow; stings if handled. Females dig into the soil in search of a beetle larva (mainly large beetles in the Scarabaeidae family) and then paralyze and lay an egg in it. After hatching, the wasp larva feeds on the paralyzed grub and then pupates next to it.

☐ **POTTER WASPS**
Eumeninae Subfamily
VESPIDAE FAMILY

L 10-30mm. Also known as "mud daubers" and "mason wasps". They are so called for building nests with mud. A nest has one or more sealed cells, each contains an egg and one or more paralyzed insects for the developing larva to feed on. Larvae pupate inside the cells and then emerge as full adults. Different potter wasp species build different style nests and hunt different insects. Adults feed on nectar. **Habitat** Areas with some vegetation, including semi-arid regions. **Activity** Solitary. Does not sting humans unless provoked.

☐ DIGGER WASPS
SPHECIDAE FAMILY

There are over 130 digger wasp species worldwide. They are so called for digging nests in the ground. Digger wasps sting and paralyze their prey, drag them into their nests, and lay eggs next to them. Adults feed on nectar. Larvae feed on the paralyzed insects. **Habitat** Areas with some vegetation in western Jordan, including semi-arid regions. **Activity** Solitary; timid; very active. Digger wasps do not sting humans unless provoked.

☐ SAND WASPS
Bembix Genus
CRABRONIDAE FAMILY

L 15-25mm. Sand wasps are so called for building nests in sandy soil. They differ from other wasps by opening and sealing their nest repeatedly as they provide their larvae with fresh insects throughout their development. Adults feed on nectar, honeydew, and sap. Larvae are fed mainly flies. **Habitat** Sandy soil in warm regions, including the river and stream banks in western Jordan. **Activity** Social, often forms colonies. Digs burrows rapidly with its forelegs.

☐ ORIENTAL HORNET
Vespa orientalis
VESPIDAE FAMILY

L 4cm. Dark-red with a yellow pattern on its abdomen and face; two large compound eyes on the sides of the head; three small ocelli on the forehead that form a triangle (see *Ocelli*). Feeds on insects such as bees. **Habitat** Nests in cavities and abandoned burrows close to water sources such as the river valleys of western Jordan, including *Wadi al-Seer*. **Activity** Active during the day. Lives in social colonies of one queen and multiple females. Males hatch in autumn and fertilize the reproductive females. Only females survive the winter to form new colonies the following spring.

Vertebrates

Vertebrates are animals with backbones or spinal columns. They include fish, amphibians, reptiles, birds, and mammals.

Freshwater Fish

A total of 25 freshwater fish species have been recorded in Jordan, only 15 are native. Among the native fish are several endemic species such as the *Aphanius sirhani* in Azraq.

☐ **CARP FISH**
Garra rufa
CYPRINIDAE FAMILY

L 10cm. Elongated body; flat belly; round snout; sucker-like mouth; two pairs of short barbels; color varies depending on habitat. Feeds on algae. Used in warm pools that lack algae to feed on the skin of patients with skin diseases, which gives it the "doctor fish" nickname. **Habitat** The *Jordan River* and wadis of western Jordan, including the *Zarqa* and *Mujib*. Farther south, the *Garra rufa* is replaced by the closely-related, endemic *Garra ghorensis*. **Activity** Bottom feeder. In fast-running water, it clings to rocks with its sucker-like mouth and scrapes off encrusted algae with its teeth.

☐ **REDBELLY TILAPIA**
Tilapia zilli
CICHILIDAE FAMILY

L 30cm. Grayish-brown body with nine faint vertical bars on each side and a yellowish belly. Females are paler than males. Spawning fish turn bluish-green with a red belly. Redbelly tilapias feed on vegetation and other fish. **Habitat** The *Jordan River*. Introduced in *Azraq* where it competes with the

endemic *Aphanius sirhani*. **Activity** Territorial. Defends its nest aggressively.

☐ PUPFISH
Aphanius sirhani
CYPRINODONTIDAE FAMILY

L 4-5cm. Males have white flanks with 8-11 dark vertical bars and a dark dorsal fin with yellow horizontal bars. Females are yellowish with numerous small brown spots and a lateral row of larger brown spots. Pupfish feed on insect larvae and small crustaceans. **Habitat** Endemic to the Azraq Oasis and the only native finfish found there. Endangered due to loss of habitat and introduced species. **Activity** Forages in shallow water among stones and vegetation.

☐ NORTH AFRICAN CATFISH
Clarias gariepinus
CLARIIDAE FAMILY

L 20-120cm. Dark, smooth skin; dorsal fin extends over much of the body; small eyes; four pairs of long barbels near the mouth used to feel for food in muddy water. Capable of breathing out of water and traveling on land for short distances. Feeds on fish, invertebrates, plankton, and rotting plants. **Habitat** Quiet waters in the *Jordan River*. The introduced *Azraq* population disappeared due to loss of habitat. **Activity** Mainly bottom feeders. Sometimes hunts near the surface in packs.

☐ RED SEA FISH

The shallow depth and lack of sea currents in the Gulf of Aqaba produce clear water and enable light-loving algae and corals to thrive. The algae and corals, in turn, provide habitats to over 1,100 fish species, around 10% are unique to the Red Sea. **Location** The *Gulf of Aqaba* and the Aquatic Park south of *Aqaba*.

Amphibians
AMPHIBIA CLASS

Amphibians start their lives as gill-breathing aquatic larvae and then transform into lung-breathing terrestrial adults. They include frogs, toads, salamanders, and newts.

☐ **LEVANT WATER FROG**
Rana bedriagae
RANIDAE FAMILY

L 10cm. Pointed snout; horizontal eye pupils; round eardrums; webbed toes for swimming; long hind legs for jumping; relatively smooth skin. Color varies from green to gray and brown; spots vary in color, size, and arrangement; some have a stripe down their back. Males are smaller than females and have two vocal sacs on their lower jaw to amplify mating calls. Levant water frogs feed on insects, small fish, and other small animals; they resort to cannibalism in dry periods. **Habitat** Valleys with flowing or stagnant water in northwestern and western Jordan. Isolated population in *Azraq*. **Activity** Sits in shallow water by day. Dives under water to avoid detection. Calls increase in the evening.

☐ TREE FROG
Hyla savignyi
HYLIDAE FAMILY

L 4cm. Green or brownish-gray body with a brown lateral stripe; long legs; adhesive toe-disks for climbing vertical surfaces; short, rounded snout. Males are smaller than females and have two vocal sacs on their lower jaw to amplify mating calls. Tree frogs feed on insects. **Habitat** Humid areas near freshwater and vegetation in northwestern and western Jordan, including the *Yarmouk River*, some areas in the *Jordan River Valley*, *Jerash*, *Salt*, lower *Wadi Mujib*, and lower *Dana Nature Reserve*. Endangered by development and water pollution. **Activity** Mainly nocturnal. Dwells among vegetation near water.

☐ GREEN TOAD
Bufo viridis
BUFONIDAE FAMILY

L 8cm. Round body; warty skin; short legs; horizontal pupils; round eardrums; color varies and changes in response to light and temperature. Males are smaller than females. Green toads feed on insects. **Habitat** Widespread near permanent and temporary freshwater sources, including the *Jordan River Valley*, *Irbid*, *Amman*, upper *Wadi Mujib*, *Petra*, *Ma'an*, *Azraq*, and *Burqu'*. **Activity** Mainly nocturnal. Lives in humid burrows and crevices. Found in water only in spring while mating. Hibernates in winter. Secretes toxins when threatened.

Reptiles
REPTILIA CLASS

Reptiles are generally characterized by scaly skin and by laying soft-shelled eggs. They include turtles, lizards, snakes, and crocodiles. They are cold-blooded, regulating their body temperature by basking in the sun, seeking shade, and other external means. This limits their activities to the warm seasons and drives them to hibernate in winter, but also enables them to conserve energy and survive on less food.

☐ **LEVANTINE TORTOISE**
Testudo graeca terrestris
TESTUDINIDAE FAMILY

L 20cm. Yellow-brown with black patches. Shell has five vertebral plates, four costal plates on each side, and 10-11 marginal plates on each side. The number of rings on the shell is determined by diet, not age. Males are smaller than females, have a longer tail, and their bottom shell is farther from the tail-base. Color contrast is greater in juveniles. Levantine tortoises feed mainly on leaves, flowers, and fruit. **Habitat** Woodlands and grasslands of western Jordan, including *Amman*, *Irbid*, *Karak*, and *Wadi Dana*. **Activity** Moves slowly. Retracts its body into its shell when threatened.

☐ STRIPED-NECK TERRAPIN
Mauremys caspica rivuluta
EMYDIDAE FAMILY

L 20cm. Low, dark green shell with yellowish patterns that become darker with age; striped neck; thin legs with long claws. Males are smaller than females. Striped-neck terrapins feed on plants, algae, carcasses, insects, and fish. **Habitat** Near permanent water in northwestern Jordan, including the *Jordan River*, *Yarmouk River*, and *Zarqa River*. **Activity** Seen mostly in or basking near water. Dives under water when threatened.

Lizards
SQUAMATA ORDER

A total of 46 lizard species have been recorded in Jordan, none of which is venomous and all are considered beneficial for keeping the insect population under control. Most lizards change color in response to their environment, some more than others. The tail of most lizards breaks off when caught by a predator, allowing them to escape and grow a new one.

 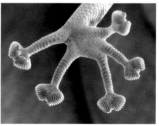

☐ SPOTTED FAN-FOOTED GECKO
Ptyodactylus guttatus
GEKKONIDAE FAMILY

L 12cm. Grayish body with irregular dark and light spots; granular scales; vertical pupils; striped tail; rounded tail-tip; adhesive, fanned toe-pads for climbing vertical surfaces. Feeds on insects, spiders, and scorpions. **Habitat** Rocky mountains in western and southern Jordan, including the *Dead Sea* region, *Wadi Mujib*, *Wadi Araba*, *Karak*, *Petra*, and *Ma'an*. **Activity** Mainly nocturnal or crepuscular. Occasionally basks in the sun by day. Hibernates in winter. Males are territorial.

☐ **SOUTHERN FAN-FOOTED GECKO**
Ptyodactylus hasselquistii
GEKKONIDAE FAMILY

L 15cm. Brownish body, sometimes with orange or pinkish blotches; loosely striped back; striped tail; pointed tail-tip; adhesive, fanned toe-pads for climbing vertical surfaces. Feeds on insects, spiders, and scorpions. **Habitat** Rocky and urban areas in southern Jordan, including *Wadi Araba, Aqaba, Wadi Rum,* and *Mudawwarah.* **Activity** Active mainly after sunset. Occasionally basks in the sun by day. Makes clicking mating calls.

☐ **NORTHERN FAN-FOOTED GECKO**
Ptyodactylus puiseuxi
GEKKONIDAE FAMILY

L 12cm. Dark with contrasting white, gray, and black spots; striped tail; brown eyes with vertical black pupils; adhesive, fanned toe-pads for climbing vertical surfaces. Feeds mainly on insects. **Habitat** Occurs in rocky regions in northern Jordan and parts of the *Dead Sea* valley. **Activity** Active in daytime and after sunset on hot days. Hibernates in winter. Retreats quickly into narrow crevices if disturbed. Males are territorial.

☐ **ROUGH-TAILED GECKO**
Cyrtopodion scabrum
GEKKONIDAE FAMILY

L 10cm. Pale body; dark spots form longitudinal rows on its back and lateral bands on its spiny tail; slender legs; pointed nose; vertical pupils; vertical ear opening; clawed toes for climbing vertical surfaces. Feeds on insects and spiders. **Habitat** Urban and rocky areas in southwestern Jordan, including *Aqaba,* southern *Wadi Araba,* and *Wadi Rum.* Also occurs in

northern Jordan in *Azraq* and *Safawi.* **Activity** Nocturnal. Commonly seen on building walls, catching insects attracted by urban lights.

☐ TURKISH GECKO
Hemidactylus turcicus
GEKKONIDAE FAMILY

L 10cm. Granular skin with variable colors and spots; triangular head with pointed nose; brown, lidless eyes with vertical pupils; clawed toes for climbing vertical surfaces. Juveniles have dark tail bands. The Turkish gecko feeds on small insects. **Habitat** Common in rocky and urban areas in all of western Jordan and in some *Eastern Desert* regions, including *Amman, Wadi Mujib, Madaba, Wadi Araba, Azraq,* and *Jafr*. **Activity** Mainly nocturnal. Attracted to light sources. Territorial, makes squeaking sounds to send territorial messages.

☐ EUROPEAN CHAMELEON
Chamaeleo chamaeleon recticrista
CHAMAELEONIDAE FAMILY

L 20cm. Skin changes color for camouflage, to communicate a mood, or in response to light and temperature conditions. Long, sticky tongue for catching prey. Long tail for holding onto branches. Fused toes that form a pair of grasping pads on each foot, each pad with either two or three small claws. Fused eyelids with only a small hole to see through. Eyes rotate independently, enabling it to see in all directions and in different directions at the same time. Lacks external eardrums. Females are larger than males. European chameleons feed on large insects, small reptiles, fruits, flowers, and leaves. **Habitat** Woodlands or shrublands of western Jordan, including *Jerash, Amman, a*nd the *Dana Nature Reserve*. **Activity** Moves slowly. Ambushes its prey. Hisses when disturbed.

☐ STARRED AGAMA
Laudakia stellio
AGAMIDAE FAMILY

L 30cm. Stout body with variable colors; blotchy cross-bands; triangular head; sharp claws for climbing vertical surfaces. The subspecies short-toed agama (*Laudakia stellio brachydactyla*) has a yellower head and darker cross-bands. The subspecies black agama (*Laudakia stellio picea*) has a black body, generally with orange cross-bands. Starred agamas feed on spiders, insects, and occasionally small lizards. **Habitat** Rocky highlands in western Jordan, including *Jerash*, *Amman*, *Karak*, *Shobak*, and *Petra*. *Laudakia stellio brachydactyla* occurs in the south, including *Wadi Rum* and *Aqaba*. *Laudakia stellio picea* occurs in the *Basalt Desert* in northern Jordan. **Activity** Basks in the sun by day. Retreats into narrow crevices when disturbed. Strongly territorial, males oversee their territory from high spots and chase off other males while bobbing their heads.

☐ PERSIAN AGAMA
Trapelus persicus
AGAMIDAE FAMILY

L 25cm. The only agama in Jordan with longitudinal bands. Gray-brown body; triangular head with a narrower neck and a pointed nose; tail longer than its body. Changes color and patterns for camouflage and in response to heat. Displaying males have a blue throat. Receptive females have rusty orange spots on their back. Persian agamas feed mainly on insects. **Habitat** Limited to the *Azraq* region. **Activity** Climbs on shrubs to bask in the sun. Males signal their dominance by nodding and flashing their blue throat.

☐ **SINAI AGAMA**
Pseudotrapelus sinaitus
AGAMIDAE FAMILY

L 25cm. Tail longer than its body; ear opening larger than its eye. Dominant males are blue, and turn yellowish-brown for camouflage. Females are yellowish-brown with a blue head. Gravid females have rusty orange spots on their back. Sinai agamas feed on insects. **Habitat** Arid, rocky regions in western Jordan and open desert regions in eastern Jordan, including *Wdi Dana*, *Wadi Rum*, *Azraq*, and *Burqu'*. **Activity** Basks motionless in the sun by day. Catches wandering insects with its sticky tongue. Males perch on big rocks to oversee and defend their territory.

☐ **TOAD-HEADED AGAMA**
Phrynocephalus arabicus
AGAMIDAE FAMILY

L 13cm. Orangish-brown body with darker, round spots; white underparts; rounded head; nostrils separated by a single scale; lacks external eardrums. Males are slightly larger than females. Dominant males have a black tail tip with white bands. Females have a pinkish undertail. Toad-headed agamas feed on ants and other insects. **Habitat** Southern Jordan, including *Wadi Rum*. **Activity** Avoids hot sand by climbing on bushes. Buries itself in the sand when threatened. Males curl their tail repeatedly to assert dominance.

□ PALE AGAMA
Trapelus pallidus
AGAMIDAE FAMILY

L 19cm. Flattened body with variable colors; tail longer than its body; about 13 dark tail-bands; ears smaller than its eyes; irregular scales, some spiny. Males have dark cross-bands that interrupt a white dorsal stripe. Females have a faint dorsal stripe. Gravid females have orange head and sides. Pale agamas feedf mainly on ants and some other insects. **Habitat** *Wadi Araba* and the *Eastern Desert*, including *Ruwayshid, Azraq, Qatranah,* and *Ma'an*. **Activity** Runs with its tail curved upwards. Climbs on bushes to avoid the hot sand. Males perch on high spots to assert dominance.

□ SYRIAN AGAMA
Trapelus ruderatus
AGAMIDAE FAMILY

L 20cm. Brownish-gray body; dark cross-bands and white, diamond-shaped dorsal spots; about 10 dark tail-bands. Males have a blue throat and fainter bars in the mating season. Gravid females have orang-yellow bars. Syrian agamas feed on insects and spiders. **Habitat** Open semi-deserts with vegetation in northwestern and western Jordan, including *Ramtha, Amman, Madaba, Karak, Tafilah,* and *Shobak*. **Activity** Timid. Basks on rocks.

□ EGYPTIAN DAB-LIZARD
Uromastyx aegyptius microlepis
AGAMIDAE FAMILY

L 75cm. Also known as "dabb" and "Egyptian spiny-tailed lizard". Large, muscular body; short rounded nose; tapered, spiny tail; relatively short digits and claws. Color varies from brown to yellow and gray, and become lighter in response to temperature. Males have a larger body and a relatively larger head than females. Egyptian dab-lizards feed mainly on leaves, fruit, and some insects. **Habitat** Flat, sandy or gravely deserts in the *Azraq* region and southwestern Jordan, including *Wadi Araba, Wadi*

Fidan, Aqaba, and *Wadi Rum*. Burrows a deep tunnel with a crescent-shaped entrance. **Activity** Basks in the sun by day near a burrow. Forages mainly in the morning. Retreats quickly into a burrow when approached. Inflates its body, hisses, and swings its tail when threatened. Hibernates in winter.

☐ **FRINGE-TOED LIZARD**
Acanthodactylus Genus
LACERTIDAE FAMILY

L 16-27cm. A total of seven *Acanthodactylus* species have been recorded in Jordan. They are characterized by fringed toes used for digging. They have variable colors and patterns, comb-like ear margin, pointy nose, large head scales, and tail longer than their body. Females and juveniles are smaller with more pronounced patterns. Fringe-toed lizards feed on insects and other smaller lizards. **Habitat** Different species occur in different deserts and semi-deserts, including *Azraq, Dana Nature Reserve, Petra, Wadi Rum*, and *Ma'an*. **Activity** Territorial and aggressive towards other lizards. Moves frequently to oversee a large territory. Usually stops in the shade and waves its tail to assert dominance. Runs long distances or hides if disturbed.

☐ **SHORT-NOSED DESERT LIZARD**
Mesalina brevirostris
LACERTIDAE FAMILY

L 16cm. Brownish or pale body; clear or faint white and brown dots; short snout; wide head; long tail. Differs from fringe-toed lizards by lacking fringes on its toes, and the two large scales on the back of its head do not touch. Feeds on insects and spiders. **Habitat** Stony, shrubby semi-deserts in central, eastern, and southwestern Jordan, including *Azraq, Ruwayshid,*

south of *Amman, Ma'an,* and *Aqaba*. **Activity** Timid. Fast runner. Raises its feet alternately to avoid the hot sand.

☐ LEBANON LIZARD
Lacerta laevis
LACERTIDAE FAMILY

L 14cm. Brownish or grayish body with a dark stripe on each side; pointed snout; a large scale between the eye and ear. Adults have small, blue spots below the stripes. Juveniles have a turquoise tail. Males are larger and more colorful than females. Lebanon lizards feed mostly on insects. **Habitat** Wooded and bushy areas in northwestern Jordan, including *Ajloun, Dibbin, Zay,* and *Salt.* Prefers oak forests. **Activity** Fast runner. Timid.

☐ BRIDLED SKINK
Mabuya vittata
SINCIDAE FAMILY

L 20cm. Generally brownish or grayish body with light, longitudinal stripes; tail is longer than its body; forelegs thinner than hind legs. Females are bigger than males. Bridled skinks feed on invertebrates and may resort to cannibalism. **Habitat** Grassy and bushy fields in western Jordan, including *Irbid, Jerash, Amman, Madaba,* and *Petra.* A small population also occurs in *Azraq.* **Activity** Timid. Moves under plant debris and hides in bushes.

☐ FESTA'S SKINK
Ablepharus rueppellii
SINCIDAE FAMILY

L 25cm. Snake-like body with small legs; thick tail longer than its body; glossy-brown color with a dark side-stripe that runs from the nose, through the eye, to the tail. Feeds on insects and other small invertebrates. **Habitat** Mainly wooded and bushy areas in the *Northern Highlands,* including *Irbid, Jerash, Dibbin, Wadi al-Seer,* and *Salt.* Also occurs farther south near water and vegetation in *Wadi Mujib, Karak, Shobak,* and *Dana.* **Activity** Timid. Forages by day under leaves and rocks.

☐ SANDFISH
Scincus scincus meccensis
SINCIDAE FAMILY

L 18cm. Reddish-yellow back with dark cross-bands; white underparts; short indistinct neck; long snout extending beyond the lower jaw; short, tapering, pointy tail; extremely smooth body scales that produce less friction than polished steel and glass. Adults have dark flank-stripes. Sandfish feed on insects. **Habitat** Sandy regions south of *Azraq* and in southern Jordan, including *Umari, Mudawwarah,* and *Wadi Rum.* **Activity** Spends most of its time hiding or searching for insects in the sand. Moves fast in a swimming motion on loose sand. Seeks shade under bushes or flat stones. Difficult to observe in the wild.

☐ DESERT MONITOR
Varanus griseus
VARANIDAE FAMILY

L 100cm; Jordan's largest lizard. Sandy-yellow, brown, or gray body; dark cross-bands; two, dark, horizontal bands on each side of its neck and head; long neck, head, and pointed nose; nostrils closer to its eyes than to its nose-tip; forked tongue used to pick up airborne scents. Adult patterns are less pronounced. Feeds on smaller lizards, rodents, insects, snails, and eggs. Although feared by locals, the desert monitor is not venomous. **Habitat** North of the *Dead Sea* and most desert habitats, including *Wadi Araba, Wadi Rum,* and *Azraq.* **Activity** Solitary. Moves during the day in search of prey and rests in burrows at night. Desert monitors are very intelligent and have hunting skills that rival those of mammals. They can track individual scent trails, and can determine both the trail's direction and age.

Snakes
SQUAMATA ORDER

A total of 36 snake species have been recorded in Jordan, some of which are venomous. Snakes are reptiles characterized by long, flexible, scaly bodies that lack limbs, eyelids, and ear openings. They have forked tongues used to pick up airborne scents. They grow throughout their lives and shed outgrown skin 3-6 times a year. Snakes perform an essential role in keeping the rodent population under control. Venomous snakes use venom to catch their natural prey and pose no risk to humans if left undisturbed.

☐ **COIN SNAKE**
Coluber nummifer
COLUBRIDAE FAMILY

L 100cm. Grayish-brown body with brown, black-rimmed, oval spots; fused tail-spots that form three dark tail stripes; flattened head wider than the neck; rounded snout; golden eyes with black, round pupils; two dark stripes below and behind each eye. Feeds on rodents, lizards, and birds. Non-venomous. **Habitat** Sunny, open fields in the highlands, including *Irbid*, *Ajloun*, *Jerash*, *Amman*, *Shobak*, and *Ma'an*. **Activity** Mainly diurnal. Active after sunset on hot days. Retreats quickly when disturbed. Hibernates in winter.

☐ **PALAEARCTIC TAIL-LINED**
Coluber ravergieri
COLUBRIDAE FAMILY

L 120cm. Grayish-brown body with dark, yellow-rimmed, rectangular markings that often fuse into a zigzag pattern; fused tail-markings that form three dark tail stripes; flattened head wider than the neck; rounded snout; golden eyes with black, round pupils; two dark stripes below and behind each eye. Feeds on rodents, lizards, birds, frogs, and snails. Non-venomous. **Habitat** Unique to northern Jordan. Reported around *Jawa*, east of *Mafraq*. **Activity** Mainly diurnal. Active after sunset on hot days. Retreats quickly when disturbed. Hibernates in winter.

☐ **CROWNED DWARF RACER**
Eirenis coronella
COLUBRIDAE FAMILY

L 35cm. Grayish body with darker cross-bands; rounded snout; golden eyes with black, round pupils; indistinct neck with a brown collar that faintly connects with an eye band. Feeds on insects and scorpions. Non-venomous. **Habitat** Western and northern Jordan, including *Mafraq*, *Amman*, *Karak*, *Petra*, and *Ma'an*. **Activity** Slow, secretive, and non-aggressive.

☐ **ROTH'S DWARF RACER**
Eirenis rothi
COLUBRIDAE FAMILY

L 30cm. Light-brown body; flat head with two black patches and a black collar; rounded snout; indistinct neck. Feeds on insects and other small invertebrates. Venomous. **Habitat** Common in rocky, humid regions or near water in the highlands, including *Ramtha*, *Ajloun*, *Amman*, *Salt*, *Karak*, *Petra*, and *Ma'an*. **Activity** Slow, secretive, and non-aggressive. Common on spring mornings under rocks.

☐ **DICE SNAKE**
Natrix tessellata
COLUBRIDAE FAMILY

L 100cm. Gray or brownish body with dark or faint chessboard pattern; lighter belly with dice-like, dark patterns; head slightly wider than the neck; yellow eyes with round, black pupils. Feeds on fish and amphibians. Non-venomous. **Habitat** Common around permanent freshwater sources in northwestern and western Jordan, including the *Jordan River Valley*, *Zarqa River*, *Amman*, and *Wadi Mujib*. Rare in *Azraq* and some regions in southwestern Jordan. **Activity** Aquatic, spends most of its time foraging in water and dives under water when threatened. Hisses if caught, feigns death, bleeds from mouth, and excretes a foul smell. Occasionally basks in the sun. Mates in large groups in spring.

☐ **DIADEM SNAKE**
Spalerosophis diadema
COLUBRIDAE FAMILY

L 100cm. Yellowish-brown body with brown, white-rimmed, oval spots; head wider than the neck; distinct dark band between the eyes that extends backwards to the jaws; golden eyes with black, round pupils. Feeds on rodents, birds, and lizards. Non-venomous. **Habitat** Western and northern Jordan, including *Amman*, *Wadi Araba*, *Wadi Rum*, and *Azraq*. **Activity** Mainly nocturnal. Active during the day on cold days. Bites repeatedly when threatened.

☐ **SCHOKARI SAND RACER**
Psammophis schokari
COLUBRIDAE FAMILY

L 125cm. Generally yellowish-brownish body with dark and light longitudinal stripes; whitish, black-spotted underparts; elongated head slightly wider than the neck; golden eyes with black, round pupils; dark eye-mask. Feeds on lizards, rodents, and birds. Mildly venomous; harmless to humans. **Habitat** The highlands, the *Azraq*, and the *Jafr* regions. **Activity** Timid. Fast. Climbs trees in search of young birds.

☐ **ARABIAN TIGER SNAKE**
Telescopus dhara
COLUBRIDAE FAMILY

L 100cm. Slender body; wider head; flat snout; vertical pupils; reddish, brownish, or grayish coloration with longitudinal spots. Feeds on lizards, birds, eggs, and bats. Venomous, but their small fangs deliver harmless quantities of venom. **Habitat** Rocky regions in the *Jordan Valley* and *Wadi Rum*. **Activity** Nocturnal.

☐ **PAINTED SAW-SCALED VIPER**
Echis coloratus
VIPERIDAE FAMILY

L 80cm. Brownish-gray body with gray, black-rimmed, oval cross-bands; triangular head; eyes close to its nose; vertical pupils. Feeds on rodents, lizards, birds, insects, and frogs. Venomous. **Habitat** Dry, rocky valleys in western Jordan including the *Jordan Valley*, *Wadi Dana*, and *Wadi Rum*. **Activity** Nocturnal. Moves mainly sideways.

□ **ARABIAN HORNED VIPER**
Cerastes gasperettii
VIPERIDAE FAMILY

L 50cm. Yellowish or reddish body with darker patches; wide head; horn-like scales (not always present); yellow eyes with black vertical pupils; dark streaks behind its eyes. Feeds on reptiles, rodents, and birds. Venomous. **Habitat** Sandy deserts including *Wadi Araba* and *Wadi Rum*. **Activity** Nocturnal. Buries its body in the sand or hides in crevices during the day. Moves sideways. Rubs its scales together to produce a warning sound when threatened.

□ **PERSIAN HORNED VIPER**
Pseudocerastes persicus
VIPERIDAE FAMILY

L 70cm. Grayish body with black patchy cross-bands; wide head; flat snout; vertical pupils; black streaks behind its eyes; horns composed of several scales (horns of the Arabian viper are single scales). Vipers adapted to the Basalt Desert are nearly black. Feeds on rodents, lizards, and birds. Venomous. **Habitat** Stony deserts and semi-deserts, including *Azraq*, *Qatranah*, and *Shobak*. **Activity** Mainly nocturnal. Avoids humans.

□ **PALESTINIAN VIPER**
Vipera palaestinae
VIPERIDAE FAMILY

L 100cm. Grayish-brown body with dark-brown, white-rimmed markings; triangular head with V-shape markings; neck is narrower than the head; orange cheek spots; brownish eyes with vertical pupils. Feeds on rodents, birds, and reptiles. Venomous. **Habitat** Northwestern Jordan, including *Irbid*, *Ajloun*, *Amman*, and the *Jordan River Valley*. **Activity** Secretive. Mainly nocturnal. Climbs on bushes.

Birds
AVES CLASS

Flight enables most birds to avoid seasonal food shortages by migrating great distances. Many birds that occur in Jordan reside in the region all year. Other birds typically breed in Europe or Central Asia and then migrate through Jordan to winter in Africa and parts of the Middle East.

Over 400 resident and migratory birds occur in Jordan. This section lists the most common or popular. The plumage of most birds varies according to age, season, habitat, and gender. This section describes the most typical plumages.

☐ **BLUE-NECKED OSTRICH**
Struthio camelus
STRUTHIONIDAE FAMILY

H 240cm; the largest of all living birds. Small, flat head; large eyes with long eyelashes and excellent eyesight; long, powerful legs; long, blue-toned, naked neck. Males have black feathers and a white tail. Females have gray-brown feathers. While most birds have four toes and some have three, the ostrich has only two. Feeds on vegetables, fruit, grasses, seeds, and small animals. **Habitat** Once common in Jordan, the subspecies Arabian ostrich (*Struthio camelus syriacus*) is now extinct. The blue-necked ostrich is currently bred in captivity in the *Shomari Reserve* for introduction into the wild. **Activity** Flightless. Fast runner and can reach speeds of up to 65 km/h.

☐ **GREAT CRESTED GREBE**
Podiceps cristatus
PODICIPEDIDAE FAMILY

L 50cm. Brown upperparts; white underparts; white face and throat; pointed, pink bill; black streak between its eye and bill. Breeding adults have a black crest and collar. The crest is shorter and the collar is absent in the winter. Great crested grebes feed mainly on fish, some insects, amphibians, and crustaceans. **Habitat** Breeds in Europe and northern Asia. Rare winter visitor to bodies of water in the *Azraq* region, *Aqaba*, and some reservoirs in western Jordan. **Activity** Swims and flies with an extended neck. Dives under water to forage.

☐ **GREAT WHITE PELICAN**
Pelecanus onocrotalus
PELECANIDAE FAMILY

L 160cm. White plumage with contrasting black wing tips; pink patches around its black eyes; yellow-pink legs; bluish bill with a red tip and a yellow, big pouch. Feeds on fish, frogs, and other small animals. **Habitat** Breeds mainly in Europe; winters in Africa and the Middle East; winters in diminishing numbers in Jordan. Migrates south through Jordan in autumn and north in spring. Occurs in *Aqaba*, *Kirbat al-Samra* (north of *Zarqa*) and *Azraq*. **Activity** Catches and carries fish with its big bill pouch.

☐ **GREAT CORMORANT**
Phalacrocorax carbo
PHALACROCORACIDAE FAMILY

L 85cm. Glossy, black plumage; some white feathers on its throat, neck, and nape; yellow throat patch. Breeding adults have a white thigh patch. Juveniles have browner upperparts and a white belly. Great cormorants feed on fish. **Habitat** Migrates south through Jordan in winter and north in spring. Occurs in small numbers in *Aqaba* and more rarely in *Azraq*. **Activity** Perches on trees near water, often with stretched wings. Dives to catch fish.

☐ **GRAY HERON**
Ardea cinerea
ARDEIDAE FAMILY

L 95cm. Gray upperparts; white underparts; black eyebrows that terminate in a drooping crest; black streaks down the front of the neck; yellow bill; long neck and legs. Feeds on fish, frogs, and other small animals. **Habitat** Migrates south through Jordan mainly in autumn and north in spring. Occurs in the wetlands and dams in *Azraq*, the *Northern Highlands*, and the *Dead Sea* region. **Activity** Roosts in colonies. Ambushes or stalks its prey, then spears it with its bill. Retracts its neck in flight.

☐ **NIGHT HERON**
Nycticorax nycticorax
ARDEIDAE FAMILY

L 60cm. White or light-gray plumage; black crown and back; red eyes; short neck and legs. Juveniles have white-spotted brown plumage. Night herons feed on aquatic animals and small mammals. **Habitat** Migrates south through Jordan in autumn and north in spring. Scarce around wetlands, rivers, and reservoirs in *Azraq*, *Aqaba*,

and the highlands. **Activity** Forages mostly at dusk by ambushing its prey. Retracts its neck in flight.

☐ **SQUACCO HERON**
Ardeola ralloides
ARDEIDAE FAMILY

L 45cm. Short neck and bill; yellow eyes; white wings. Summer adults have golden plumage and long, streaked nape feathers. Squacco herons feed on insects and aquatic animals. **Habitat** Breeds in Europe and the Middle East; winters in Africa; migrates south through Jordan in autumn and north in spring. Occurs in diminishing numbers around water in *Azraq, Aqaba,* and river valleys. **Activity** Forms small colonies. Retracts its neck in flight.

☐ **GREAT WHITE EGRET**
Ardea alba
ARDEIDAE FAMILY

L 95cm. White plumage; yellow bill; black legs and feet. Breeding adults have a darker bill, lighter legs, and ornamental dorsal feathers. Great white egrets feed on fish, frogs, insects, and other small animals. **Habitat** Migrates south through Jordan in autumn and north in spring. Occurs in diminishing numbers in wetlands and dams in *Azraq,* the *Northern Highlands,* and *Aqaba.* **Activity** Moves slowly. Retracts its neck in flight.

☐ **LITTLE EGRET**
Egretta garzetta
ARDEIDAE FAMILY

L 60cm. White plumage; black bill; black legs; yellow feet. Breeding adults have two long head feathers. Juveniles have brown legs. Little egrets feed on fish, crustaceans, and some insects. **Habitat** Wetlands and reservoirs, including *Azraq,* the *Dead Sea,* and *Kirbat al-Samra* (north of *Zarqa*). Builds stick-nests in trees and shrubs. Passage migrants fly south in autumn and north in spring. **Activity** Nests in colonies. Ambushes or runs after its prey in shallow water.

☐ **CATTLE EGRET**
Bubulcus ibis
ARDEIDAE FAMILY

L 50cm. White plumage; short, yellow bill; black legs. Breeding adults have orange crown, back, breast, and legs. Cattle egrets feed on insects. **Habitat** Near water sources and agricultural land mainly in the *Jordan River Valley.* Builds stick nests on trees, bushes, and among reeds. Passage migrants fly south in autumn and north in spring over the *Azraq,* the *Northern Highlands,* and the *Jordan Valley.* **Activity** Nests in colonies. Often feeds in flocks around cattle.

☐ **WHITE STORK**
Ciconia ciconia
CICONIIDAE FAMILY

L 100cm. White plumage; black flight feathers; red bill and legs; broad wingspan that enables it to glide for long distances. Feeds on insects, frogs, rodents, and lizards. **Habitat** Breeds in Europe; winters in Africa; migrates south through Jordan in autumn and north in spring. Flies over western Jordan including *Amman* and the *Dead Sea* region. Roosts in wetlands such as the *Kafrain Dam* (north of the *Dead Sea*) and *Kirbat al-Samra* (north of *Zarqa*). **Activity** Walks slowly. Extends its neck in flight.

☐ **SHELDUCK**
Tadorna tadorna
ANATIDAE FAMILY

L 63cm. Mostly white; dark green head; chestnut breast-ring; black belly-stripe; black flight feathers; red bill and legs. Breeding males have a red bill-knob. Juveniles have gray upperparts and white underparts. Shelducks feed on insects, snails, and other invertebrates. **Habitat** Migrates south through Jordan in autumn and north in spring. Some winter in Jordan in the *Azraq* and the *Dead Sea* regions. Occasionally breeds in Jordan after rainy seasons. Nests in abandoned burrows and among vegetation. **Activity** Spends most of its time in and around water.

☐ **WIGEON**
Anas penelope
ANATIDAE FAMILY

L 48cm. Adult males have a chestnut head; a yellowish forehead; gray back and sides; a white wing patch; pinkish breast; a white belly; a black tail; and a gray, black-tipped bill. Females are mottled brownish-gray with a white belly. Wigeons feed on vegetation. **Habitat** Migrates south through Jordan in autumn and north in spring. Winters in the *Azraq* region in rainy years. Occurs near water in *Aqaba*, the *Dead Sea*, and some reservoirs in spring. **Activity** Noisy. Forms large flocks.

☐ MALLARD
Anas platyrhynchos
ANATIDAE FAMILY

L 56cm. Males have a green head; a flat yellow bill with a black tip; brown breast; a gray body; a black lower back; and a blue speculum. Females have mottled brown plumage and dark-brown bill. Mallards feed on aquatic vegetation and some insects. **Habitat** Winter visitor to bodies of water in the *Azraq* region and rivers and reservoirs in northwestern Jordan.

Rare in summer. **Activity** Forms large, noisy flocks. Forages by dabbling in shallow water with its tail up in the air. Filter-feeds by straining food out of water and mud with its flat bill.

☐ TUFTED DUCK
Aythya fuligula
ANATIDAE FAMILY

L 40cm. Males are black with white flanks; gray, black-tipped bill; drooping crest; and orange eyes. Females are brown with paler flanks. Tufted ducks feed on aquatic insects, mollusks, and plants. **Habitat** Uncommon winter visitor and migrant through Jordan. Migrates south in winter and north in spring. Occurs in small numbers in

wetlands, reservoirs, and flood pools in *Azraq*, the *Dead Sea*, and *Aqaba* regions. **Activity** Forages by diving underwater.

☐ **GRIFFON VULTURE**
Gyps fulvus
ACCIPITRIDAE FAMILY

L 100cm. Also known as "Eurasian griffon". White head, neck, and collar; sandy-brown body; dark tail. Identifiable from below by its large, fingered wings that have a light leading-edge and a contrasting dark trailing-edge. Juveniles are paler than adults. Griffon vultures scavenge carcasses. **Habitat** Occurs in declining numbers in the rocky valleys of western Jordan, including *Wadi Mujib* and *Wadi Dana*. Nests on cliff ledges and caves. **Activity** Spends most of its time soaring in search of dead animals. Scavenges in flocks and forms loose colonies. Capable of soaring as high as 9,000 meters and diving as fast as 160 km/h. Lacks sense of smell; locates carcasses by sight. Lacks a sharp bill; waits for other scavengers to open carcasses.

☐ **EGYPTIAN VULTURE**
Neophron percnopterus
ACCIPITRIDAE FAMILY

L 60cm. White plumage; wing's trailing-edge is gray above and black below; yellow, bare-skinned pointed head. Scavenges the internal organs of dead animals and preys on small animals and eggs. **Habitat** Migrates south through Jordan in autumn and north in spring. Small numbers breed in Jordan in summer in the *Dead Sea* region, *Petra*, and *Wadi Araba*. Nests on cliffs. **Activity** Scavenges after the larger vultures finish feeding.

☐ **GOLDEN EAGLE**
Aquila chrysaetos
ACCIPITRIDAE FAMILY

L 75cm. Brown plumage with a golden-yellow nape. Juveniles have whitish wings and tail patches that turn dark gray when mature. Golden eagles feed on birds, rodents, and larger mammals. **Habitat** The Eastern Desert, including the *Azraq* and *Ba'ir* regions. Less common in the highlands. Nests on rock cliffs and trees. **Activity** Mates for life and collaborates with its partner when hunting.

☐ **SHORT-TOED EAGLE**
Circaetus gallicus
ACCIPITRIDAE FAMILY

L 65cm. Brown head and upperparts; white, brown-streaked underparts; brown wing-tips; barred underwings; banded tail; yellow eyes. Some are paler and have white heads. Feeds on reptiles and small mammals. **Habitat** Migrates south through Jordan in autumn and north in spring. Some breed in western Jordan in summer, including *Dana Nature Reserve* and *Ajloun*. Nests in trees. **Activity** Soars in search of prey.

☐ **LONG-LEGGED BUZZARD**
Buteo rufinus
ACCIPITRIDAE FAMILY

L 60cm. Colors vary from reddish to brown and white. Long legs, wings, and tail. Identifiable from below by its fanned tail and whitish, fingered wings with a dark leading-edge and a dark border. Feeds on rodents, reptiles, insects, and birds. **Habitat** Open desert margins, including the *Basalt Desert*, *Petra*, and *Wadi Rum*. Nests on cliff ledges and trees. **Activity** Hovers or soars in search of prey.

☐ **OSPREY**
Pandion haliaetus
PANDIONIDAE FAMILY

L 60cm. Brown upperparts; white head and underparts; dark eye-mask with contrasting yellow eyes; black bill. Feeds mainly on fish. **Habitat** Migrates south through Jordan in autumn and north in spring. Occurs near rivers, reservoirs, and desert pools. **Activity** Hovers over water and then dives to catch fish.

☐ **BARBARY FALCON**
Falco pelegrinoides
FALCONIDAE FAMILY

L 35cm. Bluish-gray upperparts; reddish-brown, barred underparts; dark crown; brown moustache; black eyes. Females are larger than males. Barbary falcons feed mainly on birds and occasionally on bats. **Habitat** Rocky semi-deserts, including the *Dead Sea* region, *Wadi Araba*, and *Wadi Rum*. Nests on cliff ledges. **Activity** Catches prey in midair.

☐ **KESTREL**
Falco tinnunculus
FALCONIDAE FAMILY

L 35cm. Long, narrow, pointed wings; long tail; reddish-brown upperparts with black spots; white, brown-streaked underparts; yellow legs; black claws; excellent eyesight. Males have bluish-gray head and tail. Kestrels feed on small mammals, birds, amphibians, and insects. **Habitat** Common in diverse habitats in all of Jordan. Nests on cliff ledges, buildings, and trees. Often uses nests abandoned by other birds. **Activity** Hovers in midair in search of prey and then dives to catch it.

□ **CHUKAR**
Alectoris chukar
PHASIANIDAE FAMILY

L 33cm. Gray upperparts and breast; black-striped sides; black eye-mask that extends down and across the breast; red bill, eye-rings, and legs. Feeds on seeds and insects. **Habitat** Semi-arid regions in western Jordan, including the *Dana Nature Reserve*. Less common in *Azraq*. Nests on the ground. **Activity** Often followed by multiple juveniles. Seeks water sources twice a day. Flies for short distances or runs when disturbed.

□ **SAND PARTRIDGE**
Ammoperdix heyi
PHASIANIDAE FAMILY

L 24cm. Light-brown plumage with white and brown breast stripes. Males have white forehead and cheek patches. Females lack distinct patterns, but have spotted necks. Juveniles resemble females. Sand partridges feed on seeds, insects, and fruit. They maintain a low metabolism, which enables them to survive on small amounts of food in arid habitats. **Habitat** Common in the arid rocky slopes near water sources, including the *Dead Sea* region and *Wadi Rum*. Less common in *Azraq*. Nests on shaded ground. **Activity** Flies for short distances when disturbed.

□ **CHICKEN**
Gallus gallus domesticus
PHASIANIDAE FAMILY

L 35cm. Domesticated in Vietnam over 10,000 years ago and reached the Middle East around 3,000 years ago. Males (roosters) have showy, shiny plumage; long tail; red, fleshy crest (comb); and hanging, fleshy flaps under the bill (wattles). Females (hens) have duller colors, shorter comb, and shorter wattles. Chickens feed on seeds, insects, and lizards. **Location** Domesticated. Used for meat and eggs. **Activity** Flies for short distances when disturbed. Scratches the soil in search of seeds and insects. Roosters crow loudly to proclaim their territory.

☐ COMMON CRANE
Grus grus
GRUIDAE FAMILY

☐ SPOTTED CRAKE
Porzana porzana
RALLIDAE FAMILY

L 115cm. Gray plumage; black flight feathers; black head and neck with white eye-streak running down its neck; small, red crown-patch. Feeds on vegetation, insects, small mammals, and small birds. **Habitat** Common winter visitor to the wetlands and flood pools of the *Azraq* and *Basalt Desert*. Passage migrants continue south in autumn and fly north in spring over the valleys of western Jordan and *Aqaba*. **Activity** Slow walker. Leaps with open wings during its display dance. Flies with an outstretched neck, often in flocks that form a V-formation.

L 22cm. Brown upperparts barred black and white; pale-brown, white-spotted underparts; grayish breast and eyebrows; yellow bill with a red base; green legs and long toes. Feeds on insects and small aquatic animals. **Habitat** Breeds in Europe. Winters in Africa and India. Migrates in small numbers through Jordan, south in autumn and north in spring. Occurs near water in regions such as *Azraq* and the *Zarqa River*. **Activity** Secretive and difficult to see in the wild. Walks with its tail raised up.

☐ MOORHEN
Gallinula chloropus
RALLIDAE FAMILY

L 33cm. Dark-gray plumage; dark-brown upperparts; white wing and undertail patches; red bill with a tapered, yellow tip; red forehead shield; yellow legs; long toes. Juveniles lack the red forehead shield. Moorhens feed on leaves and some aquatic animals. **Habitat** Small numbers occur near water sources, including *Azraq*, *Zarqa River*, and reservoirs. Additional small numbers migrate to Jordan in winter. Moorhens nest on the ground among dense vegetation. **Activity** Swims and forges like ducks. Walks, aided by its long toes, on mud and floating vegetation.

☐ **EURASIAN COOT**
Fulica atra
RALLIDAE FAMILY

L 38cm. Black plumage; white bill and forehead shield; red eyes; greenish legs; distinctive lobed toes. Feeds on vegetation, eggs, and small animals. **Habitat** Common winter visitor in rainy years. Scarce in other seasons and in dry years. Occurs in wetlands and flood pools in the *Azraq* region, and in smaller numbers in bodies of water in the *Jordan River Valley*, *Wadi Hidan*, and *Aqaba*. Nests on dead vegetation near the water's edge. **Activity** Dives occasionally. Runs on water on take-off.

☐ **BLACK-WINGED STILT**
Himantopus himantopus
RECURVIROSTRIDAE FAMILY

L 36cm. Black upperparts; white underparts; variable, dark pattern on head and neck; distinctive, long, red legs; long, thin, black bill. Feeds on aquatic insects, mollusks, and crustaceans. **Habitat** Shallow freshwater in *Azraq* and the reservoirs of western Jordan. Migrates through Jordan from spring through autumn. Breeds in Jordan in the summers of rainy years. Builds nests on the ground. **Activity** Noisy. Spends most of its time walking and feeding in shallow water. Defends its nest aggressively and feigns injury to divert predators.

☐ PIED AVOCET
Recurvirostra avosetta
RECURVIROSTRIDAE FAMILY

L 44cm. White plumage; black forehead, crown, and nape; black patches on wings, tail, and back; long, black, upcurved bill; bluish-gray legs. Juveniles have duller black patches. Pied avocets feed on crustaceans and insects. **Habitat** Migrates to Jordan in spring after rainy winters. Breeds in small colonies near water in *Azraq* in summer. Builds nests on the ground. Some migrate through Jordan, flying over the *Jordan Valley* and *Aqaba*. **Activity** Forages by sweeping its long bill side to side in shallow water.

☐ STONE CURLEW
Burhinus oedicnemus
BURHINIDAE FAMILY

L 42cm. Brown-streaked upperparts and breast; white belly; white wing stripe; black flight feathers with two white patches; yellow and black bill; yellow eyes. Feeds on insects, some other invertebrates, and lizards. **Habitat** Scarce summer visitor and breeder. Occurs in dry, open semi-deserts in the *Azraq* and *Dead Sea* regions. Nests on the ground. **Activity** Mostly nocturnal. Often motionless.

☐ **NORTHERN LAPWING**
Vanellus vanellus
CHARADRIIDAE FAMILY

L 30cm. Greenish-black upperparts; white belly; black breast; black crown and long crest; short, black bill; orange legs. Feeds mainly on insects and worms. **Habitat** Breeds in Europe. Winters in the Middle East, central Asia, and northern Africa. Jordan's winter population flocks to agricultural land in the *Jordan Valley* and mud-flats in *Azraq*. Migrates south in autumn and north in spring over *Azraq* and the *Jordan Valley*. **Activity** Feeds mainly at night.

☐ **SPUR-WINGED PLOVER**
Vanellus spinosus
CHARADRIIDAE FAMILY

L 26cm. Brown back; white cheeks, neck, and belly; contrasting black crown, throat, breast, bill, legs, and tail. Feeds on ground insects. **Habitat** Dry ground near wetlands and reservoirs in the *Jordan River Valley*, the *Dead Sea* region, the *Northern Highlands*, and the *Azraq* region. Nests in shallow ground depressions surrounded by stones. **Activity** Mates for life.

☐ LITTLE RINGED PLOVER
Charadrius dubius
CHARADRIIDAE FAMILY

L 15cm. Gray-brown upperparts and cap; white underparts; black bill, eye-mask, and forehead; yellow eye-rings; black collar; pinkish legs and webbed toes. Feeds on insects and worms. **Habitat** Migrates through Jordan from spring through autumn and breeds in Jordan in summer. Occurs in shallow freshwater in *Azraq* and reservoirs and river banks in western Jordan, including the *Zarqa River*. Nests on gravel near water. **Activity** Territorial. Forages in quick runs and stops.

☐ GULLS
LARIDAE FAMILY

L 30-70cm. Also known as "seagulls", a total of 12 species in the Laridae family have been recorded in Jordan. They are generally characterized by white or gray plumage, a relatively long bill, and webbed feet. Gulls feed on fish, crabs, and human scraps. **Habitat** Most gull species that occur in Jordan are passage migrants or accidental. A few are winter visitors. Gulls are most common in *Aqaba*, but may occur inland near water sources such as reservoirs and desert waterholes. **Activity** Lives in social groups. Intelligent and resourceful.

☐ RUFF
Philomachus pugnax
SCOLOPACIDAE FAMILY

L 28cm. Females and winter males have brownish upperparts with white feather margins; lighter underparts; a slightly curved, medium bill; and long legs. Breeding summer males grow showy neck and head feathers with colors and patterns unique to each individual. Ruffs feed on insects and earthworms. **Habitat** Breeds in northern Europe. Winters in southern and western Europe, Africa, and parts of Asia. Migrates south through Jordan in autumn and north in spring. Occurs in *Azraq*, *Kirbat al-Samra* (north of *Zarqa*), and desert pools. Small numbers winter in *Azraq*. **Activity** Very social. Flocks in large groups.

☐ PIN-TAILED SANDGROUSE
Pterocles alchata
PTEROCLIDIDAE FAMILY

L 35cm. Males have yellow-green head and upperparts; white belly; chestnut breast with narrow, black borders; orange face; black throat; blue eye-rings; and black eye-stripes. Females have barred upperparts and yellow breast with three black bars. Pin-tailed sandgrouse feed on seeds. **Habitat** The *Basalt Desert* and the *Azraq* region in northern Jordan. Nests on the ground. **Activity** Nomadic. Lives in flocks. Mostly seen in spring in grassy and cultivated areas and around waterholes in the morning.

☐ SPOTTED SANDGROUSE
Pterocles senegallus
PTEROCLIDIDAE FAMILY

L 32cm. Males are sandy-yellow with light-gray wing bars; gray head and breast; orange throat; black underwing margins. Females are sandy-yellow; dark-spotted upper body and breast; paler orange throat. Spotted sandgrouse feed on seeds. **Habitat** Occurs in declining numbers in arid regions, including *Ruwayshid*, *Azraq*, and *Wadi Araba*. Well-camouflaged in deserts. Nests on the ground. **Activity** Nomadic. Mostly seen in autumn mornings around waterholes.

☐ **ROCK PIGEON**
Columba livia
COLUMBIDAE FAMILY

L 32cm. Also known as "feral pigeon" and "domestic pigeon". The near domestication and breeding of the rock pigeon has produced a wide variety of colors and patterns, including solid white. The rock pigeons that are closest to their wild ancestors have a dark head and neck, a lighter upper back, a white lower back, black bars on their wings, and a black tail tip. Rock pigeons have orange eyes, orange eyelids, and gray eye-rings. The iridescent throat colors are produced by the way light reflects off the feather structure, not by pigments. Pigeons are larger than doves. Pigeons and doves drink water by sucking it, while other birds swallow water by tilting their heads up. Rock pigeons feed on seeds and human scraps. **Habitat** Occurs in urban areas and the highlands. Nests on buildings and cliffs. **Activity** Spends most of its day feeding.

☐ **TURTLE DOVE**
Streptopelia turtur
COLUMBIDAE FAMILY

L 26cm. Brown upperparts; lighter underparts; black and white stripes on the neck; spotted wings; black bill; red eyes, eye-rims, and legs. Doves are smaller than pigeons. Doves and pigeons drink water by sucking it, while other birds swallow water by tilting their heads up. **Habitat** Migrates south through Jordan in autumn and north in spring. Breeds in Jordan in summer in the *Northern Highlands* and in some semi-arid regions such as the *Dana Nature Reserve*. Nests in trees and bushes. **Activity** Timid.

☐ **EURASIAN COLLARED DOVE**
Streptopelia decaocto
COLUMBIDAE FAMILY

L 29cm. Gray-brown plumage; black bill; red legs; dark-red eyes; white eye-rings. Adults have a black half-collar on their neck. Collard doves feed on seeds and some fruit. Doves are smaller than pigeons. Doves and pigeons drink water by sucking it, while other birds swallow water by tilting their heads up. **Habitat** Highlands and valleys of western Jordan and the *Azraq* region. Nests on trees and buildings. **Activity** Mainly solitary. Visits water sources in the evening.

☐ **LAUGHING DOVE**
Streptopelia senegalensis
COLUMBIDAE FAMILY

L 25cm. Also known as "palm dove". Reddish-brown plumage; lighter head and underparts; bluish-gray wing margins; black neck spots; black bill; red legs. Feeds on seeds, grasses, and some ground insects. **Habitat** Grasslands and urban areas in the highlands, the *Jordan Valley*, *Azraq*, and *Wadi Rum*. Nests on trees and buildings. **Activity** Mates for life.

☐ **ROSE-RINGED PARAKEET**
Psittacula krameri
PSITTACIDAE FAMILY

L 40cm. Also known as the "ring-necked parakeet". Green plumage; curved red bill; long tail. Males have a black neck band that terminates under the bill. Rose-ringed parakeets feed on nuts, seeds, fruit, and vegetables. **Habitat** Introduced as a pet from West Africa, currently established in wooded areas and urban gardens in northwestern Jordan, the *Dead Sea* region, *Aqaba*, and *Azraq*. Nests in trees and wall crevices. **Activity** Noisy and capable of mimicking human speech. Roosts and nests in social colonies.

☐ **COMMON CUCKOO**
Cuculus canorus
CUCULIDAE FAMILY

L 33cm. Gray upperparts; white, dark-barred underparts; long tail; pointed wings; yellow eyes. Females have a brown breast, sometimes with brown upperparts. Common cuckoos feed mainly on caterpillars and other insects. **Habitat** Breeds in Europe; winters in Africa; migrates south through Jordan in autumn and north in spring. Migrants fly over western valleys, including *Wadi Zarqa*, *Wadi Dana*, and *Petra*. **Activity** Lays its eggs in the nests of other bird species. The unsuspecting host incubates the eggs and raises the cuckoo's youngs.

Owls

A total of 11 owl species have been recorded in Jordan. Despite their excellent eyesight, owls are unable to see nearby objects clearly and have fixed eyes requiring them to turn their heads to look around. Owls use their eyesight together with their excellent hearing to pinpoint a prey in the dark and then swoop down on it silently in complete surprise. They swallow their prey whole and then regurgitate pellets of indigestible bones and fur.

Owls are at the top of the food chain and are good indicators of an ecosystem's health. The decline of an owl population usually coincides with a habitat's destruction and a reduction of animal populations lower on the food chain.

☐ **EAGLE OWL**
Bubo bubo
STRIGIDAE FAMILY

L 65cm; the world's largest owl. Speckled, brown-black upperparts and throat; lighter underparts with horizontal streaks; brown edges on its facial-disk; brown-black tail-bars; black bill and claws. Easily identifiable by its orange eyes and ear-like feather tufts. Ear tufts are generally upright in males and drooping in females. Eagle owls feed mainly on insects, small mammals, reptiles, birds, and occasionally on larger animals such as foxes. They live up to 60 years. **Habitat** Open, rocky areas in the *Eastern Desert*, including *Azraq* and *Wadi Rum*. Nests in crevices on rocky cliffs. Threatened species. **Activity** Mainly nocturnal. Territorial, solitary, and timid. Avoids people.

☐ **LITTLE OWL**
Athene noctua
STRIGIDAE FAMILY

L 23cm. Brown upperparts with white dots; white underparts with brown streaks; long legs; yellow eyes; white eyebrows. Feeds on insects, rodents, and frogs. **Habitat** Open, rocky, semi-arid areas in all of Jordan, except for the *Central Desert*. Common in the *Dead Sea* region. Nests in tree holes, rock crevices, and burrows. **Activity** Partly nocturnal. Can be seen in daytime perching on trees and buildings.

☐ **EUROPEAN SCOPS-OWL**
Otus scops
STRIGIDAE FAMILY

L 20cm. Streaked, grayish-brown plumage with small, white blotches; paler face; small, ear-like feather tufts. Feeds on insects. **Habitat** Migrates south through Jordan in autumn and north in spring. Small numbers breed in Jordan in summer. Occurs in the highlands, including *Irbid*, *Ajlun*, *Wadi Dana*, and *Petra*. Nests in tree holes, rock crevices, and burrows. **Activity** Nocturnal.

☐ **TAWNY OWL**
Strix aluco
STRIGIDAE FAMILY

L 40cm. Red-brown or gray-brown plumage; streaked upperparts; lightly barred lower wings and tail; vertically streaked, light underparts; round head; black eyes extremely sensitive to light. Feeds on small animals, including rodents, birds, insects, lizards, and bats. **Habitat** Wooded areas in the *Northern Highlands*, including *Ajloun* and the *Dibbin Nature Reserve*. Nests in tree holes and in rock and building crevices. **Activity** Mainly nocturnal. Spends most of its time perching inactively. Defends its nest aggressively.

☐ **BARN OWL**
Tyto alba
TYTONIDAE FAMILY

L 35cm. Brown upperparts with dark and light spots; white underparts; heart-shaped face; black eyes; long legs. Ears are at slightly different levels, enhancing its directional hearing. Females are larger than males. Barn owls feed on small mammals, birds, insects, and lizards. **Habitat** Urban and rural areas in northwestern Jordan, including *Irbid* and *Amman*; and semi-deserts, including the *Azraq* region. Nests in tree holes and building crevices. **Activity** Nocturnal. Solitary or in pairs. Hunts in complete darkness.

☐ EUROPEAN NIGHTJAR
Caprimulgus europaeus
CAPRIMULGIDAE FAMILY

L 26cm. Gray upperparts with brown bars and streaks; lighter, barred underparts; gray crown with dark streaks; brown cheeks and throat; short, black bill. Males have white wing and tail spots. European nightjars prey mainly on moths and other flying insects. **Habitat** Breeds in Europe; winters in Africa; migrates south through Jordan in autumn and north in spring. Occurs mainly in the *Azraq* region and in some valleys of the *Dead Sea* region. Nests on bare ground. **Activity** Forages mainly at sundown. Lies camouflaged on stony grounds during the day.

☐ COMMON SWIFT
Apus apus
APODIDAE FAMILY

L 16cm. Gray or brownish-gray plumage; whitish throat, often difficult to see; forked tail; very short legs. Feeds on insects. **Habitat** Breeds in Europe; winters in Africa; migrates south through Jordan in autumn and north in spring; may breed in Jordan in summer. Occurs around urban areas in the *Jordan Valley* and the *Eastern Desert*. Nests in buildings and cliff crevices. **Activity** Clings to vertical surfaces and never lands on the ground. Catches flying insects in midair and swoops over water to drink.

☐ ALPINE SWIFT
Apus melba
APODIDAE FAMILY

L 21cm. Dark-brown plumage; white belly; white throat; short legs; forked tail. Feeds on insects. **Habitat** Breeds in Europe and Central Asia; winters in Africa; migrates south through Jordan in autumn and north in spring; occasionally breeds in Jordan in summer. Occurs in the highlands and valleys of western Jordan, including *Wadi Hidan*, *Wadi Dana*, and *Amman*. Rare in *Azraq* and *Aqaba*. Nests in cliff crevices. **Activity** Clings to vertical surfaces and never lands on the ground. Catches flying insects in midair and swoops over water to drink.

☐ PIED KINGFISHER
Ceryle rudis
CERYLIDAE FAMILY

L 25cm. Black and white plumage; mostly black upperparts; mostly white underparts; black eye-mask; short crest; large, black bill; black legs. Males have two black breast bands, while females have one. Juveniles have duller bands. Pied kingfishers feed mainly on fish and other aquatic animals. **Habitat** Near water and trees in northwestern Jordan, including the *Jordan River Valley* and *King Talal Dam*. Nests in burrows on river banks. **Activity** Noisy. Occasionally roosts in flocks. Hovers over water and dives to catch prey.

☐ COMMON KINGFISHER
Alcedo atthis
ALCEDINIDAE FAMILY

L 17cm. Bright blue upperparts with a green glow; orange underparts and ear patch; white throat and neck-sides; dark bill with a reddish base; red legs. Feeds on fish, insects, and crustaceans. **Habitat** Migrates south through Jordan in autumn and north in spring. Small numbers winter in Jordan. Some are suspected to breed in Jordan in summer. Passage migrants fly over the *Jordan Valley*, the *Dead Sea*, *Aqaba*, and river valleys such as *Wadi Mujib*. Nests in burrows on river banks. **Activity** Timid. Perches near water at regular locations. Swoops down to catch fish and insects.

☐ WHITE-THROATED KINGFISHER
Halcyon smyrnensis
HALCYONIDAE FAMILY

L 28cm. Blue upperparts; red-brown head, shoulders, and underparts; black wing patch; white throat and breast; large, red bill; red legs. Juveniles are duller than the adults. White-throated kingfishers feed on insects, rodents, reptiles, amphibians, and fish. **Habitat** Near water and trees in northwestern Jordan, including the *Jordan River Valley*, the *Zarqa River*, and *Wadi Mujib*. Nests in burrows on river banks. **Activity** Noisy. Looks out for prey while perching on wires and trees.

☐ LITTLE GREEN BEE-EATER
Merops orientalis
MEROPIDAE FAMILY

L 18cm. The Arabian little green bee-eater has green plumage, a blue face, a black eye-mask, slightly downcurved black bill, and elongated central tail feathers. Juveniles are duller and lack elongated tail feathers. Bee-eaters feed mainly on bees and wasps. **Habitat** Southwestern regions with acacia trees, including *Wadi Araba* and *Aqaba*. Nests in sand burrows. **Activity** Solitary, but occasionally roosts in flocks. Perches near the ground. Catches insects in midair. Removes bee stings by hitting them against hard surfaces.

☐ EUROPEAN BEE-EATER
Merops apiaster
MEROPIDAE FAMILY

L 28cm. Brown and yellow upperparts; blue underparts; yellow throat; black eye-mask and bill. Juveniles have greener upperparts. Bee-eaters feed mainly on bees and wasps. **Habitat** Migrates south through Jordan in autumn and north in spring. Some breed in Jordan in summer. Occurs in the *Azraq* region and western Jordan, including *Amman*, *Wadi Hidan*, and *Aqaba*. Nests in colonies on sandy hillsides and river banks. **Activity** Catches bees and wasps in mid air. Removes bee stings by hitting them against hard surfaces.

☐ **EUROPEAN ROLLER**
Coracias garrulus
CORACIIDAE FAMILY

L 30cm. Blue plumage; brown back; black flight feathers; black bill. Juveniles have duller colors. European Rollers feed on insects, reptiles, and frogs. **Habitat** Migrates south through Jordan in autumn and north in spring. A few breed in Jordan in summer. Occurs in the *Azraq* region and the valleys of northwestern Jordan, including *Wadi al-Seer* and *Ma'in*. Nests in tree holes and rock crevices. **Activity** Perches on high trees and wires. Rolls in display flight, hence its name.

☐ **WRYNECK**
Jynx torquilla
PICIDAE FAMILY

L 16cm. Closely related to woodpeckers. Pointed head and bill; dark eye-mask; gray, black-streaked upperparts; brown, gray-spotted wings; black shoulder spots; yellow, barred throat; lighter underparts. Feeds mainly on ants and tree insects. **Habitat** Migrates south through Jordan in autumn and north in spring. Rare in wooded and scrub areas, including

Amman, Azraq, and *Aqaba*. **Activity** Well camouflaged among vegetation and difficult to detect. Twists its neck and hisses when threatened.

☐ HOOPOE
Upupa epops
UPUPIDAE FAMILY

L 28cm. Pinkish upper body and underparts; contrasting black and white bands on wings and tail; long crest with black tips; long bill. Feeds on ground insects and worms. **Habitat** Grassy areas in the *Azraq* region and the highlands, including *Jerash*, *Amman*, *Madaba*, *Karak*, and *Wadi Dana*. Population increases with spring and summer migrants. Nests in holes in trees and walls. **Activity** Spends most of its time feeding on the ground.

☐ SYRIAN WOODPECKER
Dendrocopos syriacus
PICIDAE FAMILY

L 24cm. Black upperparts, crown, and moustache; white underparts, face, shoulder patch, and wing bars; red undertail; pointed bill for drilling into wood; sticky tongue for extracting insects from crevices. Males have a red nape. Syrian woodpeckers feed mainly on wood-boring insects, some seeds, and fruit. **Habitat** Woodlands and olive orchards in the *Northern Highlands*, including *Irbid*, *Dibbin Nature Reserve*, and *Wadi al-Seer*. Nests in tree holes. **Activity** More likely to be heard tapping on wood than seen.

□ TEMMINCK'S LARK
Eremophila bilopha
ALAUDIDAE FAMILY

L 14cm. Also known as "Temminck's horned lark". Sandy upperparts; white underparts; black eye-mask that extends to bill and cheeks; black breast band. Males have black feather-horns in summer. Temminck's larks feed on seeds and insects. **Habitat** Common in the *Basalt Desert*, *Rweishid Desert*, and *Central Desert*. Nests in shallow ground depressions lined with stones. **Activity** Forages around desert shrubs. Visits water sources to drink.

□ HOOPOE LARK
Alaemon alaudipes
ALAUDIDAE FAMILY

L 22cm. Sandy or gray upperparts; paler underparts; streaked breast; distinctive black and white flight feathers; distinctive long legs; long, slightly down-curved bill; light eyebrows; dark eye-strip and moustache. Feeds on seeds, and on some insects in breeding season. **Habitat** Common in all deserts, including the *Eastern Desert* and *Wadi Araba*. Prefers flat, sandy valleys with

low shrubs. Nests on the ground. **Activity** Solitary or in pairs. Runs and makes sudden stops on the ground. Dives down vertically in display flight.

☐ **CRESTED LARK**
Galerida cristata
ALAUDIDAE FAMILY

L 17cm. Brown, streaked upperparts; white underparts; streaked breast; long crest always erect; long, slightly down-curved bill. Feeds on seeds and insects. **Habitat** Arid or grassy plains in northern Jordan, including the *Jordan River Valley*, the *Dead Sea*, *Amman*, the *Basalt Desert*, and the *Ruwayshid Desert*. Nests on the ground. **Activity** Perches on high spots.

☐ **DESERT LARK**
Ammomanes deserti
ALAUDIDAE FAMILY

L 15cm. Brown, sandy, or gray upperparts; pale underparts; brown tail; pointed bill. Feeds on seeds and insects. **Habitat** Three subspecies with color variations occur in Jordan. Common in the rocky deserts and valleys in all of Jordan, including the *Eastern Desert* and the *Petra* region. Nests on stony grounds and in rock crevices. **Activity** Not as vocal as other larks.

☐ **BAR-TAILED LARK**
Ammomanes cincturus
ALAUDIDAE FAMILY

L 13cm. Sandy upperparts; paler underparts; reddish tail with a black tip; black wing tips; short, yellow bill. Feeds on seeds and insects. **Habitat** Occurs in small numbers in areas with scattered vegetation in the *Basalt Desert*, *Rweishid Desert*, *Wadi Rum*, and *Wadi Araba*. Nests on the ground. **Activity** Runs and makes sudden stops on the ground.

☐ BARN SWALLOW
Hirundo rustica
HIRUNDINIDAE FAMILY

L 16cm. Dark-blue upperparts; chestnut forehead and throat; dark breast band; whitish underparts; long, forked tail; pointed wings. Juveniles have brown forehead and breast band. Barn swallows feed on insects. **Habitat** Resident population occurs around villages and reservoirs in the *Jordan River Valley*. They build cup-shaped mud nests on building ledges. Migrant population breeds in Europe and winters in Africa. They migrate south through Jordan in autumn and north in spring, flying over *Azraq*, the valleys of western Jordan, and *Aqaba*. **Activity** Flies low and makes quick turns. Catches flying insects in midair.

☐ RED-RUMPED SWALLOW
Cecropis daurica
HIRUNDINIDAE FAMILY

L 17cm. Dark-blue upperparts; yellowish underparts; reddish collar and rump. Feeds on insects. **Habitat** Common summer visitor. Migrates south through Jordan in autumn and north in spring. Breeds in the *Northern Highlands* in summer, including *Irbid*, *Ajloun*, and *Salt*. Builds mud nests with a tunnel entrance under cliff, bridge, or building overhangs. **Activity** Collects mud from river banks to build nests.

☐ ROCK MARTIN
Ptyonoprogne fuligula
HIRUNDINIDAE FAMILY

L 12cm. Also known as "pale crag martin" and "African rock martin". Gray upperparts; darker gray wings and tail; white underparts. Feeds on insects. **Habitat** Common in rocky valleys of western and southwestern Jordan, including *Wadi Mujib*, *Wadi Dana*, *Petra*, *Wadi Rum*, and *Aqaba*. Nests on cliffs and buildings. **Activity** Catches flying insects in midair.

☐ **LONG-BILLED PIPIT**
Anthus similis
MOTACILLIDAE FAMILY

L 17cm. Also known as "brown rock pipit". Gray-brown upperparts; darker brown wings and tail; paler underparts; light eyebrows; long, dark, slightly down-curved bill. Feeds on seeds and insects. **Habitat** Stony slopes and valleys with low vegetation in western Jordan, including *Ajloun, Amman, Wadi Mujib, Karak,* and *Petra.* Nests on the ground. **Activity** Fans and twitches its tail up when perching.

☐ **RED-THROATED PIPIT**
Anthus cervinus
MOTACILLIDAE FAMILY

L 15cm. Brown upperparts; pale underparts; broken breast streaks; reddish face, throat, and breast. Feeds on insects and some seeds. **Habitat** Breeds in Europe and northern Asia; winters in Africa; small numbers winter in Jordan. Migrates south through Jordan in autumn and north in spring. Most common in spring in *Azraq,* near water in the *Dead Sea* region, and in *Aqaba.* **Activity** Jerks its tail repeatedly.

☐ **WHITE WAGTAIL**
Motacilla alba
MOTACILLIDAE FAMILY

L 18cm. Also known as "pied wagtail". Slender body; gray upperparts; white underparts and face; black crown, breast, and bill; long tail. Feeds on insects. **Habitat** Breeds in Europe; winters mainly in Africa; some winter in Jordan. Migrates south through Jordan in autumn and north in spring. Occurs in open urban areas and around water in northern Jordan and the *Jordan Valley,* including *Amman,* the *Dead Sea, Azraq, Petra,* and *Aqaba.* **Activity** Wags its tail constantly. Chases after insects on the ground.

☐ **WHITE-SPECTACLED BULBUL**
Pycnonotus xanthopygos
PYCNONOTIDAE FAMILY

L 19cm. Gray-brown upperparts; lighter underparts; darker tail; yellow undertail; black head; white eye-rings, which give it its name. Feeds mainly on fruit. **Habitat** Woodlands, valleys, and urban areas in western Jordan, including *Amman* and the *Dana Nature Reserve.* Nests in trees and bushes. **Activity** Active in large social groups. Charming singer.

☐ **BLUE ROCK-THRUSH**
Monticola solitarius
TURDIDAE FAMILY

L 20cm. Males are blue-gray in summer. Females and juveniles are brown. Both sexes have slightly darker wings and lighter, scaly underparts. Blue rock-thrushes feed on insects, lizards, and fruit. **Habitat** Rocky mountains and valleys in western Jordan, including *Wadi al-Seer, Wadi Dana,* and *Petra.* Nests in rock crevices and buildings. **Activity** Timid and keeps it distance by perching on high rocks.

☐ **EURASIAN BLACKBIRD**
Turdus merula
TURDIDAE FAMILY

L 25cm. Males are all black with yellow bill and eye-rings. Females are brown with brown bill and light-brown eye-rings. Juveniles are a lighter brown than females and have a speckled breast. Eurasian blackbirds feed on insects, seeds, and fruit. **Habitat** Woodlands and urban gardens in northwestern Jordan. Population and range increase with winter visitors. Builds cup-shaped nests in bushes. **Activity** Very territorial in breeding season.

☐ **WINTER WREN**
Troglodytes troglodytes
TROGLODYTIDAE FAMILY

L 10cm. Brown upperparts; paler underparts; barred wings, tail, and flanks; white eyebrows; thin bill. Feeds mainly on insects and spiders. **Habitat** Wooded areas in the *Northern Highlands*, including *Ajloun*, *Dibbin*, and *Wadi al-Seer*. Builds tubular nests with a side-entrance in buildings, trees, and hedges. **Activity** Restless. Disappears in crevices in search of prey. Tail often cocked.

☐ **BLACKCAP**
Sylvia atricapilla
SYLVIIDAE FAMILY

L 14cm. Gray plumage. Males have a distinctive black cap. Females and juveniles have a paler brown cap. Blackcaps feeds on insects and fruit. **Habitat** Breeds in Europe; winters in Africa; migrates south through Jordan in autumn and north in spring. Occurs in valleys and highlands of western Jordan, the *Eastern Desert,* and *Wadi Rum.* Small numbers winter in northwestern Jordan. **Activity** Attracted to urban gardens.

☐ **ORPHEAN WARBLER**
Sylvia hortensis
SYLVIIDAE FAMILY

L 15cm. Grayish-brown upperparts; dark head; white throat and underparts; dark pupil; lacks eye-rings. Adults have yellowish iris. Orphean warblers feed on insects. **Habitat** Breeding summer visitor to the southern rift margins, including *Wadi Dana* and *Petra*. Nests in trees and bushes. **Activity** Usually stays out of sight.

☐ SARDINIAN WARBLER
Sylvia melanocephala
SYLVIIDAE FAMILY

☐ GRACEFUL PRINIA
Prinia gracilis
SYLVIIDAE FAMILY

L 13cm. Males have gray upperparts, paler underparts, a black head, a white throat, red eyes, and red legs. Females have brown upperparts, paler underparts, and a gray head. Sardinian warblers feed on insects and some fruit. **Habitat** Common in open and bushy fields in the highlands, including *Irbid, Amman, Karak*, and *Wadi Dana*. Winters in the valleys of western Jordan and in the *Azraq* region. Nests in low shrubs. **Activity** Stealthy and difficult to observe.

L 10cm. Sandy-gray upperparts; white underparts; finely streaked crown and back; long, tapering tail; fine bill. Breeding males have a black bill. Females have a brown bill. Graceful prinias feed on insects. **Habitat** Common mainly in cultivated and tall-grassy areas in the *Jordan River Valley* and the *Dead Sea* region. Builds domed nests in shrubs and grass. **Activity** Rarely lands on the ground. Difficult to see among vegetation. Tail often cocked.

☐ SCRUB WARBLER
Scotocerca inquieta
SYLVIIDAE FAMILY

L 10cm. Sandy-gray plumage; finely-streaked crown; streaked, white breast; white eyebrows; black eye-streak; long, dark-brown, tapering tail. Feeds on insects and some weeds. **Habitat** Common in arid, stony valleys and slopes of western and southwestern Jordan, including *Wadi Mujib* and *Wadi Rum*. Less common in eastern deserts, including the *Jafr* and *Azraq* regions. Builds domed nests in low scrub. **Activity** Hops on the ground, occasionally disappearing into bushes and crevices. Tail often cocked.

□ **ROBIN**
Erithacus rubecula
MUSCICAPIDAE FAMILY

L 13cm. Brown upperparts; lighter underparts; orange face and breast; black, pointed bill. Juveniles are mottled brown and lack orange coloring on the face and breast. Robins feed on earthworms and insects. **Habitat** Common winter visitor. Occurs in urban gardens, shrublands, and woodlands, mainly in the *Northern Highlands*. Some venture to semi-deserts such as *Azraq*, *Wadi Dana*, and *Petra*. Nests in crevices and below hedges. **Activity** Often hops on the ground. Territorial and aggressive despite its small size.

□ **SPOTTED FLYCATCHER**
Muscicapa striata
MUSCICAPIDAE FAMILY

L 14cm. Brown-gray upperparts; white underparts; streaked forehead and breast; black, pointed bill; black legs. Juveniles are browner with spotted underparts. Spotted flycatchers feed on insects. **Habitat** Small numbers breed in Jordan in summer. Occurs in wooded and urban areas in the *Northern Highlands*, including *Amman*. Nests on buildings and trees. Population and range increase as it migrates south through Jordan in autumn and north in spring. **Activity** Perches and waits for prey. Catches flying insects in midair.

☐ STONECHAT
Saxicola torquata
MUSCICAPIDAE FAMILY

L 12cm. Black back, head, throat, and tail; white underparts with reddish breast; white neck-sides. Females are paler brown. Stonechats feed on insects. **Habitat** Breeds in Europe. Winters in Africa and the Near East, including Jordan. Occurs mainly in the open grassland and scrubland of northwestern Jordan and the *Azraq* region. **Activity** Jerks its tail and wings frequently. Makes calls that sound like stones hit together, which give it its name.

☐ BLUETHROAT
Luscinia svecica
MUSCICAPIDAE FAMILY

L 14cm. Breeding males have gray upperparts, lighter underparts, blue throat, white eyebrows, and red tail-base. The "red-spotted bluethroat" has a red spot in the center of its blue throat, and a black and red necklace below its throat. Non-breeding males, females, and juveniles have a light-gray throat, a back necklace, and a black moustache. Bluethroats feeds on insects. **Habitat**

Uncommon winter visitor. Occurs in small numbers around water in the *Northern Highlands* and in the *Azraq* region. **Activity** Migrant population peaks in November and March.

☐ **COMMON REDSTART**
Phoenicurus phoenicurus
MUSCICAPIDAE FAMILY

L 14cm. Males have gray upperparts, chestnut-orange underparts and tail, white belly, black face and bill, white forehead, and black legs. Females are paler and lack the black face patch. Common redstarts feed on insects. **Habitat** Breeds in Europe; winters in Africa; migrates south through Jordan in autumn and north in spring. Occurs in *Azraq* and western Jordan, including *Amman*. **Activity** Catches flying insects in midair.

☐ **DESERT WHEATEAR**
Oenanthe deserti
MUSCICAPIDAE FAMILY

L 14cm. Sandy-brown crown and back; white eyebrows; black wings and tail. Males have a black face patch that narrowly connects to the black wing patch. Females are duller with a dark eye patch. Desert wheatears feed on insects and seeds. **Habitat** Flat, bushy deserts in all of Jordan, including the *Eastern Desert* and *Wadi Araba*. Nests in burrows. **Activity** Timid. Perches on low branches or on the ground.

☐ **NORTHERN WHEATEAR**
Oenanthe oenanthe
MUSCICAPIDAE FAMILY

L 15cm. Gray upperparts; white underparts; black wings; thin, black eye and ear patch; yellowish-orange throat. Females are browner. Northern wheatears feed mostly on insects and some fruit. **Habitat** Breeds in Europe; winters in Africa; migrates south through Jordan in autumn and north in spring. Occurs in the highlands and some *Eastern Desert* regions such as *Azraq*. **Activity** Restless body movements.

☐ **RED-RUMPED WHEATEAR**
Oenanthe moesta
MUSCICAPIDAE FAMILY

L 17cm. Males have a black face, throat, neck-sides, back, and tail; black wings with some white patches; white underparts and crown; and an orange rump. Females have gray-brown upperparts; an orange crown and cheeks; and white underparts. Red-rumped wheatears feed mainly on ground insects. **Habitat** The *Eastern Desert*, including *Azraq*. Less common in *Shobak*, *Petra*, and *Ma'an*. **Activity** Nests in abandoned rodent burrows.

☐ MOURNING WHEATEAR
Oenanthe lugens
MUSCICAPIDAE FAMILY

L 15cm. Black back, wings, and throat; white crown and underparts; orange undertail; white wing patches visible in flight. Distinguished from the hooded wheatear by its white breast (black does not extend below throat). Females and juveniles are paler. The black morph of the same species has a black crown and belly, an adaptation to its habitat. Mourning wheatears feed on ground insects and seeds. **Habitat** Stony regions in southwestern Jordan, including *Petra*. Nests in rock crevices. The black morph occurs in the *Basalt Desert*. **Activity** Builds a stone platform at the nest's entrance.

☐ FINSCH'S WHEATEAR
Oenanthe finschii
MUSCICAPIDAE FAMILY

L 15cm. Males have a black face patch that connects to a black wing patch (disconnected in the black-eared wheatear); an orangish-white crown and back; white underparts; and a black tail. Females are paler brown. **Habitat** Breeds in southern Europe. Winters in northern Jordan in dry, rocky regions, including the *Eastern Desert*, *Amman*, and *Wadi Mujib*. **Activity** Ground-dweller. Rarely perches on trees.

☐ HOODED WHEATEAR
Oenanthe monacha
MUSCICAPIDAE FAMILY

L 17cm. Black back, wings, throat, and breast; white crown and underparts; mostly white tail. Distinguished from the mourning wheatear by its black breast. Females have brown upperparts, darker brown wings, and an orange rump. Hooded wheatears feed on insects. **Habitat** Arid, rocky regions of western and southwestern Jordan, including *Wadi Mujib*, *Wadi Dana*, *Petra*, *Aqaba*, and *Wadi Rum*. Nests in rock crevices. **Activity** Often catches flying insects in midair.

☐ BLACK-EARED WHEATEAR
Oenanthe hispanica
MUSCICAPIDAE FAMILY

L 15cm. Whitish crown, back, and underparts; black eye and ear patch disconnected from the black wing patch (connected in the Finsch's wheatear). Also occurs in a black-throated form, where the eye and ear patch extends to the throat. Females are browner. Black-eared wheatears feed mainly on insects. **Habitat** Migrates through Jordan from spring through autumn. Breeds in Jordan in summer. Common in the dry, rocky valley slopes in the highlands. Nests in holes. **Activity** Perches on short vegetation and rocks.

☐ WHITE-CROWNED BLACK WHEATEAR
Oenanthe leucopyga
MUSCICAPIDAE FAMILY

L 17cm. Black plumage; white rump; mostly white tail. Unlike other wheatears, the female is similar to the male. Most adults have white crowns. Juveniles and some adults have black crowns (distinguished from the black morph of the mourning wheatear by their white rump and habitat). Black wheatears feed mainly on insects and occasionally on scorpions. **Habitat** Common in arid, rocky areas of western Jordan, including *Wadi Mujib*, *Petra*, and *Wadi Rum*. **Activity** Mimics calls of other birds.

☐ ISABELLINE WHEATEAR
Oenanthe isabellina
MUSCICAPIDAE FAMILY

L 16cm. Gray-brown upperparts with a black tail and wing margins; pale underparts; light eyebrows; black bill and connecting eye-streak. Feeds on insects, mainly ants and beetles. **Habitat** Common passage migrant through Jordan in spring and autumn. Breeds in summer in the *Karak*, *Shobak*, and *Ras al-Naqb* regions. Small numbers winter in northwestern Jordan and the *Eastern Desert*. Nests in burrows. **Activity** Forages on the ground. Runs in short bursts and pauses with an upright posture.

☐ BLACKSTART
Cercomela melanura
MUSCICAPIDAE FAMILY

L 15cm. Gray upperparts; lighter-gray underparts; dark legs; thin, dark bill; black tail; white eye-ring. Males have a darker lore (the area between the eye and bill). Blackstarts feed on insects caught on the ground. **Habitat** Arid, rocky valleys in western Jordan, including the *Zarqa River*, *Wadi al-Seer*, *Wadi Mujib*, *Wadi Hidan*, and *Petra*. Nests in crevices. **Activity** Not timid. Active in the presence of people.

□ **ARABIAN BABBLER**
Turdoides squamiceps
TIMALIIDAE FAMILY

L 27cm. Gray-brown, lightly-streaked plumage; pale spots on breast; gray bill with a black tip; brown legs. Males have yellow eyes. Females have brown eyes. Arabian babblers feed on reptiles, insects, fruit, seeds, and human scraps. **Habitat** Arid areas in the valleys of western and southwestern Jordan, including *Wadi Mujib*, *Dead Sea*, *Wadi Araba*, *Wadi Fidan*, *Petra*, *Aqaba*, and *Wadi Rum*. Favors areas with acacia, tamarix, palm, and other desert trees. Nests in trees. **Activity** Territorial. Lives in wolf-like social groups with an alpha pair. Each group builds a single nest and feeds nestlings cooperatively.

□ **GREAT TIT**
Parus major
PARIDAE FAMILY

L 14cm. Black crown, throat, and collar; white cheeks; green upperparts; bluish wings and tail; white wing-bar; white tail-margins; yellow underparts with a black, central stripe. Males have a broader central stripe. Juveniles have duller colors. Great tits feed on insects and seeds. **Habitat** Woodlands and gardens of northwestern Jordan, the *Dana Nature Reserve*, and *Petra*. Nests in holes on trees and walls. **Activity** Common in urban gardens. Adapted to human presence.

□ **BLUE TIT**
Parus caeruleus
PARIDAE FAMILY

L 11cm. Blue crown, wings, and tail; green shoulders; white face and wing-bar; dark throat, collar, eye-streak, and bill; yellow underparts with a dark, central stripe; gray legs. Feeds on insects, seeds, and fruit. **Habitat** Oak woodlands and urban gardens of northwestern Jordan, including *Ajloun* and *Dibbin*. Nests in tree and wall holes. **Activity** Very active. Moves in small hops on the ground. Hangs upside down in search of insects on trees.

☐ **PALESTINE SUNBIRD**
Cinnyris oseus
NECTARINIIDAE FAMILY

L 11cm. Despite the resemblance, sunbirds are not closely related to hummingbirds. The Palestine sunbird has a long, curved bill. Males are dark with iridescent blue, green, and purple colors. Females are gray with lighter underparts. Palestine sunbirds feed mainly on nectar and occasionally on insects. **Habitat** Rocky valleys in western Jordan with acacia, oleander, and other flowering plants. Occurs in *Wadi al-Seer*, *Dana Nature Reserve*, and *Petra*. Builds nests suspended from branches. **Activity** Hovers over flowers to feed on nectar.

☐ **MASKED SHRIKE**
Lanius nubicus
LANIIDAE FAMILY

L 18cm. Black upperparts, crown, and eye-mask; white face and shoulder patch; white underparts with orangish flanks; black bill with a sharp, curved tip. Females are paler. Masked shrikes feed on small birds, insects, rodents, and lizards. **Habitat** Migrates south through Jordan in autumn and north in spring. Some breed in Jordan in summer. Common in spring in wooded areas and orchards of the *Northern Highlands*, including *Amman*. A few occur farther south in *Petra* and *Wadi Rum*. Builds nests in trees. **Activity** Impales large prey on sharp thorns to tear into them.

☐ GREAT GRAY SHRIKE
Lanius excubitor
LANIIDAE FAMILY

L 24cm. Also known as "northern shrike". Gray upperparts; white underparts; black eye-mask; black bill with a sharp, curved tip; dark legs; black wings with white patches; black tail. Feeds on insects, reptiles, rodents, and birds. **Habitat** Semi-arid regions, including the valleys of western Jordan and *Azraq.* **Activity** Solitary. Perches on the highest tree branches. Catches its prey in swooping attacks. Impales large prey on sharp thorns to tear into them.

☐ WOODCHAT SHRIKE
Lanius senator
LANIIDAE FAMILY

L 18cm. Chestnut crown and nape; black upperparts with a white shoulder patch; white underparts; black bill with a sharp, curved tip. Females are paler. Woodchat shrikes feed on insects, reptiles, rodents, and birds. **Habitat** Common summer visitor to Jordan. Occurs from spring to autumn in the highlands, including *Irbid, Ajloun, Amman,* and *Shobak.* Nests in trees. **Activity** Perches on the highest tree branches. Catches its prey in swooping attacks. Impales large prey on sharp thorns to tear into them.

☐ RED-BACKED SHRIKE
Lanius collurio
LANIIDAE FAMILY

L 18cm. Males have a distinctive chestnut back; gray crown; black eye-mask; black bill with a sharp, curved tip; reddish-white throat and belly; black tail. Females and juveniles are paler and streaked with small crescents. Red-backed shrikes feed on insects, small birds, and lizards. **Habitat** Breeds in Europe and western Asia; winters in Africa; migrates south through Jordan in autumn and north in spring. Occurs in bushy areas in the *Azraq* region and western Jordan. **Activity** Impales large prey on sharp thorns to tear into them.

☐ EURASIAN JAY
Garrulus glandarius
CORVIDAE FAMILY

L 33cm. Pink-brown upperparts; lighter underparts; black moustache, crown, lower back, and tail; blue and white wing patches. Feeds on insects, rodents, reptiles, small birds, fruit, and seeds (especially acorns). **Habitat** Woodlands and urban areas in northwestern Jordan, including *Amman* and *Jerash*. Nests in pine and oak trees. **Activity** Timid. Collects and buries acorns for winter. Attacks owls violently in the daytime to avoid falling prey to them at night. Mimics other bird calls, even while attacking them.

☐ JACKDAW
Corvus monedula
CORVIDAE FAMILY

L 33cm. Black plumage with gray nape; distinctive pale eyes. Feeds on insects, seeds, and human scraps. **Habitat** Winter visitor in declining numbers. Rare summer breeder. Occurs in the *Jordan River Valley, Ajloun,* and *Azraq*. Nests in cliff crevices. **Activity** Lives in flocks. Fast flyer compared to other crows.

☐ HOUSE CROW
Corvus splendens
CORVIDAE FAMILY

L 40cm. Glossy black plumage; dark-gray neck and breast; black bill and legs. Feeds on insects, lizards, fruit, eggs, and human scraps. **Habitat** Native to central Asia. Introduced and established in *Aqaba*. Nests on trees and buildings. **Activity** Flocks to palm trees on *Aqaba's* beachfront.

☐ **CARRION CROW**
Corvus corone
CORVIDAE FAMILY

L 47cm. Black plumage with a green or purple sheen; black bill and legs. Looks like its cousin the raven, but is smaller. Feeds on small animals, eggs, human scraps, and carcasses. **Habitat** Woodlands and urban areas of northwestern Jordan, including *Amman* and *Jerash.* Nests on tall trees, buildings, and cliffs. **Activity** Perches on high spots. Lands to scavenge available food.

☐ **BROWN-NECKED RAVEN**
Corvus ruficollis
CORVIDAE FAMILY

L 50cm. Black plumage, bill, and legs. Adults have a dark-brown nape, which may be difficult to see. Feeds on insects, reptiles, fruit, grains, human scraps, and carcasses. **Habitat** Arid regions in all of Jordan. Common in the *Dead Sea* and *Aqaba* regions and along the *Desert Highway.* Winters in *Wadi Rum.* Nests on cliffs and electricity towers. **Activity** Fearless.

☐ **FAN-TAILED RAVEN**
Corvus rhipidurus
CORVIDAE FAMILY

L 47cm. Black plumage; gray flight feathers; gray feet; short tail fanned in flight, which gives it its name. Feeds on insects, fruit, grains, human scraps, and carcasses. **Habitat** Valleys and slopes of western and southwestern Jordan. Common in the *Dead Sea*, *Petra*, and *Aqaba.* Nests in cliff crevices and on ledges. **Activity** Often soars in the sky with other ravens.

☐ **HOODED CROW**
Corvus cornix
CORVIDAE FAMILY

L 50cm. Gray body with black head, breast, wings, tail, bill, and legs. Males are larger than females. Juveniles are darker than adults. Hooded crows feed on carcasses, human scraps, and eggs stolen from other birds. **Habitat** Woodlands and urban areas in northwestern Jordan, including *Amman* and *Jerash.* Nests on tall trees and cliffs. **Activity** Perches on high spots. Scavenges available food.

☐ TRISTRAM'S STARLING
Onychognathus tristramii
STURNIDAE FAMILY

☐ CORN BUNTING
Miliaria calandra
EMBERIZIDAE FAMILY

L 25cm. Males are glossy black. Females are dark brown. Both sexes have a contrasting yellow-orange wing patch. Tristram's starlings feed mainly on fruit and occasionally on insects groomed off Nubian ibexes. **Habitat** Rocky valleys and urban areas of western and southwestern Jordan, including the *Dead Sea* region and the *Dana Nature Reserve*. Nests on rocky cliffs. **Activity** Common in flocks.

L 18cm. Streaked, gray-brown upperparts; streaked, paler underparts; irregular dark spot on breast; light moustache. Males are larger than females. Buntings feed on seeds, and feed their young insects. **Habitat** Winter visitor; rarely breeds in Jordan in summer. Occurs in northwestern fields and desert margins, including the *Zarqa River*, *Amman*, and *Azraq*. **Activity** Often perches on wires.

☐ HOUSE BUNTING
Emberiza striolata
EMBERIZIDAE FAMILY

☐ CRETZSCHMAR'S BUNTING
Emberiza caesia
EMBERIZIDAE FAMILY

L 14cm. Streaked, chestnut upperparts; paler orange underparts; light-gray head with dark streaks; dark upper bill and orange lower bill. Females are paler. Buntings feed on seeds, and feed their young insects. **Habitat** Rugged valleys and cliffs in western and southwestern Jordan, including *Wadi Mujib* and *Petra*. Nests on cliffs and building crevices. **Activity** Timid and difficult to observe. Best seen around waterholes.

L 16cm. Gray head and breast; reddish-brown moustache, throat, and underparts; streaked, black and brown upperparts; thick bill. Females are paler with streaked underparts. Buntings feed on seeds, and feed their young insects. **Habitat** Breeds in Europe; winters in Africa; migrates through Jordan in autumn and spring; small numbers breed in Jordan in summer. Occurs on rocky slopes, mainly in the northwest. Nests on the ground. **Activity** Perches on low rocks and vegetation.

☐ SINAI ROSEFINCH
Carpodacus synoicus
FRINGILLIDAE FAMILY

L 15cm. Jordan's national bird. Males have a pink head, pink underparts, and a brown back and tail. Females and juveniles are light brown, with darker brown back and tail. Both sexes have lightly streaked underparts and a thick, gray bill. Sinai rosefinches feed on seeds. **Habitat** Red sandstone cliffs in southwestern Jordan, including *Petra* and the *Dana Nature Reserve*. Nests in rock crevices. **Activity** Timid. Common in flocks.

☐ GREENFINCH
Carduelis chloris
FRINGILLIDAE FAMILY

L 14cm. Olive-green plumage; gray wings and tail with bright-yellow patches; thick, pale bill. Females are duller green. Greenfinches feed on seeds, and feed their young insects. **Habitat** Common in urban gardens and wooded areas of the *Northern Highlands* and the *Dead Sea* region. Winters in *Wadi Dana*, *Petra*, and the *Eastern Desert*. Nests in evergreen trees and shrubs. **Activity** Lives in flocks outside of breeding season.

☐ **EUROPEAN GOLDFINCH**
Carduelis carduelis
FRINGILLIDAE FAMILY

L 12cm. Red face; white cheeks; black crown; brown upperparts; white underparts with light-brown patches; black and yellow wings; ivory bill. Feeds on seeds and some insects.

Habitat Common in woodlands and gardens in the highlands, including *Irbid*, *Amman*, and *Petra*. Nests in trees. **Activity** Lives in flocks outside of breeding season.

☐ **TRUMPETER FINCH**
Bucanetes githaginea
FRINGILLIDAE FAMILY

L 14cm. Females have light-brown upperparts; darker brown wings and tail; pale underparts; and a short, thick, yellow bill. Males look similar, except in breeding season. Breeding males have a red bill; a gray head; and pinkish forehead, wings, underparts, and rump. Trumpeter finches feed on seeds and some insects. **Habitat** Common in stony areas in the *Eastern Desert*, including the *Basalt Desert*, the *Central Desert*, and *Wadi*

Rum. Less common in the valleys of western Jordan. Nests in rock crevices. **Activity** Spends most of its time running and foraging on the ground. Makes distinctive nasal sounds similar to a toy trumpet, which give it its name.

☐ **LINNET**
Carduelis cannabina
FRINGILLIDAE FAMILY

L 13cm. Gray head; brown upperparts; light underparts; black wing margins and tail; gray bill. Males have red crown and breast. Linnets feed on seeds. **Habitat** Grass and shrub fields of northwestern Jordan and some areas in southwestern Jordan such as the *Dana Nature Reserve*. Population and range increase when winter visitors arrive from the north. **Activity** Often mixes with other bird species.

☐ **SPANISH SPARROW**
Passer hispaniolensis
PASSERIDAE FAMILY

L 15cm. Distinguished from the house sparrow by a chestnut crown and black-streaked underparts. Interbreeds with the house sparrow, producing hybrids with shared characteristics. Feeds mainly on seeds. **Habitat** Near water in the valleys of western Jordan, including *Wadi al-Seer*. Population increases with winter visitors and range expands to include southwestern Jordan and the *Azraq* region. Builds domed nests or reuses nests abandoned by other birds. **Activity** Lives in large flocks.

☐ **HOUSE SPARROW**
Passer domesticus
PASSERIDAE FAMILY

L 15cm. Males have chestnut-brown upperparts; white underparts; a gray crown; white cheeks; and a black eye-mask, bill, throat, and breast. Females lack the black patches and gray crown. House sparrows feed mainly on seeds and occasionally on insects. **Habitat** Urban areas in all of Jordan, except for extreme deserts. Nests mainly in building crevices. **Activity** Adapted to human presence.

☐ **ROCK SPARROW**
Petronia petronia
PASSERIDAE FAMILY

L 14cm. Brown, barred upperparts; white, brown-streaked underparts; gray crown with black streaks; white eyebrows; faint yellow breast spot. Feeds on seeds and some insects. **Habitat** Common in arid, rocky valleys and cultivated slopes of western Jordan, including *Petra* and the *Zarqa River*. Nests in rock and wall crevices. **Activity** Forages on stony grounds.

Mammals
MAMMALIA CLASS

Mammals are warm-blooded vertebrates that include humans, canines, felines, rodents, bats, and others. They are characterized mainly by the hair or fur on their bodies and by milk-producing glands to nourish their young.

Hoofed Mammals

Hooves are enlarged toes and nails. Horses and donkeys are *odd-toed ungulates*; they walk on an enlarged middle toe adapted for running. Gazelles, camels, goats, sheep, and boars are *even-toed ungulates*; they have split-hooves and walk on their third and forth toes, adapted for movement on rough terrain. The remaining toes are vestigial.

Hoofed animals emerged around 55 million years ago (10 million years after the dinosaurs died out). The ancestors of horses were once very numerous and successful, but the spread of grasses around 20 million years ago favored even-toed ungulates with multi-chambered stomachs, better-suited to digest low-nutritional food. This is reflected in the greater diversity of even-toed ungulates in Jordan today.

☐ **ARABIAN HORSE**
Equus caballus
EQUIDAE FAMILY

L 230cm; H 155cm. The Arabian horse is one of the oldest horse breeds with recorded bloodlines and guarded purity. Domesticated around 5,000 years ago, then honed by Bedouins, the desert, and human warfare. Prized for its beauty, gentle character, intelligence, courage, strength, speed, and endurance. Played important roles throughout Arab history, in Bedouins' daily lives, and in equestrian competitions. The Arabian horse has a compact body, arched neck, broad chest, broad forehead, large eyes, small concave muzzle, and large nostrils. All the other light horse breeds descend from the Arabian horse. Colors include gray, chestnut, and occasionally black. White Arabians turn white as they age (like humans). Arabians are never spotted. The skin under their coat is always black. **Habitat** Domesticated. **Activity** Very energetic. Requires running space.

☐ PERSIAN ONAGER
Equus Onager
EQUIDAE FAMILY

L 200cm; H 120cm. Fast runner, larger than a donkey, and more horse-like. Reddish body; white belly; black, upright mane; black stripe down the back; black tail tip. Feeds on grasses, foliage, and bushes. **Habitat** Dry, grassy plains and marginal deserts in southeastern Jordan.

Once extinct in Jordan, currently bred in captivity in the *Shomari Reserve* for reintroduction into the wild. **Activity** Grazes mainly in the cooler hours of the day. Timid; avoids people and other animals. Communicates over long distances with loud, raspy brays.

☐ DONKEY
Equus asinus
EQUIDAE FAMILY

L 160cm; H 100cm. Slow, agile, patient, and has great endurance. Donkeys are closely related to horses and can mate with them: a male donkey and a female horse produce a mule; a male horse and a female donkey produce a hinny. Donkeys are smaller than horses and have longer ears, upright manes, and coarse tails. **Habitat** Native to marginal deserts. Domesticated around 5,000 years ago to carry and pull loads. **Activity** Conserves energy

when possible. Despite their limited behaviors, donkeys are very intelligent, friendly, curious, and playful when put at ease. Donkeys' misunderstood stubbornness comes from a heightened survival instinct: they freeze instead of performing an unsafe task.

☐ **DROMEDARIAN CAMEL**
Camelus dromedarius
CAMELIDAE FAMILY

L 3m; H 2m. Superbly adapted to the desert: stores fat in its hump and water in its bloodstream; tolerates high temperatures, eliminating panting and minimizing perspiration; has flat feet with broad pads for walking on sand. To protect against dust, the camel has two rows of eyelashes, small hairy ears, and nostrils that can shut tightly. Camels feed on almost any available vegetation, including thorny bushes. **Habitat** Domesticated around 3,000 years ago. Used by Bedouins for transportation and as a source of milk, meat, skin, and fiber. **Activity** Swallows food quickly, then regurgitates and chews the undigested parts. The legs on each side of their body move together, producing a wobbly walk. During mating, males gurgle, foam from the mouth, and show off an inflated throat bladder (*dulla*), commonly mistaken for the tongue.

☐ ARABIAN ORYX
Oryx leucoryx
BOVIDAE FAMILY

L 160cm; H 100cm. White with brown patches on its head, tail, and legs. Both sexes have long, slightly curved, ringed horns. The two horns appear as one from the side, which might have inspired the unicorn myth. Females have slightly thinner and longer horns. Males have a slightly larger neck and a clump of hair on its throat. Calves are light brown. The Arabian oryx is well adapted to the desert: it detects rainfall from a distance, it gets most of its water from the vegetation it feeds on, and its white coat reflects sunlight. **Habitat** Once extinct in Jordan, they are being reintroduced into *Wadi Rum Protected Area* and bred in captivity in the *Shomari Reserve*. **Activity** Moves in the cooler hours of the day. Digs shallow pits and rests in the cool sand around midday. A female leads the herd for long distances in search of vegetation, while the dominant male brings up the rear.

☐ ROE DEER
Capreolus capreolus
CERVIDAE FAMILY

L 130cm; H 70cm. Reddish upperparts (dark in winter); light underparts; gray face. Juveniles have white spots. Males have antlers in the mating season (young males have short antlers, while older males have branched antlers). Roe deer feed on vegetation. **Habitat** Once extinct in Jordan, it has been reintroduced into

the *Ajloun Woodland Reserve*. **Activity** Active in cool hours. Solitary, except in the mating season. Fast runner.

☐ GAZELLE
Gazella Genus
BOVIDAE FAMILY

L 100cm; H 70cm. A total of three gazelle species occur in Jordan. They are generally characterized by a slender body with long hind legs; a reddish-brown coat; a white belly; dark flank stripes; a black, short tail; white stripes connecting the eyes to the nostrils; and backward-bending horns. Gazelles feed on vegetation. **Habitat** The mountain gazelle (*Gazella gazella*) occurs in the mountains and foothills of southwestern Jordan, including the *Dana Nature Reserve*. The dorcas gazelle (*Gazella dorcas*) occurs in the desert plains and dry canyons of southwestern Jordan, including *Wadi Araba*. Once extinct in Jordan, the goitered gazelle (*Gazella subgutturosa*) is currently bred in captivity in the *Shomari Reserve* for reintroduction into the wild. All gazelles are endangered and protected in Jordan. **Activity** Fast runner. Moves in small herds in cooler hours. Rests in the shade around midday. Uses sight and hearing to detect predators and smell to find food. Highly territorial: males mark their territory with dung and scent-gland secretions.

☐ CATTLE
Bos taurus
BOVIDAE FAMILY

L 250cm; H 150cm. Domesticated around 8,000 years ago in Egypt and Greece. Today's dairy cows are mostly European breeds, which are smaller descendants of the earlier cattle that once roamed wild in the Middle East. **Habitat** Domesticated. Used for milk, meat, skin, and for pulling heavy loads. **Activity** Slow. Spends most of its time eating. Regurgitates and re-chews undigested food.

☐ **NUBIAN IBEX**
Capra ibex nubiana
BOVIDAE FAMILY

L 120cm; H 60cm. Sandy-brown coat; white belly; curved horns. Males have a brown stripe down their back, and larger horns with outer knobs. Nubian ibexes feed on grasses and leaves. **Habitat** Rocky, dry mountains in southwestern Jordan, including the *Mujib Nature Reserve*, the *Dana Nature Reserve*, and *Wadi Rum*. Endangered species. **Activity** Spends much of its day moving up and down steep cliffs. Moves to higher elevations in summer to avoid the heat and to lower ground in winter and spring for shelter and new grass. Fights to establish hierarchy. Males live in separate herds from females and juveniles, except during the mating season in autumn.

☐ **DOMESTIC SHEEP**
Ovis aries
BOVIDAE FAMILY

L 120cm; H 70cm. Domesticated around 10,000 years ago in the Middle East (one of the earliest domesticated animals). Males are larger than females and have larger and curvier horns. Sheep store fat in their tail. **Habitat** Domesticated. Used for milk, meat, skin, and fiber. Raised mainly in cooler highlands, but can adapt to deserts. **Activity** Very timid and has a flocking instinct that keeps it close to the herd. Gets easily stressed when separated. Huddles with the herd and keeps its head in the shade to protect against the sun.

☐ DOMESTIC GOAT
Capra aegagrus hircus
BOVIDAE FAMILY

L 120cm; H 80cm. Domesticated around 10,000 years ago in the Middle East (one of the earliest domesticated animals). Males have a pungent odor used to attract females and as a substitute for territory marking. Contrary to popular belief, goats do not eat everything. They limit their diet to vegetation, products made with vegetation such as paper, and can eat weeds toxic to other animals. **Habitat** Domesticated. Used for milk, meat, skin, and fiber. Adapts well to any environment, including dry deserts. **Activity** Nimble and curious. Explores and climbs rocks and trees to reach plants that other animals cannot.

☐ WILD BOAR
Sus scrofa
SUIDAE FAMILY

L 150cm; H 80cm. Thick, bristly coat. Colors include brown, gray, and black. Short, straight tail. Males have sharp upper and lower tusks. Females are smaller and lack tusks. Piglets are striped for camouflage. Wild boars feed on almost anything from vegetables, fruit, and nuts to small animals and young lambs. **Habitat** Along the Jordan and Yarmouk rivers, in the *Ajloun Woodland Reserve*, and the

Mujib Nature Reserve. **Activity** Mainly nocturnal. Rests in dens during the day. Aggressive when provoked and when it defends its offspring. Male lives alone, except during the mating season.

Carnivores

Carnivores are meat-eating animals. Most carnivores supplement their diet with insects and fruit, but unlike hoofed mammals, carnivores have simple digestive systems incapable of digesting low-nutrition grass. Felines occasionally eat grass to induce vomiting and cleanse their stomachs of hair-balls or bad food. Some domestic dogs occasionally eat grass, probably for the taste.

Carnivores are at the top of the food chain. They are fast, agile, and adapted for hunting animals lower on the food chain. Because they burn large amounts of calories, carnivores consume many smaller animals and keep the population of herbivores under control, promoting greener and healthier ecosystems.

☐ **GOLDEN JACKAL**
Canis aureus
CANIDAE FAMILY

L 80cm; H 40cm. Also known as "Asiatic jackal" and "common jackal". Coarse, reddish-brown coat; dark back; lighter underparts; white pattern on the throat; black tail-tip. Females are smaller than males. Golden jackals feed on small mammals, birds, insects, and fruit; and scavenge when possible.

Habitat Open deserts and around urban areas, including *Wadi Rum*, *Azraq*, and the *Dana Nature Reserve*. Endangered species. **Activity** Mainly nocturnal; strictly nocturnal in areas inhabited by humans. Mates for life. Hunts and defends its territory in collaboration with its mate. Communicates by howling.

□ **GRAY WOLF**
Canis lupus
CANIDAE FAMILY

L 130cm; H 75cm. Dense, yellowish coat; lighter underparts; distinguished from other canines by their larger body and muzzle. Successful packs hunt large animals. Smaller packs or individuals hunt smaller animals such as rodents. **Habitat** Mountains and marginal deserts in western and northern Jordan, including *Ajloun*, *Azraq*, *Wadi Dana*, and *Ma'an*. Endangered species. **Activity** Mainly nocturnal. Avoids humans. Packs follow strict social hierarchies led by an alpha male and female. They hunt cooperatively and communicate a large variety of moods with body language, low vocalizations, and loud howls heard over long distances. Highly territorial; claims large territories with scent markings.

□ **SALUKI**
Canis lupus familiaris
CANIDAE FAMILY

L 65cm; H 65cm. Also known as "Arabian hound". Domestic dog, closely related to the gray wolf. Dogs were the first animals to be domesticated around 12,000 years ago. The saluki is one of the oldest dog breeds, started over 10,000 years ago in the Middle East. It is highly valued by Bedouins for its speed, eyesight, grace, and pride. It is allowed inside tents and traded mostly as gifts. Used for hunting, it can spot a moving prey from long distances and chase it at up to 55 km/h. Bred in different colors to blend with different desert surroundings. **Habitat** Domesticated. **Activity** Very active. Requires open space. Often hunts and brings the catch to its master on its own.

□ **CANAAN DOG**
Canis lupus familiaris
CANIDAE FAMILY

L 55cm; H 55cm. Domestic dog, closely related to the gray wolf. Dogs were the first animals to be domesticated around 12,000 years ago. The Canaan dog has been used by Bedouins for thousands of years, but has not been selectively bred. It is highly intelligent, highly territorial, and difficult to transfer to a new owner. It is commonly used as a guard and herd dog. The Canaan dog has bushy tail that curls over its back. Colors include white, black, and brown, with or without patches. Bedouins believe that cropping its ears and docking its tail make it more alert. **Habitat** Domesticated. **Activity** Conserves energy when possible, but is always alert and vigilant.

☐ FENNEC FOX
Fennecus zerda
CANIDAE FAMILY

L 40cm; H 20cm. The fennec fox has the smallest body and the largest ears of all the canines. It is well adapted to the desert: the large ears dissipate heat, which minimizes panting and conserves water; the yellowish coat blends with sand and reflects sunlight; the paws are covered with hair to protect against the hot sand; and it gets most of its water from food. Feeds on insects, lizards, rodents, birds, eggs, and fruit. **Habitat** Southwestern Jordan, including the sandy desert of *Wadi Rum* and the *Dana Nature Reserve*. Rare and vulnerable species. **Activity** Nocturnal. Avoids humans. Fast digger; builds large dens with large entrances in the sand.

☐ SAND FOX
Vulpes rueppelli
CANIDAE FAMILY

L 45cm; H 25cm. Yellow-brown upperparts with a dark back; lighter underparts; long bushy tail with a white tip; pointed muzzle with a black pattern connecting the eye with the upper lip; large ears that dissipate heat, which minimizes panting and conserves water; hairy pads that protect it from hot sand. Feeds on insects, small mammals, reptiles, fruit, and human refuse. **Habitat** Semi-arid regions in the *Eastern Desert* and around *Aqaba*. Endangered species. **Activity** Lives in small groups or pairs; territorial; nocturnal.

□ **RED FOX**
Vulpes vulpes
CANIDAE FAMILY

L 75cm; H 37cm. Reddish-brown upperparts; white underparts; long, bushy tail with a white tip; black ear tips and legs; yellow eyes with vertical pupils; pointed muzzle with a black pattern. Feeds on small mammals, lizards, insects, fruit, birds, eggs, and human refuse. **Habitat** Common in all habitats, including the *Jordan Valley*, *Irbid*, *Amman*, *Karak*, and the *Eastern Desert*. **Activity** Mainly nocturnal; solitary; territorial. Fast and agile runner, aided by strong legs and a long tail used for balance.

□ **STRIPED HYENA**
Hyaena hyaena
HYAENIDAE FAMILY

L 135cm; H 75cm. Gray-brown coat with black stripes; black muzzle and ears; forelegs longer than hind legs; strong jaws capable of crushing bones, used to consume parts of carcasses uneaten by other animals. Unlike the spotted hyena of Africa, the striped hyena is mainly a scavenger, not equipped to kill large prey. It feeds on carcasses or hunts small animals such as insects, lizards, and rodents and supplements its diet with fruit. Hyenas are unnecessarily killed by humans for superstitious reasons and because of their fearsome appearance. **Habitat** Dry areas near water sources, including *Azraq*, the *Dana Nature Reserve*, the *Mujib Nature Reserve*, and parts of central Jordan. Endangered species. **Activity** Nocturnal and nomadic. Lives in small family groups, but hunts alone. Exhibits intelligent social behaviors.

☐ **CHEETAH**
Acinonyx jubatus
FELIDAE FAMILY

L 125cm; H 90cm. Slender body; yellow coat with round, black spots; black lines that run from the eyes down to the mouth. The cheetah is the fastest land animal, reaching up to 100 km/h. Feeds mainly on mammals such as gazelles and hares. **Habitat** The *Ma'in* region. Rare or extinct in Jordan. Last seen and shot in 1962. **Activity** Unlike other felines, cheetahs hunt by chasing after their prey, not by ambush.

☐ **LEOPARD**
Panthera pardus
FELIDAE FAMILY

L 175cm; H 90cm. Yellow coat with black rosettes and lighter underparts. Leopards are distinguishable from cheetahs by their muscular body, larger heads, and black rosettes instead of round spots. Leopards feed mainly on mammals such as gazelles, goats, and jackals. **Habitat** Rare or extinct in Jordan. Last seen in the rift margins in 1987. **Activity** Nocturnal and stealthy.

☐ **SAND CAT**
Felis margarita
FELIDAE FAMILY

L 50cm; H 27cm. Sandy-yellow, lightly-barred upperparts; white underparts; wide head; large, pointed ears; black tail-tip; hairy pads that protect against the hot sand. Gets most of its water from food. Feeds on rodents, insects, birds, and lizards. **Habitat** *Wadi Rum* desert. Endangered species. **Activity** Nocturnal. Uses its acute hearing to locate and dig rodents out of their burrows.

☐ **WILD CAT**
Felis silvestris
FELIDAE FAMILY

L 65cm; H 35cm. The wild cat is the ancestor of the domestic cat (*Felis silvestris catus*). Brown, lightly-barred coat; short ears. Feeds on small mammals, lizards, and birds. **Habitat** Semi-deserts of the *Azraq* and the *Dana Nature Reserve*. Vulnerable species. **Activity** Solitary; territorial; mainly nocturnal. Timid; avoids humans.

☐ CARACAL
Caracal caracal
FELIDAE FAMILY

L 80cm; H 45cm. Also known as "Persian lynx" and "African lynx". Small and fast cat with distinct, long, black ears that contribute to its excellent hearing. Long legs built for jumping and climbing. Colors include light-brown and red. Feeds on rodents and other small mammals, birds, and reptiles. **Habitat** Rocky areas in the *Southern Highlands*, including the *Mujib Nature Reserve* and the *Dana Nature Reserve*. Endangered species. **Activity** Solitary. Mainly nocturnal. Hides in crevices during the day. Difficult to encounter in the wild.

☐ JUNGLE CAT
Felis chaus
FELIDAE FAMILY

L 70cm; H 38cm. Also known as "swamp lynx". Sandy, gray coat; black ear-tips; black tail-tip and several black tail rings; faint, brown markings on face and long legs. Resembles the caracal, but they are not closely related. Juveniles have vertically striped upperparts. Jungle cats feed on rodents, hares, birds, reptiles, amphibians, and fish. **Habitat** The *Jordan River Valley*. Endangered species. **Activity** Mainly solitary. Hunts mostly in daytime by stalking and leaping on prey. Rests in dens abandoned by other animals.

☐ EUROPEAN OTTER
Lutra lutra
MUSTELIDAE FAMILY

L 80cm; H 30cm. Slender body; brown upperparts; white underparts; short legs; webbed feet adapted for swimming; small ears; black nostrils that close underwater; long whiskers; muscular, pointed tail. Males are larger than females. Otters feed mainly on fish, some insects, birds, amphibians, and other small animals. **Habitat** The Jordan and Yarmouk rivers. Builds dens on riverbanks accessible from underwater. Vulnerable species. **Activity** Territorial. Mostly solitary and nocturnal. Skillful swimmer and diver.

☐ BEECH MARTEN
Martes foina syriaca
MUSTELIDAE FAMILY

L 45cm; H 15cm. Also known as "stone marten". Slender body; brown coat with a white, forked chest-pattern; long, bushy tail; short ears and legs. Feeds on small mammals, eggs, worms, and fruit. **Habitat** Pine and oak woodlands in the *Northern Highlands*, including *Jerash*, *Ajloun*, and *Wadi al-Seer*. Rare and vulnerable species. **Activity** Mainly crepuscular. Territorial. Known for attacking chicken coops around urban areas and for damaging car engines by chewing on wires and hoses.

☐ EURASIAN BADGER
Meles meles
MUSTELIDAE FAMILY

L 70cm; H 30cm. Gray upperparts; black underparts; white head with contrasting black stripes running from the nose to the eyes and ears; white ear-tips; short tail; powerful fore claws used to dig out food. Females are smaller than males. Badgers feed mainly on earthworms, some insects, lizards, eggs, frogs, and small mammals. Supplements its diet with fruit and other plants. **Habitat** The *Mujib Nature Reserve* and northern *Jordan Valley*, including *Irbid*, *Suwaylih*, and the *Ajloun Woodland Reserve*. Vulnerable species. **Activity** Forages at night in open fields. Shares

elaborate tunnels with other clan members during the day. Territorial; marks its territory with a scent.

Insectivores

Insectivores are carnivores that feed mainly on insects. They include a few mammals, birds, fish, amphibians, insects, and even some plants.

☐ **HEDGEHOG**
ERINACEIDAE FAMILY

L 25cm; H 15cm. Three hedgehog species have been recorded in Jordan. They are generally characterized by a round body covered with harmless, hard, brown quills; a long snout; and lighter underparts. Hedgehogs have an acute sense of hearing and smell used to locate prey. They feed on insects, small rodents, and bird eggs. **Habitat** The Eastern European hedgehog (*Erinaceus concolor*) occurs in the woodlands of the *Northern Highlands*, including *Amman*. The long-eared hedgehog (*Hemiechinus auritus*) occurs in arid regions in western and northern Jordan, including *Wadi Dana*. The Ethiopian hedgehog (*Paraechinus aethiopicus*) occurs in arid regions in western and southern Jordan, including *Wadi Araba*. **Activity** Nocturnal. Hibernates in winter. Rolls into a ball when threatened.

☐ **SHREW**
SORICIDAE FAMILY

L 6cm; H 2cm. Two shrew species have been recorded in Jordan. Shrews are among the smallest mammals. Despite their resemblance to mice, they are not rodents. They are generally characterized by short gray hair; small hind legs; long, whisker-like hairs; poor eyesight; and a long nose constantly active to locate prey. Shrews burn calories at a fast rate, requiring them to consume about three times their body weight daily. They feed on crickets, worms, and spiders. **Habitat** The Etruscan pygmy shrew (*Suncus etruscus*) occurs in semi-arid regions, including *Azraq*. The lesser white-toothed shrew (*Crocidura suaveolens*) occurs in the woodlands and grasslands of western and northern Jordan, including *Ajloun* and *Azraq*. **Activity** Very active. Forages day and night. Solitary and territorial. Lives under rocks and in burrows.

Rodents
RODENTIA ORDER

A total of 25 rodent species have been recorded in Jordan. Rodents are a successful order of mammals characterized by front teeth (incisors) that grow continuously as they are worn down from gnawing on hard plant parts. They reproduce rapidly in most habitats, making them an important source of food for larger carnivores.

☐ **JERBOA**
DIPODIDAE FAMILY

L 10cm; H 6cm. Two jerboa species have been recorded in Jordan. They are generally characterized by reddish or brown upperparts, lighter underparts, short forelegs, long hind legs, and a long tail with a hairy tip used for balance. Hind legs are adapted for leaping and hopping at high speeds and for long distances. Jerboas feed mainly on vegetation. **Habitat** The three-toed jerboa (*Jaculus jaculus*) occurs in the flat, arid areas of eastern Jordan such as *Azraq*, and some arid valleys in western Jordan such as *Wadi Fidan*. The five-toed jerboa (*Allactaga euphratica*) occurs in the arid areas of eastern Jordan, including *Azraq* and *Ma'an*. **Activity** Nocturnal and solitary. Hops on its hind legs like a kangaroo.

☐ **RAT**
MURIDAE FAMILY

L 22cm. Two rat species have been recorded in Jordan: the black rat (*Rattus rattus*) and the brown rat (*Rattus norvegicus*). The more common black rat is distinguished by its darker and finer hair, smaller size, longer tail and ears, poor swimming skills, better climbing skills, and preference for warmer regions. Both species feed mainly on grains and almost any other available food. They are susceptible to diseases such as the bubonic plague, which makes them a health hazard to humans. **Habitat** Common in all urban areas. The black rat prefers high nests and warm regions (rarely found in sewers). The brown rat prefers moderate climates and commonly lives in burrows or sewers. **Activity** Nocturnal. Lives in large social groups.

☐ **HOUSE MOUSE**
Mus musculus
MURIDAE FAMILY

L 9cm. Brown or black upperparts; lighter underparts; short hair; long tail; females have five pairs of nipples, while males have none. The house mouse feeds mainly on seeds and plants. Because mice have a similar biology to humans, they are used in laboratories to study diseases and test drugs. **Habitat** Occurs in all habitats, including deserts. Common in urban areas in proximity to humans. **Activity** Mainly nocturnal. Territorial. Agile climber and swimmer. Often stands on hind legs while foraging.

☐ **GOLDEN SPINY MOUSE**
Acomys russatus
MURIDAE FAMILY

L 12cm; H 5cm. Sandy-brown upperparts with spiny hair; white underparts; small, white patches below each eye and behind each ear; black palms, tail, and eyes; tail shorter than body; rounded ears. Feeds on seeds, insects, snails, and vegetation. **Habitat** Well-adapted to desert conditions. Common in rocky, arid areas in *Azraq, Jerash, Amman, Madaba, Petra, Aqaba,* and the *Jordan Valley.* Nests in rock crevices. **Activity** Mainly diurnal. Lives in small social groups.

☐ **FAT SAND RAT**
Psammomys obesus
MURIDAE FAMILY

L 15cm; H 6cm. Yellowish-brown upperparts; lighter underparts; almond-shaped eyes; hairy tail with a black tail-brush; black nails. Distinguished from other gerbils by its small rounded ears. Feeds on vegetation with high water and salt content. Conserves water by producing highly concentrated urine. **Habitat** Common in sandy plains with some bushy vegetation, including *Azraq,*

Ma'an, and *Aqaba.* Lives in elaborate burrows with multiple entrances built under bushes. **Activity** Mostly solitary. Active during the cool hours of the day in summer. Basks in the sun in winter.

☐ **PERSIAN SQUIRREL**
Sciurus anomalus
SCIURIDAE FAMILY

L 20cm. The only squirrel species in Jordan. Grayish-brown upperparts with dark dorsal hair; yellowish-brown underparts; bushy tail used for balance; dark feet; sharp claws used for climbing trees. Feeds mainly on pine seeds, some fruit, and leaves. **Habitat** Pine and oak woodlands in the *Northern Highlands*, including the *Dibbin Nature Reserve*. Rare in *Ajloun* and *Jerash*. Nests in tree holes or on thick branches. Endangered species. **Activity** Diurnal. Territorial; marks its territory with urine and feces. Collects and stores acorns in cavities and below ground.

☐ CRESTED PORCUPINE
Hystrix cristata
HYSTRICIDAE FAMILY

L 75cm; H 30cm. Large rodent with a tail and lower body covered with long quills (modified, hollow hairs with prickly tips). Long claws used for climbing trees and digging burrows. Feeds on roots, tree bark, and fruit. Porcupines are not closely related to hedgehogs. They are distinguished by a round nose, more hair, longer quills, and they do not roll into a ball. **Habitat** Mountainous areas in western Jordan, including the *Dana Nature Reserve* and the *Dead Sea* region. **Activity** Nocturnal; moves slowly; climbs trees in search of food. Raises its quills and retreats backwards when threatened. Swings its tail in self-defense. It is a myth that the porcupine shoots quills; quills snap off only after sticking to another object.

☐ PALESTINE MOLE RAT
Nannospalax ehrenbergi
SPALACIDAE FAMILY

L 17cm; H 6cm. Small, skin-covered, blind eyes (uses touch, hearing, and smell to navigate); reduced ears and tail; short limbs; powerful front teeth (incisors) located outside the lips. Feeds on roots, bulbs, seeds, fruit, and insects. **Habitat** Grasslands and agricultural areas in western Jordan, including *Jerash*, *Amman*, and *Shobak*. **Activity** Solitary; spends most of its time underground; occasionally forages above ground. Digs elaborate underground tunnels, leaving mounds of soil on the surface. Digs temporary, shallower runways in the mud, leaving pushed up soil on the surface. Stores food in special tunnel chambers.

Bats

CHIROPTERA ORDER

A total of 24 bat species have been recorded in Jordan, all are insectivores except the fruit-eating "Egyptian fruit bat". Bats are the only mammals capable of true flight (not just gliding); bat wings are membranes that stretch between elongated fingers. Most bats use echolocation for navigation; they determine distances by emitting high-frequency sounds and then detecting their echo delays.

☐ EGYPTIAN FRUIT BAT
Rousettus aegyptiacus
PTEROPODIDAE FAMILY

L 15cm. The only fruit-eating bat and the largest bat in Jordan. Soft, light-brown fur; darker wings; pointed ears; long, dog-like snout; short tail; long claw on second finger. Males are larger than females. Egyptian fruit bats feed on fruit; they pollinates trees and propagates seeds in the process. **Habitat** Common in northwestern Jordan, including *Irbid*, the *Jordan River Valley*, the *Zarqa River*, and *Amman*. **Activity** Nocturnal. Lives in large social colonies. Hangs upside down in trees or caves during the day. Uses echolocation for navigation. Less active in cold weather, but does not hibernate.

☐ MEDITERRANEAN HORSESHOE BAT
Rhinolophus euryale
RHINOLOPHIDAE FAMILY

L 5cm. Grayish-brown upperparts; paler underparts; darker wings; horseshoe-like nose, which gives it its name. Distinguished from other bats by its finger anatomy that prevents the wings from wrapping around the entire body. Feeds on insects such as moths and beetles. **Habitat** Woodlands and olive groves in the *Northern Highlands*, including the *Dibbin Nature Reserve* and

Jerash. Prefers caves near water sources. Endangered species. **Activity** Nocturnal. Roosts in colonies. Hangs upside down at rest. Uses echolocation for navigation.

☐ CAPE HARE
Lepus capensis
LEPORIDAE FAMILY

L 50cm; H 30cm. While hares resemble rabbits, they are larger, have longer legs, and nest in camouflaged depressions above ground (not in burrows). Only hares are found in the wild in Jordan. The cape hare has a grayish-brown coat, a black tail top, long ears, and long hind legs. Feeds on grasses and shrubs. **Habitat** There are two subspecies in Jordan. The *Lepus capensis arabicus* occurs in deserts, including the *Azraq* region, central Jordan, and the *Jafr* basin. The *Lepus capensis syriacus* is slightly larger with a lighter coat; it occurs in the *Northern Highlands* and the *Dead Sea* region. **Activity** Mainly nocturnal and crepuscular. Solitary, except in mating season when females box and fight off males. Fast runner.

☐ ROCK HYRAX
Procavia capensis
PROCAVIIDAE FAMILY

L 50cm; H 25cm. Despite their small size, rock hyraxes are closely related to elephants and have tusk-like front teeth. The rock hyrax has a thick, brown coat; lighter underparts; a pointed head; small ears and tail; short legs; and rubbery feet that provide excellent traction when climbing rocks. The rock hyrax feeds on grasses, leaves, roots, and fruit. **Habitat** Rocky valleys in southwestern Jordan, including the *Dana Nature Reserve* and *Wadi Rum*. Lives in crevices and burrows abandoned by other animals. Endangered species. **Activity** Lives in herds with a territorial dominant male. Spends most of its time resting. Regulates its body temperature by basking in the sun or huddling with other hyraxes. Retreats quickly to crevices when approached.

Tracks

Tracking animals in the wild begins with identifying their feeding grounds, shelters, escape routes, and travel trails. The presence of animals in an area may be confirmed by rubbing marks, hairs and feathers, food remains, scat, and tracks.

Tracks, in particular, yield a wealth of information such as the exact species involved, its travel direction, speed, behaviors, weight, age, and much more.

Tracks vary due to ground conditions, track age, and many other factors. The best way to become familiar with tracks is by examining them immediately after encountering an animal, noting any differences produced by different ground conditions, animal characteristics, and animal behaviors.

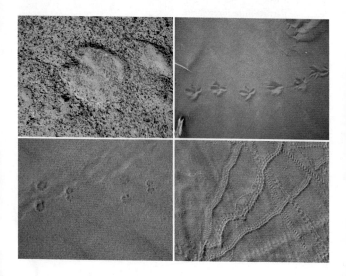

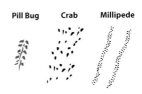

Pill Bug   Crab   Millipede

☐ LEGLESS INVERTEBRATES

Earthworm, snail, slug

Legless invertebrates leave meandering trails without any footprints. The width of the trail can determine the size of the invertebrate. The habitat type and other clues can determine to which exact species the track belongs. Earthworm trails usually start and end with small dirt mounds pushed up from underground runways. Slugs and snails usually leave slimy trails that become flaky white when dry.

☐ MANY-LEGGED INVERTEBRATES

Pill bug, crab, millipede, centipede

Invertebrates with over eight legs generally leave trails of many small footprints. The width of the trail can determine the size of the invertebrate. The habitat type and other clues can determine to which exact species the track belongs. Pill bugs have 14 legs and leave diagonal leg prints with drag marks. Crabs have eight legs, two claws, and walk sideways; they leave one line of dotted prints. Centipedes and millipedes leave two lines of dotted footprints.

☐ EIGHT-LEGGED INVERTEBRATES

Spider, scorpion

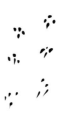

Spiders and scorpions have eight legs. They leave two parallel lines of footprints generally grouped in fours. The width of the trail can determine the size of the invertebrate. The habitat type and other clues can determine to which exact species the track belongs. If the trail has a tail-drag mark, then it belongs to a scorpion.

☐ SIX-LEGGED INSECTS

Beetle, cricket, grasshopper

Among six-legged insects, the most identifiable tracks belong to beetles, crickets, and grasshoppers. They leave two parallel lines of footprints generally grouped in threes. Some legs trail behind and leave backward-pointing prints, while other legs make sideways prints that sometimes produce cross marks. If a track starts and ends abruptly, it likely belongs to a flying insect that landed temporarily. If a track ends at a small dirt mound, it likely belongs to a burrowing beetle. If a track has gaps, it likely belongs to a hopping insect such as a grasshopper.

☐ AMPHIBIANS
Frog, toad

Amphibians have elongated, webbed, five-toed hind feet; the second toe from the outside is the longest. The fore feet are smaller with only four toes and leave footprints that point inwards. The footprints are grouped at intervals when produced by hopping. Tree frogs have adhesive toe disks for climbing vertical surfaces; they leave footprints with round toe tips. Toads are larger and heavier than frogs; they leave stockier footprints with more drag marks.

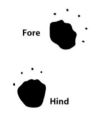

Fore

Hind

☐ TURTLES

Turtles leave footprints with large circular footpads, the fore prints with five claw marks and the hind prints with four. Depending on the turtle's weight, speed, and ground conditions, the trail may have feet, tail, and underbody drag marks. It may also show claw and claw-drag marks without footpads.

☐ LIZARDS

Most lizards have elongated, five-toed hind feet (the second toe from the outside is the longest) and smaller five-toed fore feet. Lizards tend to run with raised bodies to avoid the hot sand and generally leave only claw scratches instead of complete footprints. Their tracks, however, are identifiable by a tail-drag mark in the middle of alternating left and right scratchy prints. Fan-footed geckos have sticky toe-pads for climbing vertical surfaces; they leave padded marks at the tip of each finger. Print size and habitat type can determine to which exact species a track belongs. Some lizards dig burrows in the sand for shelter and for laying eggs. The burrows are generally identifiable by their crescent-shaped entrances.

☐ SNAKES

Snakes produce trails of curvy lines (without footprints). The lines are continuous and almost straight when produced by slow, undulating motion. They are curvier and less defined in some parts when moving faster, intermittently pushing the body off the ground. Snakes that live in sandy deserts, such as the Arabian horned viper, move rapidly sideways (sidewind) and leave a series of S-shaped marks. The width of the trail can determine the size of the snake. The habitat type can determine to which exact species the track belongs.

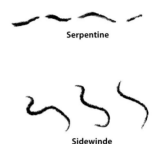

Serpentine

Sidewinde

☐ BIRDS

Small perching birds, which spend much of their time in trees, generally hop when they land on the ground and leave two parallel lines of paired footprints. Larger birds walk on the ground and leave a single line of alternating left and right footprints.

Most birds have four toes that leave three toe prints pointing forward and one pointing backward. The backward-pointing toe in birds that run (chicken, chukar, partridge, quail, crane) is higher up on the leg and usually leaves a small or no print. Woodpeckers have two toes pointing forward and two pointing backwards for clinging on vertical surfaces; they leave X-shaped footprints. Ostriches have only two tows that leave two toe prints with a detached claw print. Kingfishers have toes fused for part of their length; they leave footprints with a larger central pad. Birds of prey (eagle, vulture, falcon, etc.) have strong toes with sharp claws; they leave thick toe prints with detached, pointed claw prints. Ground birds (chicken, chukar, partridge, quail) have stout toes and nails for scratching the ground; they leave thick, blunt toe prints. Swimming birds (duck, goose, swan, gull) have three webbed toes for paddling; they leave fan-shaped footprints. Cormorants and pelicans have four webbed toes; they leave fan-shaped footprints that point inward. Wading birds (heron, stork) have partially webbed toes for walking in mud; they leave toe prints webbed at the base. Coots have lobed toes that leave padded toe prints.

Print size and habitat type can determine to which exact species a track belongs.

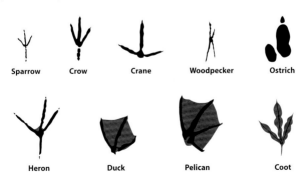

| Sparrow | Crow | Crane | Woodpecker | Ostrich |

| Heron | Duck | Pelican | Coot |

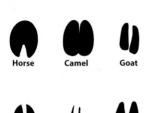

☐ HOOFED MAMMALS

Horse, onager, donkey, camel, oryx, gazelle, goat, sheep, boar

Horses, onagers, and donkeys are odd-toed ungulates. They walk on an enlarged middle toe and leave prints of single hooves with a round leading edge. Camels, oryxes, gazelles, goats, sheep, and boars are even-toed ungulates. They walk on their third and fourth toes and leave prints of split hooves. Print variations and size can determine to which exact species a track belongs.

☐ CANINES

Jackal, wolf, dog, fox

Canine footprints show four toes with detached claw marks. The fifth toe that corresponds to our thumb is higher up on the leg and rarely leaves a print. The overall shape of each footprint is oval, the space in the middle forms an X, the two sides are almost symmetrical, and the two outer toes are almost triangular. Fore prints are slightly larger and have straight heel sides, while hind prints are slightly smaller and have concave heel sides. Female canines have wider hips than shoulders; if the hind prints are farther from the travel line than the fore prints, the track belongs to a female. Print variations, size, travel pattern, animal waste, and habitat type can determine to which exact species a track belongs. For example, wolves leave large prints over 10 cm in diameter and travel in straight lines, while domestic dogs leave smaller, meandering prints.

☐ FELINES

Cheetah, caracal, cat, leopard

Feline footprints have four toes. The fifth toe that corresponds to our thumb is higher up on the leg and rarely leaves a print. Felines retract their claws when traveling and rarely leave claw prints. If they do, they are closely attached to the tear-shaped toe prints. The overall shape of each footprint is circular, with the two sides asymmetrical. The toe print most forward corresponds to our middle finger; align your hand with a print to determine if it was made by a right or left foot. Fore prints are slightly larger and have straight heel sides, while hind prints are smaller and have concave heel sides. Female felines have wider hips than shoulders; if the hind prints are farther from the travel line than the fore prints, the track belongs to a female. Print size, travel pattern, animal waste, and habitat type can determine to which exact species a track belongs.

☐ MUSTELIDS

Otter, marten, badger, polecat

Mustelid tracks show all five toes with attached claw marks in both the fore and hind footprints. Very complex heel prints are produced by several pads that form an arc. The sides of each footprint are asymmetrical.

☐ RODENTS

Mouse, rat, squirrel, porcupine

Rodent tracks show four front toes, five hind toes, complex heel prints produced by several pads, and a gallop traveling pattern. Each group of prints is produced by landing a fore foot first, followed by the other fore foot, and then by landing both hind feet outside and ahead of the fore feet. All rodents, hares, and rabbits produce this same pattern. The tracks of tree dwellers, such as squirrels, are distinguished by their side-by-side fore prints. Porcupine tracks are an exception in that they do not show a gallop pattern and have large heel prints produced by a single pad. Porcupine tracks show all feet pointing inwards with tail-drag marks in the middle.

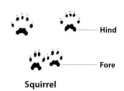

Hind

Fore

Squirrel

Porcupine

☐ HARES

Hares are gallop walkers. Each group of prints is produced by landing a fore foot first, followed by the other fore foot, and then by landing both hind feet outside and ahead of the fore feet. All hares, rabbits, and rodents produce this same pattern. Hares have furry feet, which produce feathery prints, each with four toes. Most animals and humans have a right dominant side. While moving, the dominant leg absorbs most of the weight as the leg on the other side swings forward. While turning, the non-dominant leg swings with longer strides to produce a turn around the more anchored dominant side. In gallop walkers, the fore

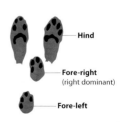

Hind

Fore-right
(right dominant)

Fore-left

foot that lands first and ahead of the other fore foot is the dominant one, which indicates the direction the track will likely turn if the animal was being chased.

Notes

Notes

Acknowledgements

Thanks to the many individuals and organizations that have supported and contributed to this book over the years. Special thanks to Omama Maani, Mohd Maani, and Habeeb Maani.

Thanks to all the scientists and authors whose books and articles provided a wealth of research material for this book. Thanks to all the photographers and organizations listed under Picture Credits for contributing the photographs that made this book possible. Many thanks to the following for their help with various tasks: Khawla Ishakat, Omama Maani, Mohd Maani, Habeeb Maani, Leen Maani, Bana Maani, Sulafa Maani, Suzanne Popkin, Dina Maani, Nafila Maani, Anees Maani, Karma Hijawi, Aram Khlief, Majd Hadad, Jude Maani, David Boyles, Shannon Berry, Ashraf Elhalah, and Maha Rasheed.

Picture Credits

Each photograph is listed by its page number, followed by one letter indicating the photograph's order on the page from top left to bottom right.

Mohd Maani 6-7, 9b, 10d, 11b, 12c, 14b-e, 15a, 16a &c, 17b, 21a &c, 22c, 23a, 31c-d, 33d-e, 40a-c, 44b-c & e-f, 45b, 47b-c, 49a-c, 51b & d-e, 55a-b & d, 56d, 57a-d, 58a, 59a, 61a-c, 62a-b, 63a-d, 64a-d, 65a & d, 66c, 67c, 68b, 69b, 70a, 73a-b, 74a, 75b-c, 76a & c-d, 77c-d, 78b-c, 79a-c, 81c, 82a-b, 83a-b & e, 84d, 85a-c, 89d, 90a-b, 93c, 94a-b, 95a & c, 99a-e, 100a, 101d, 102b, 106a, 108-109, 111a, 114b & e, 115a, 117a-d & g, 118c & e, 119b, 120a-b & d, 121a, 122c, 123a-c, 124b & d, 125b-c, 126a-b & d & g, 127a, 129c-e, 130b-c, 131c, 132b & d-f, 133c & f, 134e-f, 135c, 137c, 139c,

Anees Maani 13a & c, 18c, 19d, 20b, 23b, 35a & d, 40d, 51a, 53e, 54a-c, 71b, 72b, 78a, 89a & c, 90c, 92a, 97a-c, 98a, 107b, 112a & e, 113b, 114d, 115b-c, 118b, 124a, 133e, 135b, 138d, 139d, 140c, 143d, 144a, 146c, 147c, 148b, 151a, 152d, 153e-f, 154c, 156b, 158c-d, 161a, 163c, 169c, 170a, 171a & c, 172b & e, 176d, 177d, 178e, 180e, 185d, 187f, 188a, 189a & c, 197a-b, 200c, 201c, 203a-b, 205d, 206a, 208b, 209a, 210a, 211c, 212a, 213a & c & e, 219c, 223c, 227b, 229c, 234a, 242b, 246f, 253d, 270a, 271a, 272a, 273a, 275d, 277d, 278a, 279d, 286a-b, 289b, 293c, 302c, 303a-b, 306a-b, 309b, 313b, 314a & c, 316c, 317d, 319a, 320a, 324b, 325b, 327a, 330a, 331a, 333a, 336a-b, 338a, 341a, 342a, 345b, 347b

Karma Hijawi 9c-d, 17c, 25b, 36-37, 45c, 66b, 69a & c, 72e, 86-87, 89e, 91a-b, 92b & d, 93a, 96b-d, 101a, 112c, 118a, 121b-d, 122a-b, 125d, 126f, 128a, 129b, 130a, 133b, 134a, 137a & e, 142c, 145a & c, 147a-b & d, 148a, 149b & d, 154d, 155c, 157b, 158a, 160b, 162b, 163a & e-f, 166d-e, 167a & c, 169b, 170b, 171b, 172c-d, 175d-e, 179a, 181c-d, 184b, 185b, 186b-c, 188e, 191c-d, 193b, 195b, 198a & c, 200a & d, 202a & d-e, 205e, 206e-f, 208c-e, 220c, 246a & c, 248b, 260b & e-f, 262b, 276c, 278b, 279c, 294b, 319b, 333c, 353a

Sulafa Maani 12e, 19a, 51c, 100d-e, 134c, 138c, 142b, 143a-b, 149a, 156d, 165c, 167e, 170c & e, 179c, 183b 188c, 199a, 227a, 238d, 244a, 245a, 253b, 254c, 264b, 275e

Gudrun Kroner 52c, 80c, 251c, 291a-c, 293b, 296a, 297a, 300b, 301b, 309c

Aram Khlief 77b, 97d, 277c, 300d-e, 328b, 346a-b, 348a

Nafila Maani 44d, 73c, 128b, 169a, 287a

Majd Hadad 29a, 101b, 356b-c

F. Radcliffe copyright 2005: 41a, 43a, 74b

Leen Maani 21b
Sahel Maani 189b
Sinan Maani 27c
Khaled Al-Masri 338b
Rieke Peichert 300c

Royal Society for the Conservation of Nature 100b, 126c, 191a, 269a, 281a, 282a-b, 283a, 284a & c-d, 285a-c, 307a, 312d, 320b, 344b, 351b, 352a-d, 355a

Jordan Tourism Board North America 31b, 100c, 101c

Department of Antiquities of Jordan 39a-c

U.S. Geological Survey 17a

U.S. Fish and Wildlife Service 343a

© **Boris Nikolov & Iva Hristova** 289a, 295b, 310b, 314b, 318a-b, 328c, 332b, 333d

Jens Eriksen 301d, 304b, 307c, 313c, 317b, 321b, 322d, 325a, 330c

Miloš Anděra 349b, 354b
Jiri Bohdal 301c, 307b
Robert Pickett/Papilio 350a
Adrian Pingstone 278c
Tim Vickers 346c

Agency: Dreamstime.com
© Photographers: **Adeeb Atwan** 80a; **Andrew Blankley** 325c;

Mark Bond 348c; **Paweł Borówka** 93b; **Alexey Bushtruk** 351a; **Paul Cowan** 80b & e; **Peter Cullen** 28c; **Dragoneye** 239d; **Mark Eastment** 292d; **Stefan Ekernas** 297b; **Adrian Fortune** 290c; **Michelle Galloway** 296c; **Charles Gouin** 345a; **Alinta Giuca** 340a; **Hkratky** 348b; **Anita Huszti** 341d; **Jennyhorne** 306c; **Jeridu** 265d; **Jruffa** 295c; **Kaarsten** 292c; **Anna Kravchuk** 301a; **Vladimir Liverts** 355b; **Mccoy24** 308b; **Chris Moncrieff** 298a; **Uwe Ohse** 329a; **Michael Pettigrew** 252a; **Mikko Pitkänen / Studio Foxy** 218a; **Michael Rolands** 354a; **Luis Seco** 62c; **Kristian Sekulic** 292a & b, 299b; **Photoka** 300a, 332a; **Sherwoodimagery** 293a; **Smileyjoanne** 306d; **Tze roung Tan** 288c; **Michael Willis** 309a; **Ariy Zimin** 80d

Agency: Luckyoliver.com
© Photographers: **Rick Olson** 295a; **Christian Riedel** 288a; **Miguel Melissa Schalke** 335a; **Angelo Silva** 288b

Agency: iStockphoto.com
© Photographers: **Heiko Grossmann** 344a; **Andrew Howe** 350b; **Liz Leyden** 290d, 299a; **Paul Morton** 294a; **Kim Seidl** 9a; **Dragan Trifunovic** 269b; **Jan Zoetekouw** 304a

Agency: Fotolia.com
© Photographers: **JohanSwanepoel** 308a

Cover Photographs

Front Black Iris, Petra, Desert Monitor, and Mujib Gorge by Mohd Maani. Tree Frog and Striped Hyena by Anees Maani. **Back** Hollyhock, Eurasian Jay, and Wadi Hidan by Mohd Maani. Hasa Fort by Jarir Maani. **Spine** Black Iris by Mohd Maani. **Flap** Illustration by Jarir Maani.

Illustrations

Jarir Maani 8a, 26a, 27b, 41b, 42a, 43b, 50, 104a-b, 116a, 222a, 230a, 357a-d, 358a-c, 359a-b, 360a-c, 361a-c

Jarir Maani, Sari Maani, Sinan Maani 18a-b, 38b, 60

Habeeb Maani 102a, 110a

Index